Fundamental Laws of Physics

This book is in the

ADDISON-WESLEY SERIES IN PHYSICS

Fundamental Laws of Physics

by

F. WOODBRIDGE CONSTANT

Trinity College

ADDISON-WESLEY PUBLISHING COMPANY

READING, MASSACHUSETTS

PALO ALTO · LONDON

Fundamental Laws of Physics

by

F. WOODBRIDGE CONSTANT

Trinity College

ADDISON-WESLEY PUBLISHING COMPANY

READING, MASSACHUSETTS

PALO ALTO · LONDON

Preface

This is primarily a textbook for a liberal arts physics course at the college level; however, it is not the kind of physics book that is filled with facts and formulas, but rather one that is concerned with the philosophy, the methods, and the fundamental concepts and postulates of physical science. This book could well be used as the basis for an honors course in a secondary school. It is hoped that it will also serve to inform some intelligent adult readers who are not physicists how physicists go about their work and what they have discovered of fundamental importance.

In most nontechnical colleges and universities the students who do not major in science take one laboratory science course. If this course is to be their only glimpse, while in college, of what science is like and what it is about, is it not wise to make this course one which does not require the memorization of soon-forgotten facts, but which does impart an understanding of the methods and fundamental principles of physical science? Should not a knowledge of the concepts and basic postulates formulated by the world's greatest scientists of the past and present be of value to those who may become leaders of business, industry, government, the law, and other professions?

This book is based upon affirmative answers to these questions. Physics is taken as the basic science and the laws of physics are shown to form the foundations of astronomy, chemistry, and physical science in general. The role of mathematics and that of philosophy are also stressed. In these respects this is a book on physical science with physics as its core. This is explained in Chapter 1. It is also hoped that this chapter will help to supply the all-important motivation to study physics.

Chapter 2 contains a review of the formal mathematics to be used throughout the book. In Chapter 3 the physicist's vocabulary is developed; the meaning of definition and the reasons for making the definitions that we do make are explained and illustrated. Chapter 4 discusses the experimental method and Chapter 5 the theoretical method in science. These five introductory chapters are followed by fifteen chapters, each devoted to a separate fundamental law, or postulate, of physics. This means that each chapter is built around one central theme. The steps leading to the discovery of some of our fundamental laws and the way in which the physicist's viewpoint of these laws has changed are regarded as dramatic and exciting episodes in the development of man's thinking. The basic laws are illustrated by discussing their applications to topics of current interest such as skiing, the motion of satellites, atomic accelerators, radio waves, mass-energy equivalence, space travel, optical pumping, radioactive decay, and nuclear fission and fusion. The chapters are pretty much independent of one another. The final chapter brings one to the frontiers of physics and offers a glimpse into the future.

The true nature of physical science cannot be understood and appreciated without the use of mathematics. Hence, concise mathematical statements of laws, rigorous step by step derivations of ensuing relationships, and carefully worked examples are included in this book. However, all of the fundamental laws are also stated and explained in nonmathematical language, so that the more difficult theoretical sections (for example, Sections 6–6 through 6–11, 7–4, 8–6, 8–9, 10–3, 10–4, etc., plus a good deal in electromagnetism and relativity) *may* be omitted if desired.

To balance the necessarily theoretical summarizing of the basic postulates of physics, a set of twenty-six laboratory experiments will be found scattered at the ends of the various chapters to which they respectively pertain. These experiments illustrate the methods and fundamental laws of physics and present the student with the opportunity of measuring each of the universal constants appearing in these laws. These experiments are presented in the same conceptual and philosophical vein as is the text itself. A selected set of these experiments may be chosen to suit a specific course.

In 1957 Dr. John V. N. Dorr set up the first Pre-College Summer Science Center at the Loomis School in Windsor, Connecticut. Since then summer science centers for talented secondary school students have been sponsored throughout the United States by the National Science Foundation, with the purpose of stimulating more of our young people to choose careers in science. The program of the Loomis Center was built around a basic course which was intended to supplement the usual secondary school physics courses and to make the latter more meaningful. Such a course offered an opportunity to break away from the teaching of facts in the common encyclopaedic way and to present instead the things discussed in this book. This proved to be a successful experiment and it has been repeated every year since 1957.

Many physics texts have tried to include everything explainable on an elementary level, and with the continued addition of new topics such books have grown larger and larger. The time to cut back has come. Many familiar topics such as hydrostatics, calorimetry, thermal conduction and expansion, and the lens equation have been omitted from the present book, but those who are interested in any of these things may easily find and read about them in other texts. It is indeed hoped that readers of this book will want to explore further the exciting world of physics and to follow its future development, and that they will find the study of physics interesting and enjoyable.

Hartford, Connecticut   F. W. C.
January 1963

Contents

CHAPTER 1. UNDERSTANDING SCIENCE

1-1 The importance of science today 1
1-2 The need to understand science 1
1-3 Must science be regarded as unduly difficult? 3
1-4 Why study physics? 4
1-5 Physics and philosophy 5
1-6 Uncertainty in physics 8
1-7 Physics and mathematics 9

CHAPTER 2. REVIEW OF MATHEMATICS

2-1 Multiplication and division; powers of ten and significant figures . . 14
2-2 Square roots 15
2-3 Algebra 16
2-4 Infinite series 17
2-5 Geometry 19
2-6 Trigonometry 21
2-7 Graphs and proportionality 23

CHAPTER 3. DEFINITIONS AND UNITS

3-1 The role of definition in physics 31
3-2 Fundamental quantities and units 33
3-3 Some derived quantities 37
3-4 Units for derived quantities 39
3-5 Selecting units of convenient size; prefixes 40
3-6 Relations between British and mks units 42
3-7 Summary 43

CHAPTER 4. THE EXPERIMENTAL METHOD. ERRORS.

4-1 The role of experiment in physics 45
4-2 Controlled experiments 46
4-3 Empirical laws 48
4-4 The accuracy of a measurement 50
4-5 Sources of inaccuracy or error 50

4–6   Systematic errors 51
4–7   Random fluctuations and residual instrumental errors 52
4–8   The accuracy of a single reading 54
4–9   The accuracy of the average of several readings 55
4–10 The possible error in a combined result 56
4–11 The establishment of empirical laws 57
4–12 The need for humility in science 60
      Experiment 1. Determination of π 62
      Experiment 2. The investigation of free fall 64
      Experiment 3. The period of a pendulum 65
      Experiment 4. Hooke's law 66

CHAPTER 5. THE THEORETICAL METHOD. LAWS, HYPOTHESES, AND THEORIES

5–1   Theorizing. 67
5–2   The purposes of a theory 68
5–3   The role of mathematics in physical theory 71
5–4   What does the failure of a theory signify? 73
5–5   What are some of the great theories in physics? 75
5–6   Fundamental and restricted laws 75
5–7   What are the fundamental laws of physics? 76
5–8   The role of constants in physics 77
5–9   Pure mathematics contrasted with theoretical physics 80
      Experiment 5. Stacking blocks 83

CHAPTER 6. NEWTON'S LAW OF MOTION

6–1   Galileo's famous experiments on motion 84
6–2   The concept of force 86
6–3   The concept of mass 88
6–4   Newton's law of motion. Fundamental Law I 90
6–5   Weight 91
6–6   Addition of forces. Concept of a vector 92
6–7   The components of a vector 95
6–8   The special case of statics 98
6–9   Linear motion 100
6–10 Motion in two or three dimensions 101
6–11 The meaning of the derivative 103
      Experiment 6. The speed of sound 107
      Experiment 7. Ball rolling down a trough 108
      Experiment 8. The force table 109

CHAPTER 7. NEWTON'S ACTION-REACTION LAW

7–1   Introduction 110
7–2   Newton's action-reaction law. Fundamental Law II 110
7–3   The physical explanation of locomotion 112
7–4   Application of Newton's laws to physical systems 115
7–5   Collisions and explosions. The conservation of momentum 117
      Experiment 9. Colliding cars 123

CHAPTER 8.   NEWTON'S LAW OF GRAVITATION

8–1   What kinds of force exist in nature? 124
8–2   An historical survey of planetary theories 125
8–3   Centripetal acceleration and centripetal force. 127
8–4   Centrifugal force 129
8–5   Newton's law of gravitation. Fundamental Law III. 130
8–6   Newton's test of his law of gravitation; the motion of the moon . . . 131
8–7   Inertial mass versus gravitational mass 133
8–8   The determination of G 133
8–9   Velocity and period of satellites 135
8–10   The cause of gravitational forces 136
       Experiment 10. The nature of circular motion 138
       Experiment 11. The Cavendish experiment 139

CHAPTER 9.   THE CONSERVATION OF ENERGY PRINCIPLE

9–1   Work 141
9–2   Energy 144
9–3   Kinetic energy 145
9–4   Potential energy 146
9–5   The conservation of mechanical energy 149
9–6   Internal thermal energy 152
9–7   Chemical energy 154
9–8   Heat 155
9–9   The conservation of energy principle. Fundamental Law IV 157
9–10   Summary of important forms of energy 159
       Experiment 12. Inclined plane 161

CHAPTER 10.   THE DEGRADATION OF ENERGY PRINCIPLE

10–1   The statistical approach 163
10–2   The hypotheses of the kinetic theory of gases 163
10–3   The concept of pressure in kinetic theory 164
10–4   The concept of temperature in kinetic theory 166
10–5   Heat engines 168
10–6   The second law of thermodynamics. Fundamental Law V 171
10–7   The unavailability of energy; entropy 172
10–8   The direction of natural processes 173
10–9   The statistical interpretation of the degradation of energy 173
       Experiment 13. The gas thermometer 177

CHAPTER 11.   HUYGENS' PRINCIPLE OF WAVE PROPAGATION

11–1   Definition of a wave 178
11–2   Types of waves 179
11–3   Objective versus subjective approaches to sound and light 183
11–4   Wave propagation in three dimensions 185
11–5   Huygens' principle of wave propagation. Fundamental Law VI . . . 187
11–6   Reflection of waves 188
11–7   Refraction of waves 190
11–8   Diffraction and interference of waves 192

11–9   Theories of light 195
       Experiment 14. The grating 198
       Experiment 15. The speed of light. 199

CHAPTER 12.   COULOMB'S LAW OF ELECTROSTATIC FORCE

12–1   Electric charge 200
12–2   Coulomb's law of electrostatic force. Fundamental Law VII 201
12–3   The electric field 204
12–4   Lines of force 206
12–5   Electric potential 208
12–6   The Millikan oil-drop experiment 214
12–7   Capacitance 215
12–8   Energy of the electric field 217
       Experiment 16. Fields 219
       Experiment 17. Coulomb balance 220

CHAPTER 13.   AMPERE'S LAW OF MAGNETIC FORCE

13–1   The electric current 222
13–2   The magnetic force 225
13–3   Ampere's law of magnetic force. Fundamental Law VIII 227
13–4   Comparison of the magnetic with the electric force 229
13–5   The magnetic field 230
13–6   Properties of magnetic fields contrasted with those of electric fields . . 236
13–7   The action of electric and magnetic fields on charged particles . . . 237
13–8   The cyclotron and its successors 240
       Experiment 18. Ampere balance 243
       Experiment 19. Electrolysis 244
       Experiment 20. The ratio e/m for electrons 245

CHAPTER 14.   FARADAY'S LAW OF ELECTROMAGNETIC INDUCTION

14–1   Introduction 247
14–2   Definition of electromotive force 248
14–3   Motional electromotive force 249
14–4   Magnetic flux 253
14–5   Faraday's law of electromagnetic induction. Fundamental Law IX . . 255
14–6   Lenz's law 255
14–7   Mutual inductance and self-inductance 257
14–8   Energy stored in a magnetic field 260
14–9   Faraday's law applied to fields in free space 262
       Experiment 21. Joule heating 266
       Experiment 22. Faraday's law 267

CHAPTER 15.   MAXWELL'S LAW OF MAGNETOELECTRIC INDUCTION

15–1   Historical introduction 269
15–2   The conservation of charge 270
15–3   Extension of Coulomb's law to a nonsteady state 272
15–4   Maxwell's displacement current 273

15–5   Maxwell's postulate. Fundamental Law X 274
15–6   Comparison between Maxwell's and Faraday's laws. 275
15–7   Electromagnetic waves 277
15–8   Some pure speculation 280

CHAPTER 16.   THE RELATIVITY PRINCIPLE

16–1   Introduction 281
16–2   Inertial systems 281
16–3   The principle of relativity. Fundamental Law XI 282
16–4   The Michelson-Morley experiment 283
16–5   Relativity derivation of the Lorentz space-time transformation . . . 286
16–6   The Lorentz-Fitzgerald contraction 288
16–7   Simultaneity and relativity 289
16–8   The apparent slowing of moving clocks 291
16–9   The transformation and addition of velocities 293
16–10 Relativistic dynamics and variation of mass with velocity 294
16–11 Einstein's mass-energy relationship 297

CHAPTER 17.   THE QUANTUM PRINCIPLE

17–1   The need for a new principle 301
17–2   Blackbody radiation 302
17–3   The photoelectric effect 306
17–4   Atomic spectra and energy states 310
17–5   The dual nature of light 315
17–6   The Compton effect 316
17–7   The dual nature of atomic particles 318
17–8   The uncertainty principle 321
17–9   The quantum principle. Fundamental Law XII 323
       Experiment 23. The photoelectric effect 326

CHAPTER 18.   PAULI'S EXCLUSION PRINCIPLE

18–1   Introduction 328
18–2   Quantum numbers 330
18–3   Quantum states 331
18–4   Evidence that electrons cannot be crowded into the quantum states of
       lowest energy 332
18–5   The heat capacities of metals 332
18–6   Atomic diameters 334
18–7   The periodic table of the elements 335
18–8   Pauli's exclusion principle. Fundamental Law XIII 339
18–9   Chemical bonds. Valance 342
       Experiment 24. Monomolecular layers 348

CHAPTER 19.   THE CONSERVATION OF MATTER PRINCIPLE

19–1   The conservation of matter in physical processes 350
19–2   The conservation of matter in chemical processes 351
19–3   Nuclear chemistry 252

19–4   Particle conservation in artificial nuclear transmutations 356
19–5   Particle conservation in radioactive transformations 358
19–6   Pair annihilation and pair production 362
19–7   Conservation of elementary particles. Fundamental Law XIV . . . 364
       Experiment 25. Statistical fluctuations in the background radiation . . 367
       Experiment 26. Exponential decay 368

CHAPTER 20. NUCLEAR FORCES AND THE SEARCH FOR ADDITIONAL PRINCIPLES

20–1   Nuclear energy 370
20–2   Nuclear forces 375
20–3   The weak interactions of elementary particles 376
20–4   Symmetry in nature 376
20–5   Other problems 379
20–6   General philosophical principles 380
20–7   Goedel's theorem. 380

APPENDIX 1. Sines and Cosines of Common Angles 385

APPENDIX 2. Universal Constants 386

APPENDIX 3. Useful Data 387

ANSWERS TO PROBLEMS 391

INDEX 399

CHAPTER 1

Understanding Science

1–1 The importance of science today

Today almost everyone is talking about science. As we look around us at the many devices that have been recently invented with the avowed purpose of making our lives more comfortable and interesting, we realize that we are indebted to science for this new way of life, and so science seems to be wonderful and beneficial. Then when we consider the terrible destructive power of modern weapons, also developed through science, we feel that science may not always work for the good of mankind. However, whether the accomplishments of science are for good or evil, we all admit their importance. For this reason alone, educated people naturally will, and should, want to know more about science: its nature, its methods, and its philosophy.

In the Soviet Union the importance attached to science is evident in many ways. Every high-school student must study physics not for one but for three or four years. A Russian scientist ranks near the top of the Soviet hierarchy in both salary and social prestige. Scientific achievements vie with athletic prowess in capturing the admiration and enthusiasm of the Russian public.

In the western world our regard for science is shown in different ways. Fortunately we are beginning to realize the importance of more education in science, but not in the regimented manner of the Russians. We can see that good scientists are in great demand and that the supply is inadequate. We may also notice that our advertising world recognizes the importance of science; it goes to great pains to explain "scientifically" why one kind of cigarette or pill is superior to those of other brand names, or why the inclusion of a special ingredient, say "X-19," makes a certain brand of toothpaste or face cream excell all rivals. We are also quick to acclaim the startling new advances in science, such as that into outer space.

1–2 The need to understand science

While nearly everyone admits the importance of science, the need to study and understand it is not so universally granted. There is a common feeling that science is difficult and that studying it should be left to those who have an aptitude for it and will become (or are) scientists.

There is no doubt about the fact that we need to train more good scientists. To do this we must find the young people who have the necessary ability, and we must interest them in science to the extent that they will further their study of it. This means that we must show these people the true nature of science and the ex-

1

citement, not of mystifying demonstrations, but of real discovery and achievement. This is one purpose of this book.

A second reason for understanding the nature of science is gradually being realized. We are training our college students with the hope that they will be qualified eventually to occupy positions of leadership and prestige. Whatever the type of their job, the chances are great that an understanding of science will be an important asset to them. Consider the example of our industrial leaders; in the interests of economy they must be familiar with the latest technological developments, and they must assign an important share of their company's expenditures to research. Consider also our political leaders: they are constantly being confronted with scientific problems, such as those involving water power and other sources of energy, radio and television communication, military weapons, radioactive fallout, etc. Scientific committees are set up in our Congress, and other committees call in scientists to give expert testimony. Can our lawmakers understand these professional scientists? Not unless the scientists can express themselves clearly and their questioners have learned something of the *language of science*.

Modern science touches on all fields of thought and endeavor: religion, the law, the fine arts, social studies, etc.

Clerical authorities generally look upon the laws of nature as God's laws for the physical world, and the fact that scientists find these laws to be comprehensive, yet simple and few in number, furnishes a strong argument for belief in the omniscience and wisdom of God.

In legal affairs we find, time and again, that scientific methods are employed, and that scientific evidence enters into the testimony of a case.

In order to show the relation between science and the fine arts, we shall later contrast the objective view of sound (the description of the frequency, intensity, etc., of its waves) with the subjective view of the musician, and we shall contrast the objective view of color with the artist's subjective view. We shall see that the two viewpoints complement one another, just as a description of a man's physical appearance plus a description of his character and behavior gives a more complete picture of the whole man than would either description alone. As another example of the relation between science and the arts, take the poet who, in his way, describes the same relationships in our physical world that the scientist sums up in a mathematical law.

Finally we come to the social sciences, which, by their very name, claim a close relationship to the natural sciences. This is because they all employ, to a lesser or greater extent, scientific methods and reasoning, and because there are many analogies between concepts in, say, economics and concepts in physics. There is a delight in discovering such analogies, and there is also the danger of setting up false ones. Here we again see the need for understanding what science is.

A third reason for studying science in any liberal curriculum is that it is a method of inquiry, a way of going about the discovery of what the world around us is like. The distinction between science and the humanities is not so much one of subject matter as one of methods. There are situations that can best be met through faith. Some discoveries and some wise decisions are the result of intuition and hunches. The artist is guided largely by feeling and emotion, which are important parts of our experience. The scientific method is another important way of adding to our knowledge and of solving our problems. It also involves imagination and intuition, but its most important ingredients are reasoning without prejudice and experimental observation. A scientist will say: "Let's reason this out." He will in this manner prove that when a satellite encounters air resistance, it does not slow down but speeds up! If the scientist cannot convince us of this through arguments involving the laws of mechanics and, quite possibly, some impressive-looking equations, he will resort to the experimental method and obtain data taken from observations of the motion of an actual satellite as it came into our atmosphere.

We can all benefit from an understanding of the methods of science. Such an understanding will help us to judge values, to sift ideas and recognize half-truths and propaganda for what they are, and thus to form our individual opinions.

While we should not pretend that science will, or can, solve all of the world's problems, we must admit that the methods of science can be of great help to us; learning these methods should, therefore, be a part of a liberal education.

In early 1958 the U.S. Senate Committee on Labor and Public Welfare conducted hearings on science and education for national defense. In the course of the hearings, President L. A. DuBridge of the California Institute of Technology said: "Again we hear the cry: 'Do not forget the liberal arts!' To that, of course, there is a simple reply: Science *is* one of the essential liberal arts. It ranks along with literature, art, music, as one of the finest and most elevating achievements of the mind of man. A liberal arts education does not deserve the name if it includes no science."

During the same hearings Dr. I. I. Rabi of Columbia University said: "I feel that in this scientific age every person who has been through school should have some feeling for science, and some feeling for the world about him, because it is science which is moving and changing the world and if he is entirely ignorant of this he is just being tossed about.

"It is true not only for the general public, and I feel very strongly it should be true for people who in the future will be in government, and who in the future will be occupying your seats, gentlemen, in the Senate and the Congress and the executive departments of the Federal Government and of the State governments and city governments and municipalities.

"They simply have to have some kind of capacity to understand what is happening in the world of science, to be somewhat familiar with what it is all about."

1–3 Must science be regarded as unduly difficult?

Probably the student's chief objection to science courses is that they seem to be exceptionally difficult. There are two main reasons for this.

First, most introductory courses in, say, physics try to expose the student to *all* of the accumulated knowledge in that subject. Ideas, definitions, laws, formulas, and facts follow one another so rapidly that the student is bewildered and left behind; he cannot understand it all, so he tries vainly to keep up by memorizing. We shall see that there are things, such as definitions and fundamental principles, which must be memorized in physics, but memorizing alone will not get the student far, and it will deprive him of the great mental satisfaction that comes with understanding. Obviously, the objection that physics covers too much must be met by not trying to teach all of the facts, interesting though they may be. A physics course should not be an encyclopedic description of nature, nor should it furnish cookbook rules for solving problems. We shall consider presently what the ingredients of a physics course should be.

The second reason why a student may avoid physics is that it *requires him to think!* While this may be an objection on the student's part, it is not one from the point of view of education. The only problem is how to teach the student to use his mind. Mental inertia must be overcome, and once it has been, progress will be more rapid. Every intelligent person derives deep satisfaction from grasping new ideas and developing his powers of thought. Thought training must be developed gradually at first. If a physics course does not have too much ground to cover, a topic may be discussed at greater length and in greater depth, and the student may ask for a fuller explanation of points that he does not understand. Understanding should be insisted on. The student should realize that learning physics requires effort; however, if he is willing to work at understanding it, he will not find it unduly difficult, but enjoyable and perhaps even exciting.

The following suggestions regarding study methods are offered as a help to the student.

(1) *Concentrate* on your work.
(2) *Avoid interruptions.* Work alone part of the time.
(3) Feel sure of *success*.
(4) *Reflect* as you read.
(5) *Be alert* for new ideas.
(6) Enjoy *overcoming obstacles*.
(7) Devote enough *time* to your studies.

1–4 Why study physics?

We have already discussed the reasons for understanding *science*. Now let us consider why we should study *physics* in particular. The reasons will be enumerated.

(a) *In science, physics occupies the most central position.* Physics is the key science. It employs logic and mathematics on the one hand, and it leads to such practical developments as engineering and technology on the other. Physics is also used in forming the basic explanations in chemistry, geology, meteorology, astronomy, etc., and physical methods and instruments are used in biology, psychology, medicine, etc.

(b) *Physics is concerned with the basic laws of nature.* Consider the physical (inanimate) world in which we live; it appears to operate according to certain fixed principles, such as Newton's law of gravitation and the conservation of matter principle. We learn about these principles from infancy through personal experience. We also learn from the accumulated experience of others. This knowledge is vital. We cannot alter the way nature works, but we can put its laws to our use if we know what they are. Thus we learn not to jump out of a window, but utilize the stairs when we want to descend from an upper floor. We put gravity to our use when we use a water tank to supply water to a town, or when we run a clock with a falling weight. We get pleasure from gravitational forces, which the law of gravitation describes, when we ski down a graded slope. So it is with the other principles of our physical world. Is it not, then, a good thing to study and understand these principles more thoroughly? That is what a physics course enables us to do, for the laws of nature form the basis for all branches of physics. Physics investigates the world in which we live.

(c) *Technological developments follow from the fundamental discoveries of physics.* To understand, more than superficially, the principles of radio or rocketry, we must first learn the basic laws of physics. In a scientific career a certain amount of "know-how" may qualify one to be a technician, but the top jobs and the more interesting ones require a knowledge of fundamentals.

(d) *The study of physics is excellent mental training.* The study of physics teaches us new ideas, how to think and reason, how to use logic and its close relative, mathematics.

(e) *Physics teaches us how to observe.* We shall discuss presently the experimental method in which observations are made as accurately as possible and in a controlled manner. We shall also discuss how experimental and theoretical physics fit together.

1–5 Physics and philosophy

The deeper understanding of the physical world is closely related to philosophy. Many excellent books have been written on this subject, and references to some of them are given at the end of this chapter. In this book, philosophical implications will be discussed as we go along. This is a traditional approach, for before science covered as much knowledge and became as specialized as it is today, it was customary to teach it under the name of "natural philosophy." It is important to retain some of this approach.

Philosophy has been defined as "man's thinking about his thinking." By this we mean that in philosophy, man tries to gain a greater perspective of his accomplishments by stepping aside, as it were, and looking at them more from a distance. So in physics we shall introduce definitions, units, various kinds of laws and theories, and then we shall also ask ourselves what these things really mean. What is a law? What is a theory? Does physics answer the question of *how* the world behaves, or the question of *why* it behaves as it does? The answers to these questions are philosophical.

Logic is a branch of philosophy. It is concerned with methods of reasoning and hence enters into physical thought. We shall encounter most frequently the following types of logic.

(1) *Inductive* reasoning, in which one proceeds from specific cases to a general principle. The laws of physics are most often arrived at in this way.

(2) *Deductive* reasoning, in which one proceeds from the general principle to the specific case. Whenever laws are applied to a particular problem, this type of reasoning is employed.

(3) Reasoning by *analogy*, in which successful reasoning in one branch of physics suggests a similar line of reasoning in another area. For example, many mechanical systems have electrical and acoustical analogues, with similar theories for each.

(4) *Abductive* reasoning, in which one postulates the existence of a fact quite different from anything observed, yet a fact from which, according to known laws, something observed necessarily results. A good example is Maxwell's postulate and theory of electromagnetic waves (Chapter 15).

The *syllogism* is a familiar example of logical reasoning. Perhaps the most famous syllogism is the following, which dates back to the Greeks:

All men are mortal.	(*P*)
I am a man.	(*S*)
Therefore I am mortal.	(*C*)

We call *P* the primary premise or hypothesis, *S* the secondary premise, and *C* the conclusion. If *P* and *S* are true, then *C* must be true. It is instructive to examine this syllogism more closely, because it involves a line of reasoning analogous to that frequently encountered in physics.

The first requisite for logical reasoning is a clear definition of terms. In the syllogism above we must know what we mean by *man* (or *men*); the Greeks undoubtedly took this term to include the human inhabitants, but not the gods, of their world.

The next step is to establish the validity of our premises. The primary premise *P* appears to be fairly sound because it has been observed to hold true in billions of special cases, without an exception. Thus by inductive reasoning we establish the hypothesis *P*. Premise *S* follows from the definition of *man*.

Our syllogism concludes with a step in deductive reasoning. The hypothesis *P* is applied to a special case, which is "I." What is the conclusion? It is that I and every other living person are mortal. But is this conclusion absolutely certain? We cannot be 100% sure of the premise *P* because we cannot be absolutely sure of the future. For instance, how do we know that new medical discoveries will not some day prolong life indefinitely? We may say that this seems most unlikely and not worth considering, which is equivalent to saying that *P* is very nearly 100% certain. Then the conclusion *C* must also be nearly 100% certain, and we might as well treat it as a fact and conduct our lives accordingly. If this conclusion seems to you to be too obvious to justify its proof, it is because you have already gone through the above reasoning many times, consciously or unconsciously. The results of this sort of reasoning continually affect the way we plan our lives; for example, we reason that the sun will light the earth tomorrow, that spring will follow winter, etc. Just as some common predictions, such as those about weather and climate, are less certain than others, so we shall see that physical predictions also have varying degrees of certainty.

The logic employed in physics does not usually follow the strict form of the syllogism, although it could frequently be put in that form if so desired. The above example was given mainly to illustrate what is meant by logical reasoning and to show that its conclusions are not always equally reliable. In inductive reasoning one assumes that what is known to be true in a finite number of cases is true in general. Since one can never test the validity of a postulate in an *infinite* number of cases, even if one could think of all such cases, inductive reasoning involves extrapolation, with its attendant risk of uncertainty. Hence when one applies such a postulate to a new, untested situation, the conclusion arrived at deductively is also subject to some uncertainty. For illustration let us take the famous episode of Sir Isaac Newton and the apple.

Whether or not the story of the apple is fiction, we do know that Newton was the first person to relate the force pulling the moon toward the earth (and that pulling the earth toward the sun) to the force that makes objects fall toward the ground. Through inductive reasoning he arrived at the universal law of gravitation. This law states that between any two bodies there exists a mutual attractive force F which is proportional to the product of the masses (m_1 and m_2) of the two bodies and inversely proportional to the square of their separation s, or

$$F = G \frac{m_1 m_2}{s^2},$$

$$(1\text{--}1)$$

where G is the constant of proportionality. This equation is the mathematically concise way of saying that if either mass alone is doubled, the force will be doubled, if either mass alone is tripled, the force will be tripled, if one mass is doubled and the other tripled, the force will be six times as great, while if the separation alone is doubled or tripled, the force will be respectively one-fourth or one-ninth as great as before, and so on.

Newton postulated that G must always have the same value, whatever the attracting bodies, but experimental confirmation of this postulate was not possible during Newton's lifetime. Furthermore, Newton actually observed a gravitational force to exist only in those cases where one of the masses was large, namely that of the earth or the sun. More than 100 years later Cavendish devised a delicate method of detecting and measuring the gravitational attraction between two metal balls of ordinary size (i.e., with diameters of a few inches). Cavendish not only verified that the law of gravitation applied to such bodies, but he also determined the value of G. We shall see that once G is known, we may calculate the mass of the earth, which comes out to be about what we would expect from other considerations. One could sum up the reasoning of Cavendish in the following syllogism:

All bodies with mass obey the law of gravitation.   (P)
Metal balls are bodies with mass.   (S)
Therefore the law of gravitation applies to such balls.   (C)

As in the case of our first syllogism, terms must be clearly defined. The definition of mass will be carefully explained later. The first premise is Newton's brilliant hypothesis. Since it was only an "educated guess," the conclusion reached from it could not be regarded by Cavendish as certain until he had tried his experiment; however, Newton's great reputation made Cavendish feel that the chances were good that the conclusion would be verified. It was!

It is interesting to note here that some of Newton's hypotheses and the conclusions drawn from them have not met the test of experiment. For example, Newton reasoned about light in a way that amounted to the following:

Moving particles that are attracted toward a medium which they are about to enter will be speeded up and so move faster in the new medium. (Inductive reasoning.) (*P*)

Light consists of particles that are attracted toward a denser medium. (Abductive reasoning. Newton made an "educated guess" which accounted for the observed bending of light upon entering a new medium.) (*S*)

Therefore light travels faster in a denser medium. (Deductive reasoning.) (*C*)

Many years after Newton's lifetime, it became possible to measure the speed of light in different media and with sufficient accuracy to check the above conclusion *C* experimentally. It was found that light travels more *slowly* in glass and water than in air, so that *C* is false! This means that either *P* or *S* is false. Now *P* is based on Newton's law of motion, which states that a force produces acceleration, and this law is still accepted as one of the fundamental principles of nature; hence the faulty premise must be *S*. The present view is that while light is emitted and absorbed as though it consisted of particles (of energy), light is propagated as a wave motion, and is not attracted by glass and water surfaces. Newton offered postulate *S* as an unverified guess; this time he was wrong!

We shall see that conclusions which are verified experimentally lead to new experimental techniques and practical applications, while conclusions found to be false force us to revise our postulates and reasoning, all of which is to the good. The reasoning part of physics constitutes its theoretical side; we see that theoretical and experimental physics are closely related and mutually dependent.

1–6 Uncertainty in physics

It is worth noting that the element of probability enters into all of our conclusions in science. It is *almost* 100% certain that day will follow night (do not forget that eclipses do occur!), and that the law of gravitation will apply to a laboratory experiment. But what about the result of tossing a coin? Will it land "heads" or "tails"? The conclusion in this case must be couched in statistical terms, and even the predictions of probability theory may not be borne out in a limited number of trials. The trouble here is that we do not have complete information, such as that giving the exact manner of flipping the coin each time. In tossing coins, the randomness of the results is usually desired, but in physical experiments we make every effort to reduce the uncertainty to a minimum. That there is an ultimate minimum, based on Heisenberg's uncertainty principle, need not concern us in nonatomic experiments. In any case the scientist must be humble in his assertions and refuse to answer with an absolute "Yes" or "No" any questions regarding his conclusions. In the social sciences, vagueness of definitions and lack of information make it still more impossible to give definite answers to such questions as "Was Napoleon a success?" or "Is College X better than College Y?" Answers to questions in science should be qualified and not dogmatic. An understanding of this point is necessary to an understanding of physics.

1–7 Physics and mathematics

While it is important to understand the physicist's point of view, or philosophy, it is equally necessary to be able to understand his language. Language is a tool for communicating ideas. In physics this is done through the use of our native language and mathematics. The latter has the advantage of being the *universal language;* it is used by scientists throughout the world.

Good science writing, whether or not it contains mathematics, should consist of clear and complete sentences. For example, suppose that we have defined a quantity x and then we define y as the square root of x and z as the reciprocal of y; we may then say: "By definition (that of y in terms of x),

$$\sqrt{x} = y. \tag{a}$$

"If we square each side of the equation, we get

$$x = y^2. \tag{b}$$

"Also by definition (that of z in terms of y),

$$z = 1/y, \tag{c}$$

so that (upon solving this equation for y),

$$y = 1/z. \tag{d}$$

"If we substitute equation (d) in equation (b), we obtain the equation

$$x = (1/z)^2 = 1/z^2." \tag{e}$$

The above quotation contains four complete sentences. The equality signs are read as "equals" and so play the role of verbs. The slash sign reads "divided by," a past participle, and y^2 reads "y squared." (The parenthetic statements are only for clarity and may be omitted.) We see that mathematics is in some respects a form of shorthand.

In physics, mathematical symbols are used to stand for ideas or concepts, which philosophers call mental *constructs.* Mass, force, and distance were such quantities in the law of gravitation, Eq. (1–1). The physicist defines a construct in such a way that it can be measured experimentally, either directly, or indirectly through the measurement of other related constructs. Philosophers call this measuring process *relating the construct to the plane of perception*. We shall explain later just how to determine the mass of a ball, the force on it, and its distance from another ball. For these quantities we may then substitute the symbols m, F, and s. These quantities will become part of our *vocabulary*.

The mathematical operations that we shall encounter are also defined and represented by symbols. We have already learned the meaning of such operational symbols as $=$, $/$, and $\sqrt{}$. Others, such as sin, cos, log, and $\sum$ will be explained when we have use for them. When used in our mathematical sentences, they are the *verbs* in our new vocabulary.

A mathematician sets up a branch of his subject in much the way one would invent a new game. He invents a set of self-consistent rules, and then he plays the game accordingly. Frequently, as in the case of Newton, a brilliant mathematician has also been a physicist, and then he has been careful to choose rules for his mathematical game which will make the resulting branch of mathematics useful in physics. But it has been interesting to note that even those branches of mathematics invented by "pure mathematicians," have also turned out to be useful to physicists. The rules or axioms introduced into arithmetic, algebra, geometry, calculus, vector analysis, etc., may be looked upon as additional *rules of grammar* in our mathematical language. Playing the game, or using the mathematics, must be done logically, just as a language must be used grammatically.

We will illustrate what has just been said with a famous Smith-Jones-Robinson type of problem. Problems of this sort were invented by Lewis Carroll of *Alice in Wonderland* fame, but this particular version is a modification of one by another Englishman named Henry Dudney.

I. Here are the rules. Smith, Jones, and Robinson are the engineer, brakeman, and fireman on a train, but not necessarily in that order. On the same train are three passengers; we shall call them "Mr. Smith," "Mr. Jones," and "Mr. Robinson." One of these passengers lives in Chicago, one in Omaha, and one in Los Angeles. These rules may be clarified by drawing two arrays of rows and columns (these are called *matrices*) as shown in Fig. 1-1. Let us adopt the notation that a "1" in a cell means that the pairing indicated by that cell is correct, while a "0" will mean that the pairing is incorrect. The rules of our game then amount to

	Engineer	Brakeman	Fireman
Smith			0
Jones		1	
Robinson			

	Los Angeles	Omaha	Chicago
Mr. Smith		1	
Mr. Jones			
Mr. Robinson	1		

Fig. 1-1. The Smith-Jones-Robinson problem. Sufficient information has been given to fill in the remaining squares.

saying that *each row and each column of both matrices must have one "1" and two "0's" in it.*

II. Here is the set-up for a particular game or problem.

(a) Mr. Robinson lives in Los Angeles.

(b) Smith beats the fireman at poker.

(c) The brakeman lives in Omaha.

(d) Mr. Jones is no good at mathematics.

(e) The passenger with the same name as the brakeman's lives in Chicago.

(f) One passenger, a distinguished theoretical physicist, lives in the same town as the brakeman.

Who is the engineer?

III. Here is the solution of our problem. Because of (a) we put a "1" in the lower left-hand corner of the right-hand matrix. From (b) we see that the fireman is not Smith and so put a "0" in the upper right-hand corner of the left-hand matrix. From (c) and (f) we know that the physicist lives in Omaha, so he cannot be Mr. Robinson; nor can the theoretical physicist be Mr. Jones because of condition (d). So the physicist must be Mr. Smith, and hence Mr. Smith lives in Omaha. This means we have a "1" in the middle of the top row of the right-hand matrix.

With two "1's" located in the right-hand matrix, we can fill in all of the other squares from our rule that each row and column can only have a single "1." Mr. Jones then lives in Chicago, and so from (e) the brakeman is Jones. Smith is not the fireman nor the brakeman, so *he* must be the engineer.

If the reader solves problems similar to this, he will probably find logic and mathematics are both interesting and enjoyable. In the following problems, we will encounter the kind of logic found in mathematics and theoretical physics. Do *not* be discouraged if you can solve only two or three of these problems; they are not physics and you may not care for puzzles and games.

PROBLEMS

1. Prove that in a game of ordinary ticktacktoe it is always possible for either player to avoid defeat.

2. Three men are blindfolded and told that either a red or a green hat will be placed on each of them. After this is done, the blindfolds are removed. Each man is asked to raise a hand if he sees a red hat and to leave the room as soon as he is sure of the color of *his* hat. All three men raise a hand, but for several minutes no man leaves. Finally one man, more astute than the rest, gets up and goes out. What color was his hat, and how did he reason it out?

3. An explorer is in a region inhabited by people, each of whom either tells the truth all the time or lies all the time. The explorer comes to a fork in the road and wants to find out which road will lead him to the main village. He spies a native and, pointing to one of the roads, asks the native this question: "If I were to ask you if this is the road to your main village, would you answer Yes or No? Explain whether or not the explorer will get the information he desires. Assume that the explorer does not know whether the native is a truth-teller or a liar.

4. The explorer in problem 3 meets two of the natives of the strange tribe of truth-tellers and liars. "Are you a truth-teller?" he asks the taller one. "Goom," the native replies. "He say 'Yes,'" explains the shorter native, who speaks English, "but him big liar." Find out whether each native spoke the truth or lied.

5. In the following, addition of two four-digit numbers yields a five-digit sum. Each letter represents throughout one and only one numeral. What are the numbers involved?

$$
\begin{array}{r}
S\ E\ N\ D \\
M\ O\ R\ E \\
\hline
M\ O\ N\ E\ Y
\end{array}
$$

6. In the following, a four-digit number divided by a two-digit number yields a three-digit quotient. Each letter stands for one and only one numeral. Find the numbers involved.

$$
\begin{array}{r}
A\,N\ \overline{\smash{)}\,E\ A\ S\ Y\ }\,O\,N\,E \\
\underline{A\ N} \\
U\ N\ S \\
O\ E\ S \\
V\ B\ Y \\
V\ B\ Y
\end{array}
$$

7. In the following, an eight-digit number divided by a three-digit one yields a five-digit quotient. Each x may be any numeral. Find the numbers involved.

$$
\begin{array}{r}
X\,X\,X\ \overline{\smash{)}\,X\,X\,X\,X\,X\,X\,X\,X\ }\,X\,7\,X\,X\,X \\
\underline{X\ X\ X\ X} \\
X\ X\ X \\
X\ X\ X \\
X\ X\ X\ X \\
X\ X\ X \\
X\ X\ X\ X \\
X\ X\ X\ X
\end{array}
$$

8. This Smith-Jones-Robinson type of problem was devised by Raymond Smullyan while working for his doctorate at Princeton University. To celebrate the armistice of the First World War, three married couples had dinner together. The following facts relate only to these six, and only their first and last names are involved:

(a) Each husband is the brother of one of the wives, so that there are three brother-sister pairs in the group.
(b) Helen is exactly 26 weeks older than her husband, who was born in August.
(c) Mr. White's sister is married to Helen's brother's brother-in-law. She (Mr. White's sister) married him on her birthday, which is in January.
(d) Marguerite White is not as tall as William Black.
(e) Arthur's sister is prettier than Beatrice.
(f) John is 50 years old.

What is Mrs. Brown's first name?

9. A person arranges the cards in one or more decks according to a preconceived rule. Can you find the rule in each of the following two cases (S stands for spades, H for hearts, D for diamonds, and C for clubs):

(a) 3H, 6H, 9D, JS, 8S, 7S, 5C, 4D, 9S, 6D, JH, QH, KC, 10H, JD, QS, 2D, 3C, 2H, 4H, 7H, 8H, 9C, 8C, 6C . . . ?

(b) 3H, 5S, 6C, 10C, 9C, 7D, 4H, 9H, 2C, 8C, JC, 6S, 9S, QH, 5H, 5D, 5C, 7S, 7H, 4D, 8D, QD, 3D, 3S . . . ?

The solution of this sort of problem requires inductive reasoning. You must work toward the general rule according to which each given sequence of two consecutive cards is possible.

REFERENCES

BRIDGMAN, P. W., *The Logic of Modern Physics*, Macmillan, 1927.

BRONOWSKI, J., *The Common Sense of Science*, Harvard Univ. Press, 1953.

BROWN, G. B., *Science, Its Method and Its Philosophy*, Norton, 1950.

CAMPBELL, N., *What is Science?* Dover, 1952.

COHEN, M. R., and E. NAGEL, *An Introduction to Logic and Scientific Method*, Harcourt-Brace, 1934.

CONANT, J. B., *Science and Common Sense*, Yale Univ. Press, 1951.

CONANT, J. B., *On Understanding Science*, Yale Univ. Press, 1947.

FEIGL, H., and M. BRODBECK, *Readings in the Philosophy of Science*, Appleton-Century-Crofts, 1953.

FRANK, P., *Modern Science and Its Philosophy*, Harvard Univ. Press, 1949.

FRANK, P., *Philosophy of Science*, Prentice-Hall, 1957.

GARDNER, M., *The Scientific American Book of Mathematical Puzzles and Diversions*, Simon and Schuster, 1959.

HEISENBERG, W., *Philosophical Problems of Nuclear Science*, Pantheon, 1952.

KASNER, E., and J. NEWMAN, *Mathematics and the Imagination*, Simon and Schuster, 1940.

MADAMARD, J. S., *An Essay on the Psychology of Invention in the Mathematical Field*, Dover, 1954.

MARGENAU, H., *The Nature of Physical Reality*, McGraw-Hill, 1950.

NORTHRUP, F. S. C., *Logic of Sciences and the Humanities*, Macmillan, 1947.

POINCARÉ, H., *The Foundation of Science*, Dover, 1952.

REICHENBACH, H., *The Rise of Scientific Philosophy*, Univ. of California Press, 1951.

WHITEHEAD, A. N., *Science and the Modern World*, Macmillan, 1925.

WIENER, P. P., ed., *Readings in Philosophy of Science*, Scribner, 1953.

CHAPTER 2

Review of Mathematics

From what has been said in the last chapter, it should be evident that one cannot really understand physics without bringing into its study both philosophy and mathematics. Perhaps a physics book with a minimum of mathematics in its pages would seem easier to read than, say, this one, but such a book would not give the reader the true picture of how the physicist goes about his work and expresses his ideas. Since it is the purpose of this book to present such a picture, mathematics will not be avoided. On the other hand, when more advanced mathematics is introduced, it will be carefully explained and illustrated.

Mathematics has been called the "Queen of the Sciences" because of its beauty of form and importance to the other sciences. Physics, with its central position, then might well be termed the "King of the Sciences."

We shall review in this chapter those aspects of pre-college mathematics which are particularly related to physics.

2–1 Multiplication and division; powers of ten and significant figures

Calculations in physics frequently involve the multiplication and division of several numbers. The numbers will vary from very small ones, such as 0.000000589, to very large ones, such as 603,000,000,000,000,000,000,000,000. Here the smaller number is the wavelength of sodium light, in meters, and the larger number is the number of molecules in 18 kilograms (about 40 pounds) of water. (The larger number is Avogadro's number per kilogram-mole.) Since we shall have to handle numbers ranging so greatly in size, it is necessary to introduce the *power-of-ten notation*. In doing this we shall adopt the custom of writing one and only one figure in front of the decimal point. We write

$$0.000000589 = 5.89 \times 10^{-7}$$

(the decimal point was moved seven places to the right), and Avogadro's number becomes

$$603 \times 10^{24} = 6.03 \times 10^{26}$$

The notation we are adopting has the advantage of shortening our numbers by eliminating the zeros used to mark off the decimal point. How many zeros there are in numbers such as the above depends upon the choice of units. For example, the wavelength of sodium light may also be expressed as 0.0000589 centimeters, 0.000589 millimeters, 5890 angstroms, etc. We shall discuss units later, but the point to note here is that the zeros we are referring to are not what are termed *significant figures*. The 5, 8, and 9 above (and the 6, 0, and 3 in Avogadro's number) are to be regarded as having significance within the accuracy of the experimental method by which they were determined, otherwise there would be no point in introducing them; 6.03×10^{26} is regarded as a better estimate of the value of Avogadro's number than, say, 6.04×10^{26} or 6.01×10^{26}. In most cases we shall restrict ourselves to three significant figures, the limit that can be handled by a *slide rule*. For greater accuracy in calculations we must resort to logarithms, calculators, or long division and multiplication, but the reader is strongly urged to acquire and learn to use an inexpensive slide rule with which one can multiply, divide, square, and take square roots.

In multiplying and dividing several numbers the steps are as follows:

(1) Write each factor in the power-of-ten notation.

(2) Multiply and divide the significant figure factors, using three-figure accuracy unless otherwise instructed.

(3) Collect powers of ten. Powers of ten in the denominator change sign when brought up into the numerator. Powers of ten in the numerator are added.

EXAMPLE. Find the value of $(1.76 \times 10^{-8}) \cdot (3.55 \times 10^6) \cdot (4.4 \times 10^{-2})/(1.60 \times 10^5)$.

Solution. In the number 1.60×10^5 the 0 is a significant figure. We find that $1.76 \times 3.55 = 6.2480$, which should be rounded off to 6.25. Then $6.25 \times 4.4 = 27.5$ and $27.5/1.6 = 17.2$.

The powers of ten collect as follows:

$$10^{-8} \times 10^6 \times 10^{-2} \times 10^{-5} = 10^{-9}.$$

The answer then is 17.2×10^{-9}, which should be expressed as 1.72×10^{-8} if we adopt the standard form of one significant figure before the decimal.

2–2 Square roots

Two cases arise: (1) We are asked to extract the square root of a number involving an *even* power of ten. The steps are to (a) take the square root of the significant figure factor, and (b) halve the power of ten.

(2) We are asked to extract the square root of a number involving an *odd* power of ten. In this case we must move the decimal point one place to the right, reducing the power of ten by one, and then follow the steps in (1).

The extraction of the square root of a number is very easy with a slide rule. However, as an alternative to the slide rule, the following method of approximations may be used. Make a good two-figure estimate of the square root, divide this into the number given, and average the resulting quotient with your estimate. The result will be surprisingly accurate if the estimate and the quotient found differ by only 10 or 15%. If the first estimate is not sufficiently accurate, we can proceed by using the first answer as the estimate; this is the *method of successive approximations*.

EXAMPLE 1. Find $\sqrt{2}$ by the approximation method.

Solution. It should be evident that the answer lies between 1 and 2 (whose square is 4). Suppose that we estimate 1.5. Dividing 2 by 1.5, we get 1.33. The average of 1.50 and 1.33 is 2.83/2 = 1.415. The correct value is 1.414.

EXAMPLE 2. Find $\sqrt{4.96}$ by the method of successive approximations.

Solution. As a first approximation, we take 2.0. Then 4.96/2.0 = 2.48. The average of 2.00 and 2.48 is 4.48/2 = 2.24. This suggests that 2.2 is the best two-figure estimate, or second approximation. Then 4.96/2.2 = 2.25+, and the average of 2.20 and 2.25+ is 2.23, the third approximation. For three-figure accuracy, further approximating is not called for.

EXAMPLE 3. $\sqrt{4.96 \times 10^{-8}} = \sqrt{4.96} \times 10^{-4} = 2.23 \times 10^{-4}$.

EXAMPLE 4. $\sqrt{4.96 \times 10^{-9}} = \sqrt{49.6 \times 10^{-10}} = 7.04 \times 10^{-5}$.

2–3 Algebra

It was pointed out in the last chapter that physicists introduce symbols to represent defined concepts such as mass, force, and distance. Relations between such concepts are then expressed as equations relating the symbols for these concepts. These equations, which are of an algebraic nature, are manipulated together, and equations expressing new relations between concepts are derived. All theoretical work of this kind involves a thorough knowledge of algebra.

Occasions will arise when a symbol stands for a physical quantity whose value is known or given. Even in such cases it is advisable *not* to substitute the numerical value for the symbol until *after* all of the mathematical manipulations have been completed. It is best to follow this procedure, for it will be easier in the long run, and it will help one to concentrate his attention on *relations between quantities*. In physics these relations are much more important than the answers to numerical problems.

ILLUSTRATION. *Velocities of satellites.* A satellite of mass m circles the earth at a height h, moving with a speed v. We are told that the pull of gravity on the satellite must equal $mv^2/(R + h)$, where R is the radius of the earth. The problem is to find values of v corresponding to various values of h.

Solution. Refer to Eq. (1–1) and consider m_1 to be the mass of the earth, which will be represented by the symbol M, and consider m_2 to be m, the mass of the satellite. Then $m_1 = M$ and $m_2 = m$. Since s refers to the center-to-center distance between the bodies attracting each other, $s = R + h$. For the earth and satellite the gravitational attraction is then given by

$$F = \frac{GMm}{(R + h)^2}. \tag{2-1}$$

We equate this to the expression giving the required pull (since gravitational attraction must supply the pull) and obtain

$$G \frac{Mm}{(R + h)^2} = \frac{mv^2}{(R + h)}.$$

We may cancel the factor m and a factor $(R + h)$ on each side of the last equation, which leaves the equation

$$\frac{GM}{R + h} = v^2, \quad \text{or} \quad v^2 = \frac{GM}{R + h}.$$

We take the positive square root of each side and obtain

$$v = \sqrt{GM/(R + h)}. \tag{2-2}$$

This tells us that v varies inversely as the square root of $(R + h)$.

The numerical values of G, M, and R are known and may be found in this book by referring to the appendixes. If these values are substituted in Eq. (2–2), we find that when $h = 0$, v is approximately equal to 1.8×10^4 miles/hour. The value of Eq. (2–2) as a relationship will now become apparent. The earth's radius is about 4000 miles, so that if h is only a few hundred miles, $R + h$ will be, percentagewise, only a little bigger than R itself, and hence the value of v will still be around 1.8×10^4 miles/hour. If, on the other hand, we let $h = 3R = 12,000$ miles, we see that v will be half what it was before, or 9×10^3 miles/hour. If we let $h = 63R$ (a little more than the distance to the moon), we find that $v = 1.8 \times 10^4/8 = 2.25 \times 10^3$ miles/hour, which is slightly less than the moon's velocity relative to the earth.

Equation (2–2) furnishes another piece of information that we would have missed had we from the start used numerical values for G, M, and R. Equation (2–2) applies to a satellite circling *any* attracting body of mass M and radius R. Since G is believed to be a universal constant, we may say that for a constant value of $R + h$, the value of v will vary directly as the square root of M, the mass of the attracting body. As the mass of the earth is close to 81 times that of the moon, lunar satellites require, for a given value of $R + h$, one-ninth the velocity of an earth satellite. Thus if $R + h = 4000$ miles, a lunar satellite must move with a speed of $1.8 \times 10^4/9 = 2 \times 10^3$ miles/hour; as the moon's radius is about 1000 miles, the orbit of this satellite would be 3000 miles from the moon's surface.

2–4 Infinite series

Infinite series are encountered throughout physics. An infinite series is an infinite sum of terms such that any term, say the rth one, is determined by a rule that is fixed for the given series. For example, the series

$$1 + \tfrac{1}{4} + \tfrac{1}{27} + \tfrac{1}{256} + \cdots \tag{2-3}$$

is the same as

$$\frac{1}{1^1} + \frac{1}{2^2} + \frac{1}{3^3} + \frac{1}{4^4} + \cdots,$$

so that in (2–3) the rth term is defined by ruling that it is $1/r^r$.

The *binomial theorem* gives a series expansion for a binomial raised to the nth power. This theorem states that

$$(1 + x)^n = 1 + nx + \frac{n(n - 1)}{2!} x^2 + \frac{n(n - 1)(n - 2)}{3!} x^3 + \cdots, \quad (2\text{-}4)$$

where 2! stands for 1×2, 3! for $1 \times 2 \times 3$, etc., and n is a rational number such as 2 or $\frac{1}{2}$. For our purposes we may and shall assume that x is less than unity ($x < 1$).

In the series expansion of Eq. (2–4), we know that *the sum of all the terms* in the series has a definite value, namely $(1 + x)^n$. In a case like this, where there is a definite sum, the series is said to *converge*. There are numerous ways of testing a series for convergence, but the following two are those used most frequently.

(1) A series *converges* if its terms alternate in sign and decrease successively in magnitude.

(2) A series *converges* if, as r increases indefinitely, the ratio of the magnitude of the $(r + 1)$th term to that of the rth term approaches a value less than unity.

EXAMPLE 1. Let us expand $1/\sqrt{1 + x}$ by the binomial theorem.

Solution. First note that $n = -\frac{1}{2}$, since,

$$1/\sqrt{1 + x} = (1 + x)^{-1/2}.$$

From Eq. (2–4) we have

$$(1 + x)^{-1/2} = 1 - \tfrac{1}{2}x + \tfrac{3}{8}x^2 - \tfrac{5}{16}x^3 + \cdots.$$

Since we have assumed that $x < 1$, this converging series satisfies both of the convergence tests given above.

EXAMPLE 2. *The geometric series.* The series

$$1 + \tfrac{1}{2} + \tfrac{1}{4} + \tfrac{1}{8} + \cdots$$

is convergent because the ratio of the $(r + 1)$th term to the rth term is always $\frac{1}{2}$, or less than 1. The sum of this series is seen to be 2. Note that it is the expansion of the binomial $(1 - \tfrac{1}{2})^{-1} = 1/(1 - \tfrac{1}{2})$.

In general, the geometric series is

$$1 + x + x^2 + x^3 + \cdots, \quad (2\text{-}5)$$

and this series converges if $|x| < 1$ and not if $|x| \gtrless 1$. ($|x|$ means "magnitude of x.")

EXAMPLE 3. *The harmonic series.* This is the series

$$1 + \tfrac{1}{2} + \tfrac{1}{3} + \tfrac{1}{4} + \tfrac{1}{5} + \cdots.$$

This series does not converge; it does not meet either of the tests given above. By taking successively larger and larger groups of terms, we may collect any number of factors, each greater than $\frac{1}{2}$. Thus

$$\tfrac{1}{3} + \tfrac{1}{4} > \tfrac{1}{2}, \quad \tfrac{1}{5} + \tfrac{1}{6} + \tfrac{1}{7} + \tfrac{1}{8} > \tfrac{1}{2}, \quad \tfrac{1}{9} + \tfrac{1}{10} + \cdots + \tfrac{1}{16} > \tfrac{1}{2}.$$

2–5 Geometry

In elementary physics only a limited amount of geometry is called for. However, one should be familiar with the properties of right triangles and circles, and one should be able to recognize the equations representing rectangular parabolas and hyperbolas.

(a) *The right triangle.* We shall make frequent use of the *Pythagorean theorem*, namely,

$$A^2 + B^2 = C^2, \tag{2–6}$$

where A and B are the sides and C is the hypotenuse of a right triangle (Fig. 2–1).

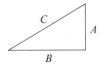

Fig. 2–1. Right triangle.

Note that an equilateral triangle may be divided into two 30°-60°-90° triangles (Fig. 2–2). Let l represent the length of each side of the equilateral triangle; then the 30°-60°-90° triangles each have a hypotenuse of length l and a small side of length $l/2$. If we let h be the length of the large side of the 30°-60°-90° triangles, we know from Eq. (2–6) that

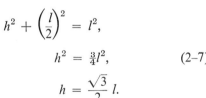

$$h^2 + \left(\frac{l}{2}\right)^2 = l^2,$$

$$h^2 = \tfrac{3}{4}l^2, \tag{2–7}$$

$$h = \frac{\sqrt{3}}{2}\, l.$$

Fig. 2–2. 30°-60°-90° triangles.

Another special right triangle of importance is the 45°-45°-90° triangle. This is half of a square (Fig. 2–3). Let l be the length of a side of the square; then from Eq. (2–6) we see that the length of the diagonal must be $\sqrt{2}l$.

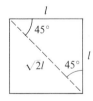

Fig. 2–3. 45°-45°-90° triangle.

(b) *The circle.* If r is the radius of a circle, the circumference $c = 2\pi r$ and the area $A = \pi r^2$.

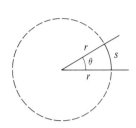

FIG. 2–4. Definition of angle in radians.   FIG. 2–5. Rectangular parabolas.

(c) *Angles.* It is common practice to say that a right angle is 90°, and that when the radius of a circle makes a complete revolution, the angle through which the radius turns is 360°. This choice of 360° for a revolution is arbitrary and based on custom. In physics, angles are defined in a more natural way, as follows.

About the vertex of an angle, whose magnitude we shall call θ, describe a circle of radius r (Fig. 2–4.) The lines enclosing the angle will intercept an arc of the circle. Let s be the length of this arc. The angle θ is then *defined* as the ratio of s to r, or

$$\theta = \frac{s}{r}. \tag{2–8}$$

If we apply this definition to the angle in a complete revolution, we see that for this case $s = c = 2\pi r$ and

$$1 \text{ revolution} = \frac{2\pi r}{r} = 2\pi. \tag{2–9}$$

In this book, angles will be regarded as pure numbers independent of our choice of units for length, mass, time, etc. However, to distinguish between angles measured in degrees and angles measured in radians, according to Eq. (2–8), we shall in the latter case express them as θ *radians.* Thus one revolution (360°) = 2π radians, 90° = $\pi/2$ radians, and 57° are approximately equal to one radian. The word *radian* is used as a label, and it does not have any connection with centimeters, inches, etc.

(d) *The parabola.* Take the x-axis to be horizontal, the y-axis vertical, and let the axes intersect at the point O (Fig. 2–5). If a parabola passes through O, its equation will be

$$y = ax^2, \tag{2–10}$$

where a is a constant, if it is symmetric about the y-axis. Its equation will be

$$x = ay^2, \tag{2–11}$$

if it is symmetric about the x-axis (Fig. 2–5). In physics we can usually choose our axes so that the parabola satisfies either Eq. (2–10) or Eq. (2–11).

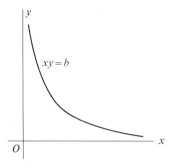

FIG. 2–6.   Positive arm of a rectangular hyperbola.

(e) *Hyperbolas.* When a hyperbola is asymptotic to the *x*- and *y*-axes, its equation becomes

$$xy = b, \qquad (2\text{–}12)$$

where *b* is constant. Figure 2–6 shows such a hyperbola for the case where *b* is positive, and only positive values of *x* and *y* are considered.

2–6 Trigonometry

Even if the reader has not studied trigonometry, it will pay him to spend a few minutes learning what the sine and cosine of an angle are.

Consider the right triangle shown in Fig. 2–7; *A* and *B* are its sides and *C* its hypotenuse. The *sine* of the angle θ is *defined* as the ratio of the length of the side opposite θ to the length of the hypotenuse. It is conventional to shorten the word *sine* to *sin*. Then by definition,

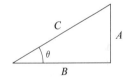

$$\sin \theta = \frac{A}{C}. \qquad (2\text{–}13)$$

FIG. 2–7.   Definition of the sine and cosine: $\sin \theta = A/C$, $\cos \theta = B/C$.

In a similar manner the *cosine* of θ, which is shortened to *cos* θ, is defined as the ratio of the length of the side adjacent to θ to the length of the hypotenuse, or

$$\cos \theta = \frac{B}{C}. \qquad (2\text{–}14)$$

It will be sufficient in this book to restrict ourselves to the case where θ is between 0° and 90°, as in Fig. 2–7.

To understand what sin θ and cos θ mean, consider the following points.

(1) sin θ and cos θ are pure ratios. For a given angle, the value of sin θ, or of cos θ, is independent of the units used to measure *A*, *B*, and *C*. Of course *A*, *B*, and *C* must be measured in the *same* units.

TABLE 2–1

θ	$\sin \theta$	$\cos \theta$
0°	0.000	1.000
30°	0.500	0.866
36.9°	0.600	0.800
45°	0.707	0.707
53.1°	0.800	0.600
60°	0.866	0.500
90°	1.000	0.000

(2) Since the hypotenuse of a right triangle is longer than either side, $\sin \theta$ and $\cos \theta$ must have values between 0 and 1 when θ is between 0° and 90°.

(3) From (1) it follows that one may prepare a *table* giving the values of $\sin \theta$ and $\cos \theta$ for various values of θ. Such tables are found in most physics books (see Appendix 1).

As $A \rightarrow 0$ (meaning "as A approaches zero") in Fig. 2–7. $\theta \rightarrow 0°$, $\sin \theta \rightarrow 0$, and $\cos \theta \rightarrow 1$. As $B \rightarrow 0$ in our triangle, $\theta \rightarrow 90°$ (or $\pi/2$ radians), $\sin \theta \rightarrow 1$, $\cos \theta \rightarrow 0$.

The values of $\sin \theta$ and $\cos \theta$ for $\theta = 30°$, 45°, and 60°, respectively, may be found from Section 2–5(a). For $\theta = 30°$ we have, from the definition of $\sin \theta$ and Fig. 2–2,

$$\sin 30° = \frac{l/2}{l} = 0.500,$$

$$\sin 60° = \frac{\sqrt{3}l/2}{l} = 0.866.$$

Similarly, we find that

$$\cos 30° = \sin 60° = 0.866,$$
$$\cos 60° = \sin 30° = 0.500.$$

For $\theta = 45°$, we have (see Fig. 2–3)

$$\sin 45° = \frac{l}{\sqrt{2}l} = 0.707,$$

$$\cos 45° = \sin 45° = 0.707.$$

Table 2–1 lists the values of $\sin \theta$ and $\cos \theta$ most frequently used in this book.

(4) Since for every value of θ there are corresponding values of $\sin \theta$ and $\cos \theta$, we may think of $\sin \theta$ and $\cos \theta$ as being *functions* of θ. This concept of a function of a variable is an important one. We know that for every value of a variable x there is a corresponding value of x^2, and that x^2 increases as the magnitude of x increases, but at a more rapid rate. We say that x^2 is a *function of* x. Other functions of x are $\sqrt{x}$, $3x^2 + 2x - 5$, $\log x$, $\sin x$, and $\cos x$. So $\sin \theta$ is a function

of θ which for small values of θ (say less than 15°) increases nearly proportionally with θ, and which for larger values of θ increases less rapidly than θ and reaches a maximum value of 1 when $\theta = 90°$. Cos θ is another function of θ which decreases as sin θ increases. In fact we should note that

$$\sin^2 \theta + \cos^2 \theta = 1. \tag{2-15}$$

Can you prove this? (Use the Pythagorean theorem.)

(5) Equations (2–13) and (2–14), defining sin θ and cos θ, may be rewritten so as to enable us to find either side of a right triangle, given the hypotenuse and the angle θ. Thus in Fig. 2–7,

$$A = C \sin \theta, \qquad B = C \cos \theta. \tag{2-16}$$

The values of sin θ and cos θ may be found from Appendix 1. It is because Eqs. (2–16) are so useful in physics, and because the sine and cosine give a broader meaning to the function concept, that a little trigonometry has been introduced here.

(6) It is interesting to note that, although the proof is beyond the scope of this book, sin x and cos x may be expanded as converging power series in x, as follows:

$$\sin x = x - \frac{x^3}{3!} + \frac{x^5}{5!} - \frac{x^7}{7!} + \cdots,$$

$$\cos x = 1 - \frac{x^2}{2!} + \frac{x^4}{4!} - \frac{x^6}{6!} + \cdots. \tag{2-17}$$

In these series expansions, x must be expressed in radians. Equations (2–17) enable us to compute sin x and cos x to as high a degree of accuracy as we may desire.

2–7 Graphs and proportionality

Graphs play a very important role in physical science. When experimental data are presented in graphical form, the significance of the data may be comprehended more quickly. Frequently a graph tells the whole story. Graphs are also drawn to represent a theoretical relationship; such a graph tells us what to expect if the postulates of the theory are correct. Finally, the theoretical curve and the points representing experimental data taken in a test of the theory are often presented on the same graph for comparison.

As in the case of the law of gravitation, Eq. (1–1), the laws of physics frequently express a proportionality between two or more physical quantities.

In the following discussion we shall take for purposes of illustration the case where a quantity, represented by the symbol y, has a value that is proportional to the square of the value of another quantity x so that we may write

$$y \propto x^2,$$

or, if we let k represent the proportionality constant,

$$y = kx^2. \tag{2-18}$$

Experimental proof of a relation such as that stated in Eq. (2–18) consists of measuring the value of y for several values of x and then seeing whether the paired values of x and y fit the proportionality. The "fit" may be established in several ways, as follows.

Numerical method of checking a proportionality. Suppose that $y = y_1$ when $x = x_1$, $y = y_2$ when $x = x_2$, $y = y_3$ when $x = x_3$, etc., and that we want to see whether or not these values fit the proportionality stated in Eq. (2–18). First we substitute y_1 for y and x_1 for x and find that

$$k = y_1/x_1^2.$$

Next we substitute y_2 and x_2 and again solve for k. We get

$$k = y_2/x_2^2.$$

If the proportionality holds, k should be a constant, and so we must have

$$\frac{y_1}{x_1^2} = \frac{y_2}{x_2^2} = \frac{y_3}{x_3^2} = \cdots. \tag{2-19}$$

If this is so, the proportionality is verified, otherwise not.

Method of graphing y against x. Suppose that on a graph we let the vertical axis represent y and the horizontal axis x, and that we plot the experimentally determined paired values (x_1, y_1), (x_2, y_2), (x_3, y_3), etc. If we connect the points with a smooth curve, what sort of curve should we get in order to be able to say that our data verify Eq. (2–18)? Reference to Section 2–5(d) will indicate that the graph should be a parabola with a vertical axis.

Method of seeking a straight line graph. This is the best method of all. Since all experimental data are subject to some error, an equation such as Eq. (2–19) may be roughly, but not exactly, satisfied. This leaves one somewhat in doubt concerning verification of the indicated proportionality. Method (2) has a different disadvantage, namely that it is hard to tell whether or not a curve that resembles a parabola really is one. There are many curves that look much like part of a parabola. A small segment of a parabola differs little from a small segment of a circle. How can we differentiate a parabola from other curves? The answer is this: Do not plot y against x, but plot y against x^2, for then we should get a *straight line* if Eq. (2–18) holds true.* Furthermore, if the experimental values of y and x^2 lead to points that are not *exactly* on a line, we can draw the line that passes (to

---

* For example, if $k = 2$, then when $x = x^2 = 0$, $y = 0$; when $x = x^2 = 1$, $y = 2$; when $x = 2$, $x^2 = 4$, $y = 8$: The points $(0, 0)$, $(1, 2)$, and $(2, 8)$ do *not* fall on a line, but the points $(0, 0)$, $(1, 2)$, and $(4, 8)$ *do*.

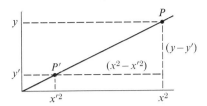

FIG. 2–8.   Finding the slope of a line.

the best of our estimation) through the *midst* of the points, and from this line we can obtain an estimate of how closely the proportionality was obeyed. The scatter of the points around the line should not exceed the possible experimental error, if the law is valid. If such a line cannot be drawn, etiher because the scatter of the points is too great, or because the points indicate a curved graph, then Eq. (2–18) is not verified.

Suppose that plotting y against x^2 leads to a linear graph and that we want to calculate k in Eq. (2–18). How is this done? The procedure is to find the *slope* of this line. Pick two points, P and P', *on* the line and near opposite ends (Fig. 2–8). Find the values of y and x^2 at P and the corresponding values, y' and $(x')^2$, at P'. Then let m designate the ratio of the change in the quantity plotted vertically (here it is y) to the corresponding change in the quantity plotted horizontally (here it is x^2). We may call m the *physical slope* of the line. In our example m will have the units of y divided by those of x^2. Then

$$m = \frac{y - y'}{x^2 - (x')^2}.$$

From Eq. (2–18) we find that

$$y = kx^2, \qquad y' = k(x')^2,$$

so that

$$m = \frac{kx^2 - k(x')^2}{x^2 - (x')^2} = k.$$

The value of the physical slope is that of k.

A few words of advice in regard to graphing may prove helpful.

(1) Choose horizontal and vertical scales which will permit one to plot all the data and to extrapolate the resulting curve as far as desired.

(2) Choose coordinate scales which will utilize as much of the space available as possible. This will reduce errors due to plotting and make it possible to carry to the graph more of the information contained in the data.

(3) Choose coordinate scales that are as simple as possible and yet compatible with (1) and (2). This will make it easier to plot and read points on the graph. When attempting to satisfy (1), (2), and (3), a compromise is frequently necessary.

(4) When plotting, say, x^2 and not x, be sure to label the axis and scale of values accordingly, using this scale when finding k.

(5) When choosing the points (P and P') to be used in computing the physical slope of a line, disregard experimental points. A graph is better than any one point, because it represents an *averaging* of all data.

We shall conclude this section by summarizing those various types of proportionality relationships most likely to be encountered in physics.

(a) *Direct relationships.* Suppose that

$$y^n = kx^m, \tag{2-20}$$

where n and m are positive rational numbers. The constancy of the ratio y^n/x^m may be tested for all paired values of x and y. To obtain a straight line graph, we should plot y^n against x^m, and the slope will be k.

(b) *Inverse relationships.* Suppose that

$$y^n = \frac{k}{x^m}, \tag{2-21}$$

where n and m are positive; then the product $x^m y^n$ should be a constant. As the value of x increases, that of y decreases. It would be best to plot y^n against $1/x^m$, for then we would obtain a straight line of slope k.

(c) *Trigonometric relationships.* Suppose that

$$y = A \sin x, \quad \text{or} \quad y = A \cos x.$$

To obtain a straight line, plot y against $\sin x$ (or $\cos x$). The graph of y versus x is the so-called *sine wave* or *cosine wave* curve.

(d) *Exponential relationships.* Suppose that

$$y = y_0 a^{-kx}, \tag{2-22}$$

where y_0, a, and k are constants. This is called an *exponential* relationship. The minus sign in front of k is introduced because in most physical examples of this type k will then be a positive quantity. If k is positive and a is greater than unity, then as x is allowed to increase in equal steps (say $x = 0, 1, 2, 3$, etc.), y will be found to decrease by equal *fractional* amounts. Thus when $x = 0$, $y = y_0$, while when $x = 1$, the value of y (call it y_1) will be $y_1 = y_0/a^k$. When $x = 2$, the value of y will be $y_2 = y_0/a^{2k}$. It then follows that

$$\frac{y_1}{y_0} = \frac{y_2}{y_1} = \frac{y_3}{y_2} = \cdots = \frac{1}{a^k}, \quad a \text{ constant.}$$

This is an important characteristic of the exponential relationship.

The method of seeking a straight line graph in this exponential case is to plot the logarithm of y against x. Then if Eq. (2-22) holds, we will obtain a straight line, otherwise not. Let us consider why this is so.

The logarithm of a number y to the base a is defined as the power to which one must raise a to obtain the given number.

This is written as $\log_a y$. By this definition

$$\log\left(\frac{y}{y_0}\right) = \log_a a^{-kx} = -kx. \tag{2-23}$$

Next we must note that the logarithm of the ratio of two numbers is equal to the difference between the logarithms of those numbers, or

$$\log\left(\frac{y}{y_0}\right) = \log y - \log y_0,$$

so that

$$\log y = \log y_0 - kx.$$

This equation states a linear relationship between $\log_a y$ and x. For positive k, the line will have a negative slope, and it will not pass through the origin ($x = 0$, $y = 0$) unless $y_0 = 1$ ($\log y_0 = 0$).

The base a will usually be either 10 or e. The latter stands for a transcendental number such as π, and it may be defined as follows:

$$e = 1 + \frac{1}{1!} + \frac{1}{2!} + \frac{1}{3!} + \cdots. \tag{2-24}$$

Just as we need to introduce π in geometry, we need to use e in higher mathematics, such as the calculus. Transcendental numbers may be computed to any number of significant figures, but never exactly. Thus

$$e = 2.71828\ldots.$$

Logarithms of numbers are commonly computed and tabulated for the base 10. These are called *common logarithms*. The logarithm of a number to the base e is approximately 2.3 times its common logarithm. The usual notation is to write

$$\log y \quad \text{for} \quad \log_{10} y$$

and

$$\ln y \quad \text{for} \quad \log_e y.$$

EXAMPLE 1. Suppose that the data yield the following paired values for x and y:

x	1	4	10	16	25	100
y	60	30	19	15	12	6

What is the relation between x and y?

Solution. Since y decreases as x increases, the relation might be an inverse one or an exponential one. The latter possibility is ruled out because as x increases from 4 to 10, y decreases by over one-third, while when x increases from 10 to 16 (again a gain of 6), y decreases by less than one-fourth. Thus equal increases in x do not result in equal fractional changes in y.

It will be noted that the product $y\sqrt{x}$ is always equal to 60, so the relation is

$$y = \frac{60}{\sqrt{x}}.$$

EXAMPLE 2. X-rays and radioactive gamma rays are generally absorbed as they pass through absorbing material such as lead. If y represents the intensity of the radiation from a given source after the radiation has passed through x sheets of lead, each sheet being of the same thickness, the data might be as follows:

x	0	1	2	3	4	5
y	1000	100	10	1	0.1	0.01

Is the absorption exponential?

Solution. Note that as x increases by unit increments, y decreases each time to one-tenth of its previous value, i.e., an increase in x of unity results in a 90% decrease in y. The absorption does follow an exponential relationship.

If we compute $\log y$ for each value of y given, we obtain the following paired values:

x	0	1	2	3	4	5
$\log y$	3	2	1	0	-1	-2

The relation between $\log y$ and x is thus

$$\log y = 3 - x,$$

which is a *linear* relationship. Therefore the graph of $\log y$ against x will be a straight line. The relation between y and x is

$$y = \frac{1000}{10x} = 1000 \times 10^{-x}.$$

EXAMPLE 3. A radioactive source is found to have an activity that decreases with time. Let y represent the activity and x the number of days since the activity was first measured. Our data might read as follows:

x	0	1	2	3	4
y	1000	707	500	354	250

The graph of y against x is shown in Fig. 2–9. Is the decay in activity exponential with regard to the time?

Solution. We see that for each unit increase in x there is a decrease in y of just under 30%. If we compute $\log y$ for each value of x, we find the following pairs of values:

x	0	1	2	3	4
$\log y$	3.00	2.85	2.70	2.55	2.40

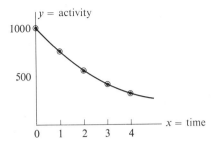

FIG. 2-9. Exponential decay of a radioactive source.

Since log y decreases at a steady rate of 0.15 as x increases in steps of one day, the graph of log y against x will be a straight line with a negative slope. Thus the activity does decay exponentially with the time.

The time required for the activity to decrease by 50% is called the *half-life*. In this example the half-life is two days; in any two-day period the activity at the end of the period is half what it was at the start of the period.

For further illustrations and discussion of exponential relationships, refer to Experiment 26 following Chapter 19.

PROBLEMS

1. Evaluate $10^5 \times 10^{-2}/(10^4 \times 10^{-5})$.
2. Evaluate $8 \times 10^{-5}/(2 \times 10^{-2})^2$.
3. Evaluate $(6.67 \times 10^{-11})(6.02 \times 10^{26})/(250 \times 10^2)(6.38 \times 10^6)^2$.
4. Find (a) $\sqrt{10}$, (b) $\sqrt{1000}$, (c) $\sqrt{2.52 \times 10^{-7}}$.
5. Given that one distance is three times another and that their sum is 100 centimeters. Find the two distances.
6. Given

$$\frac{1}{p} + \frac{1}{q} = \frac{1}{f}.$$

Solve for f in terms of p and q, then find the value of f when $p = 12$ and $q = -6$.

7. Given $F = GMm/R^2$ and $F = mg$, where $G = 6.67 \times 10^{-11}$, $g = 9.8$, and $R = 6.4 \times 10^6$. Find an expression for M in terms of known quantities, then find the numerical value of M.

8. Expand $(1 + x)^{3/2}$ by the binomial theorem.

9. Evaluate $\sqrt{10}$ by expanding $(9 + 1)^{1/2} = 3(1 + \frac{1}{9})^{1/2}$.

10. Test the following series for convergence. If the series converges, find its sum.
(a) $\frac{1}{2} + \frac{1}{4} + \frac{1}{6} + \frac{1}{8} + \frac{1}{10} + \frac{1}{12} + \cdots$ (b) $\frac{1}{2} - \frac{1}{4} + \frac{1}{6} - \frac{1}{8} + \frac{1}{10} - \frac{1}{12} + \cdots$

11. Find, to three significant figures, the number of degrees in one radian.

12. Find the acute angles of a 3-4-5 right triangle.

13. Explain how, by means of trigonometry and suitable instruments, you could measure the height of a tower.

14. Explain how, by means of trigonometry and suitable instruments, you could measure the width of a river.

15. If you move 200 feet in a southeast direction, how far did you move east and how far south?

16. Express 10° in radians, then use the series expansions of Eqs. (2–17) to find sin 10° and cos 10° to three significant figures.

17. The distance s that a body falls from rest in a time t is given by $s = \frac{1}{2}gt^2$, where s is in feet, t in seconds, and $g = 32$ ft/sec². Suppose that you have measured t for $s = 9$, 16, and 25 feet; what values of t should you obtain in each case? What quantities would you plot to obtain a straight line graph? What should the physical slope of your line be?

18. Suppose that in arbitrary units you measure the pressure p and volume V of a gas and find that when $p = 80$, $V = 15$, when $p = 60$, $V = 20$, and when $p = 50$, $V = 24$. What sort of proportionality exists between p and V? What type of curve would a graph of p against V give? What quantity should you plot against V to get a straight line graph?

19. The period P of a simple pendulum is found to depend on the length l as follows. When $l = 36$ cm, $P = 1.2$ seconds, when $l = 64$ cm, $P = 1.6$ sec, and when $l = 100$ cm, $P = 2$ sec. What sort of proportionality exists between P and l? What quantities should be plotted in order to obtain a linear graph, and what should the physical slope of the line be?

20. If a radioactive sample has an initial activity of 1000 and one day later the activity is 900, what will the activity be 2, 3, 4, and 6 days after the start? At what time will the activity be equal to 500? What quantities should you plot in order to obtain a linear graph?

21. If two sheets of lead cut out half of the radiation from an x-ray tube, how many similar sheets will cut out seven-eighths of the original radiation? (Assume an exponential relationship.)

CHAPTER 3

Definitions and Units

3–1 The role of definition in physics

As we said earlier, definitions in science correspond to a vocabulary in a language. If we are to understand science and scientists, we must first learn the language used by them. Scientists try to be very clear in their definitions of terms in order that such terms will always mean the same thing; only in this way can scientists communicate with one another, as well as with nonscientists, and only in this way can a body of scientific knowledge be built up and passed along from one generation to the next.

In a science such as physics, the choice of what concepts are to be defined and how they are to be defined is made by those people who are developing a new branch of the subject. While these pioneer workers are free to make arbitrary choices, they are naturally guided by the principle that their definitions must be *useful*. While a concept may at first be vaguely conceived, its definition must be clarified before it can be adopted by others and become part of our scientific vocabulary, just as new words are taken into and become part of a language. Definitions thus adopted we must accept and learn ourselves. This requires memorization, and it is one instance in physics where memorizing is not only justified but necessary.

Various kinds of concepts are introduced in physics, but to be clear and meaningful they must all have some association with measurement and numbers. Some concepts such as "axis," "inertial system," etc., provide reference frames for measurement. Concepts such as "atom," "electron," and "particle" have associated with them numerically measurable quantities such as "mass," "charge," or "angular momentum." Most important of all are those concepts, which we shall call *quantities*, whose definitions consist of statements of how they are to be measured. Thus the length of a table is defined in terms of the operation of measuring its length with a tape, ruler, or other instrument. It is with this last type of concept that we shall be concerned in this chapter.

While the scientist insists on giving an operational definition to a concept such as length, we frequently find that such concepts also have an *intuitive meaning* for us. Thus we associate length with distance and extension in space, mass with inertia and quantity of matter, temperature with heat and cold, etc. This intuitive meaning is usually an indication that the concept recurs frequently in our physical world; this is a sign that the concept is a useful one which deserves being given an exact definition and being added to our scientific vocabulary. However, the intuitive meaning may not be as exact as the scientific definition.

There are other guideposts that point the way to useful definitions. A quantity is usually worth defining if it will help us to *relate other quantities*, or if the quantity has *interesting properties* of its own. Let us take a few examples.

Density will be defined as the ratio of mass to volume, thus relating two quantities that are defined previously. Density is then found to have an interesting property; as long as we deal with a homogeneous substance, such as water at a certain temperature, we find that the mass is proportional to the volume, i.e., mass over volume is a *constant*, and so the density of the substance has a definite value that may be measured once and for all and listed in a table. With such a table of the densities of various substances at hand, we may compute the mass of *any* volume of one of the listed substances. This means that density is a useful concept. In everyday life we learn to associate a high density with lead and stones, a low density with cork, cotton, gases, etc. For similar reasons we find it useful to define such quantities as specific heat capacity, coefficient of thermal conductivity, coefficient of expansion, index of refraction relative to air, etc.

Mass was referred to in the definition of density. Its definition is complicated by the fact that physicists and engineers have not agreed on a common approach to it; this has resulted in greater confusion and difficulty in understanding the meaning of mass. But let us just consider here why mass is a useful quantity. We shall see that the definition of mass is such that for a given object the mass is *constant*, independent of the object's position or motion, provided that we confine ourselves to motion involving speeds much less than that of light. Mass is then a *property of an object*, just as density is a *property of a substance*. On the other hand, the mass of one piece of lead will not, in general, be the same as that of another piece of lead, and so we cannot prepare a table of masses for various *substances* as we do a table of densities. However, the masses of celestial bodies and elementary particles have been measured and listed. In certain special cases the mass of a body may be marked on the body.

The *gravitational constant G* is defined by Eq. (1–1). Its importance lies in the fact that it appears to be a *universal constant*, independent of the attracting bodies or their separation. Once measured, the value of G may be listed in a table along with other important constants.

Summarizing, we see that quantities may be useful because they are constant (1) for a given material, (2) for a given object, (3) for the observable world.

Physicists do not introduce new definitions just for the fun of it, or to give students more to learn! For example, one *could* define a new quantity, let us call it a person's *spread*, as the ratio of the person's weight (on household scales) to his age. This quantity would vary tremendously from person to person and for the same man or woman it would vary from year to year, even hour to hour. In other words, "spread" has no constant properties, and even its value in a given instance might not be too informative, because what might be a healthy "spread" for one 40-year old man might not be for another. Similarly, the ratio of the weight (gravitational pull of the earth on) to the volume of an earth satellite would be a useless concept because the weight of a satellite depends on how far it is above the earth.

3–2 Fundamental quantities and units

We saw that the definition of density presupposed that of mass and volume. Evidently we must start somewhere and this is done by defining first of all what we shall call our *fundamental quantities*. Quantities defined in terms of the fundamental ones will be called *derived quantities*.

The choice of fundamental quantities is arbitrary and so is their number. However, physicists have found it most convenient to take *three* quantities as fundamental in mechanics, then to add one more in thermodynamics, and a fifth in electromagnetism. It should be stressed that this is not the only possibility, but it is the conventional choice and a good one, and we shall confine ourselves to it.

Physicists and engineers agree in taking *length* and *time* as two of the fundamental quantities in mechanics; physicists choose *mass* for the third, engineers choose *force*. Since mass and force will be found to be related as follows,

$$\text{Force} = \text{mass} \times \text{acceleration},$$

the definition of one leads to that of the other.

Since we cannot define fundamental quantities in terms of ones previously defined, we must fall back on our *intuitive* ideas, based on everyday experience, of what these quantities are, and then we must define explicitly how they are to be *measured*. The important point is that a definition should mean the same thing to everybody so that when different people measure, say, the diameter of a certain cylinder in meters, each will, within the limits of experimental error, arrive at the same value. While we rely on our senses to tell us what we *mean* by length, mass, time, and temperature, we must remember that our senses can mislead us and should not be used to *measure* the magnitude of such quantities.

(a) *Length.* Our senses give us the concept of distance and extension in space. Such quantities were first measured crudely by using the spread of one's hand, the length of one's foot, etc. Then it was decided to adopt a standard of length and this was chosen to be one ten-millionth of (10^{-7} times) the distance between the equator and poles of the earth. The trouble with such a standard is that it is not easy to measure it accurately, and so as time went on and better methods were found, the length believed to correspond to the defined standard had to be changed. Finally, it was decided to make a rigid bar of noncorrosive platinum-iridium alloy and mark on it two fine lines separated by a distance about equal to about 10^{-7} times the equator-to-pole distance; the distance between these two lines was then adopted as our standard unit of length, and it is called *one meter* (abbreviated m). The meter is now legally defined in this way. The standard bar is kept in the "Bureau des Poids et Mesures" in Sèvres, France.

Standard meter bars have been prepared for other countries by direct comparison with the one in France. Secondary standards may be checked against the standard one, cheaper measuring sticks against secondary standards, and so on.

(b) *Mass.* With our senses we recognize the existence of matter, and so we want to be able to measure *quantity of matter*. For this purpose we use the *mass* of a body. While mass will be defined concisely in Chapter 6, where it will be identified with a body's inertia to a change in its state of motion, suffice it to say here that the mass of a body is very nearly proportional to the number of heavy elementary particles (neutrons and protons) contained in the body. Thus in this sense the mass of a body is a measure of the quantity of matter in the body.

The present standard of mass, which is called *one kilogram* (abbreviated kg) is taken to be that of a piece of platinum alloy also kept at Sèvres, France. Standards of mass for other countries, secondary standards, tertiary standards, etc., are prepared by comparison through *weighing*. We should here raise the question, "Is weight the same as mass?" The answer is "No," but at a given location *weight is proportional to mass* and the proportionality factor (called *g*) is nearly constant over the earth's surface. The pans of a balance are so close together that the variation in *g* from one pan to the other can never be detected; hence masses can be compared through weighing. The standard kilogram was chosen so as to have a mass nearly equal to that of a cube of water one-tenth meter on a side.

(c) *Time*. Our senses make us aware of the passage of time. We observe certain rhythmic events, such as the beat of a pendulum. If we use this to mark time, we find that other events repeat themselves at fixed time intervals, and this makes us feel that a pendulum clock is a good device for indicating equal time intervals. Your heartbeat, on the other hand, is a poor timer because when we compare our heartbeat with periodic phenomena in the physical world (pendulums, vibrating springs, rotation of the earth, etc.) we find that either our heartbeat rate changes, or else all the above-mentioned physical phenomena suffer changes in period. We rule out the latter possibility as unlikely and recognize that our heartbeat probably varies. What physical phenomenon, then, shall we take to measure time? The present standard is based on the *mean solar day*, which is divided into 24 hours of 3600 seconds each. The *second* (abbreviated sec) is the universal unit of time in physics. More recently it has been found that certain "atomic clocks" are more scientific timekeepers than our rotating earth, but for our purposes we may take the second to be 1/86,400 of the mean solar day.

(d) *Temperature*. From our sense of touch we learn the difference between hot and cold, but we also find that lukewarm water feels hotter if just before testing it with our hand we plunge our hand into cold rather than hot water. We also observe many properties of the physical world that vary with temperature, and it would seem better to use one of these properties of nature to measure temperature than to rely on our variable sense of touch.

In choosing which temperature-dependent property of nature to use to define and measure temperature, physicists look for one which is, if possible, independent of the particular substance used. While different solids and different liquids do not expand proportionately, different gases are found to expand at the same rate, provided that the pressure* of the gas is about one atmosphere or less. Since the volume of a gas varies rather rapidly with temperature, it is more convenient to keep the volume of the gas constant and measure its pressure at various tempera-

---

* Pressure is defined by Eq. (3–11); it is the push of the gas against unit area of the containing walls.

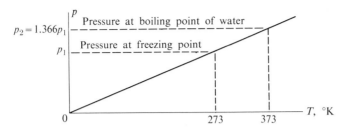

FIG. 3–1. Kelvin temperature scale.

tures. Again it is found that different gases behave similarly. For example, if a bulb containing a constant volume of gas is surrounded by water boiling under a pressure of one atmosphere, then the pressure p_2 of the *gas* will be 1.366 ($= 373/273$) times its pressure p_1 at the freezing point of water, i.e., $p_2/p_1 = 373/273$. For our purposes we may *define an absolute temperature scale* by (1) taking the temperature T to be proportional to the pressure p of a gas at constant volume, and (2) by assigning 100 degrees to the interval between the freezing and boiling points of water (Fig. 3–1).

Let T_1 be the absolute temperature of the freezing point of water and T_2 that of the boiling point. From condition (1)

$$\frac{T_2}{T_1} = \frac{373}{273},\tag{3-1}$$

and from condition (2)

$$T_2 = T_1 + 100°,\tag{3-2}$$

so that we have

$$\frac{T_1 + 100}{T_1} = \frac{373}{273},$$

from which we find that

$$T_1 = 273°,\tag{3-3}$$

or the freezing point of water is 273° absolute.

At any temperature T we have

$$\frac{T}{T_1} = \frac{p}{p_1}, \qquad T = \frac{273p}{p_1}.\tag{3-4}$$

The experimental method for calibrating a gas thermometer and using it to measure, say, room temperature is discussed in Experiment 13 at the end of Chapter 10. We shall call the absolute temperature the *Kelvin* temperature after Lord Kelvin, who first proposed this scale, and write $T_1 = 273°K$, $T_2 = 373°K$, etc.

(e) *Electric charge.* An electric current is regarded as a flow of electric charges, just as a current of air or water is considered to be a flow of molecules. Electric

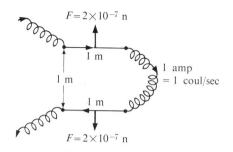

FIG. 3–2.   Definition of the coulomb or ampere.

currents must be measured by utilizing some effect associated with them; the effect now chosen for defining the unit of current (called the *ampere*) is the force that arises between two parallel wires when a current flows through the wires in series. The unit of charge, called the *coulomb* (abbreviated coul), is defined as the quantity of electricity that flows in one second past any point in circuit carrying a current of one ampere, that is,

$$1 \text{ coulomb} = 1 \text{ ampere-second.}$$

Because of this relation between the ampere and the coulomb, it really makes little difference whether we regard current or charge as the basic concept and the ampere or coulomb as the basic unit. But since a choice must be made, we shall choose the coulomb as our basic unit. The definition, which will be better understood later, is as follows: One *coulomb* is that charge such that if a current of one coulomb per second flows in each of two parallel wires one meter long and one meter apart (Fig. 3–2), then the resulting force between the wires is 2×10^{-7} newtons. (The newton will be defined presently.)

We shall henceforth take length, mass, time, temperature, and charge as our fundamental quantities, and generally we shall take the meter (m), kilogram (kg), second (sec), degree Kelvin (°K), and coulomb (coul), respectively, as the basic units for these quantities. This system of units is called the mksKc system, or, if we refer only to mechanical units, the mks system.

Much can be said for the mks system, and that is why we shall favor it in this book, but unfortunately it is not the only system in use. One may read books and articles in which the cgs (centimeter-gram-second) system is employed. We will also find many instruments calibrated in terms of cgs units. These units will, therefore, be introduced from time to time so that the reader may become familiar with them. They are related by powers of ten to the corresponding mks units. The basic conversion relations are as follows:

$$1 \text{ centimeter} = 0.01 \text{ meter} \quad (1 \text{ cm} = 10^{-2} \text{ m}),$$
$$1 \text{ gram} = 0.001 \text{ kilogram} \quad (1 \text{ gm} = 10^{-3} \text{ kg}).$$

Our general public and our engineers are most familiar with such traditional *British units* as the foot and the pound. In order for a scientist to communicate with others he must, then, be able to convert from metric to British units and vice versa. A table for doing this (Table 3–1) will be found in Section 3–6.

3–3 Some derived quantities

In order to illustrate how we define quantities other than our basic ones, the definitions of some derived quantities that are useful in mechanics will be given. Other quantities will be defined as we come to them; it will be our rule to define each one in terms of previously defined quantities.

(a) *Area.* The area (A) of a square is defined as the square of the length of a side. Other areas are defined and measured by counting the number of unit squares and fractions thereof contained in the given area. While our unit of area will be the *square meter* (m^2), small fractions of this unit may be used in computing an unknown area.

(b) *Volume.* The volume (V) of a cube is defined as the cube of the length of a side. Other volumes are defined and measured by counting how many unit cubes are contained in them. Our unit of volume will be the *cubic meter* (m^3).

(c) *Speed.* If a body travels a distance s in a time t, its *average speed* ($\bar{v}$) is defined as s/t, or

$$\bar{v} = \frac{s}{t}. \tag{3–5}$$

The *instantaneous speed* (v) is defined as the limit of the ratio s/t when t is made very small. (This will be discussed more fully later.)

(d) *Acceleration.* If a body is moving in a fixed direction and its speed changes from v_1 at the time t_1 to v_2 at the time t_2, its *average acceleration* ($\bar{a}$) in the given direction is defined as

$$\bar{a} = \frac{v_2 - v_1}{t_2 - t_1}. \tag{3–6}$$

When we consider constant accelerations in this book, we may take Eq. (3–6) as also giving us the definition of *instantaneous acceleration* (a). Let us write Δv for ($v_2 - v_1$) and Δt for ($t_2 - t_1$), then

$$a \equiv \frac{\Delta v}{\Delta t}. \tag{3–7}$$

The symbol "Δ" means "change in."

(e) *Momentum.* The momentum of a body moving in a given direction is taken to be in that direction and to have the magnitude μ defined as the product of the mass and speed of the body, or

$$\mu = mv. \tag{3–8}$$

(f) *Force.* The force acting on a body is taken to be in the direction of the resulting acceleration and is defined as the product of the mass and acceleration. Letting F be the magnitude of the force, we have

$$F = ma. \tag{3–9}$$

(g) *Density.* The density (ρ) of a body is defined as the ratio of its mass to its volume, or

$$\rho = \frac{m}{V}.$$
(3–10)

(h) *Pressure.* The concentration of force on a given area, called the pressure (p), is defined as the ratio of the force to the area, or

$$p = \frac{F}{A}.$$
(3–11)

(i) *Work.* When a force F pushes a body a distance s in the direction in which the force is acting, work is said to be done by the force. The amount of work (W) is defined as the product of the force and the distance moved, or

$$W = Fs.$$
(3–12)

(j) *Energy.* When work is performed "something" is transferred from one form and place to another form and place. This something is called *energy*. When W units of work are done by an agent, we say that W units of energy are transferred. If the agent is part of a system, call it A, which furnishes food or fuel to the agent, and if the agent does his work by pushing against something which is part of another system B, then we think of the work W as corresponding to the transfer of W units as energy from system A to system B. System A has given up this energy and B has gained it. We shall see that there are many forms of energy, and for each a formula will be developed according to the above concept and the definition of work. Since energy is measured by the amount of work needed to transfer the energy, energy and work are measured in the same units.

(k) *Power.* Power is defined as the rate of doing work. In other words, if a machine performs an amount of work W in a time t, its power output (P) is defined as

$$P = \frac{W}{t}.$$
(3–13)

(l) *Period.* The period (T) of an event that repeats itself at regular intervals of time is the time of one such interval.

(m) *Frequency.* In periodic phenomena the frequency (f) is defined as the number of periods in unit time, or

$$f = \frac{1}{T}.$$
(3–14)

Thus if the period is one-tenth second, the frequency $f = 10$ per second.

Summary. Note that each new quantity was defined in terms of our fundamental quantities and/or derived quantities previously defined. Observe also that when symbols for the various quantities are introduced, the definition of a derived quantity may be expressed as a mathematical equation. Such equations may be combined and manipulated according to the rules of mathematics.

EXAMPLE. Suppose that a constant force F acts against a piston of area A and moves it a distance s. Show that the work done equals the product of the pressure p on the piston and the change in volume ΔV (that is, the volume swept out by the piston as it moves through the distance s, as in Fig. 3–3).

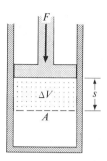

Solution. From Eq. (3–12) we have

$$W = Fs.$$

From Eq. (3–11) we see that

$$F = pA,$$

which we substitute in Eq. (3–11), getting

$$W = pAs.$$

FIG. 3–3.   Work done in moving a piston.

From the definition of volume, $As = \Delta V$, the volume swept out by the moving piston, so that we finally obtain the equation

$$W = p \, \Delta V.$$

3–4 Units for derived quantities

For each fundamental quantity we defined a unit in terms of which that quantity is measured. It is equally necessary to associate units with derived quantities; we shall see that such units are defined by the formula defining the derived quantity.

When we measure the magnitude of some quantity, say the length (l) of a table, our answer must consist of two parts, namely, (1) the unit(s) employed, and (2) the number of such units contained in l. Thus our answer might be 2.54 m, which could also be expressed as 254 cm, 100 in., 8.33 ft, 2.78 yards, etc. We see from this that the numerical part of our answer may have various values, such as 2.54 and 2.78, but that for a given choice of units there is only one correct numerical answer.

When we define the units for derived quantities we do so in such a way as to lead to a useful system. Such a system results if we adopt the following rule.

Rule: When physical quantities are mutliplied or divided together, or raised to the nth power, their corresponding units are respectively multiplied, divided, or raised to the nth power, like algebraic quantities.

As a result of this rule, units must behave as do algebraic quantities and hence *in any physical equation the units on each side must be essentially the same.* This makes good sense, for we know that we cannot equate pounds to feet per second, or kilograms per cubic meter to seconds. It is also common knowledge that we cannot add or subtract different kinds of quantities. Two meters plus three seconds do not equal five of anything. If you ever derive an equation which violates the statements above, you may be sure that your equation is not correct and that you have made some mistake.

From Eq. (3–5) and the above rule we see that when we take the meter (m) as our unit of distance and the second (sec) as our unit of time, we must take the meter per second (m/sec) as our *unit of speed* in the mks system. From Eq. (3–6) or (3–7) the mks *unit of acceleration* is seen to be the meter per second per second, or the meter per second squared (m/sec^2).

From the definition of momentum and Eq. (3–8) we see that the mks *unit of momentum* is the kg-m/sec.

The mks *unit of force* is, according to Eq. (3–9), the kg-m/sec^2. As we shall have frequent occasion to refer to force and its unit, and since kg-m/sec^2 is a rather awkward combination, we shall follow the custom of giving a single name, the *newton*, to this combination. Then by definition

$$1 \text{ newton } = 1 \text{ kg-m/sec}^2. \tag{3–15}$$

This mks unit of force will be written as n.

From the definition of density and Eq. (3–10) the mks *unit of density* is seen to be the kg/m^3.

The mks *unit of pressure* is, according to Eqs. (3–11) and (3–15), the newton per square meter (n/m^2), which is equivalent to kg-m/(sec^2-m^2). This last expression may and should be simplified by canceling the m in the numerator with one of the m's in the denominator, that is,

$$1 \text{ n/m}^2 = 1 \text{ kg-m/(sec}^2\text{-m}^2) = 1 \text{ kg/(sec}^2\text{-m}) = 1 \text{ kg/(m-sec}^2).$$

The mks *unit of work* or *energy* is, according to Eq. (3–12), the newton-meter (n-m), or the kg-m^2/sec^2. It is also customary to give a new name to this combination of units and to call it a *joule* (abbreviated j). Then by definition

$$1 \text{ joule } = 1 \text{ n-m } = 1 \text{ kg-m}^2/\text{sec}^2. \tag{3–16}$$

The mks *unit of power* is, according to Eq. (3–13), the joule per second, which is also called the *watt*. Then by definition

$$1 \text{ watt } = 1 \text{ j/sec } = 1 \text{ n-m/sec } = 1 \text{ kg-m}^2/\text{sec}^3. \tag{3–17}$$

Light bulbs and other electrical devices are rated in watts, so here we see that our mks unit is a familiar household one.

The mks unit for *period* is just the second, while for *frequency* it is per second, or (1/sec) = sec^{-1}. It is true that in measuring frequency we count something such as waves, oscillations, vibrations, revolutions, etc., but this counting process itself only involves the integers 1, 2, 3, 4 . . . and not any physical units. In the statements "vibrations per second" and "revolutions per second" we must consider the words "vibrations" and "revolutions" as telling us what is being counted, but we must not regard these words as part of the mks system of units.

3–5 Selecting units of convenient size; prefixes

Man is free to choose for his fundamental units ones of convenient size. In fact, it is mainly for this reason that it is preferable to introduce a unit for electric charge that is independent of mechanical units; the coulomb was so chosen that a coulomb per second would be the same as the ampere in terms of which electrical engineers had for some time been calibrating their instruments. Man is not, however, free to choose the size of the derived units in any given system such as the mks system. For example, once we have chosen the size of the meter and that of the second, the size of the meter per second is fixed. Fortunately the meter per second, newton, joule, and watt are not inconvenient units for measurements in everyday life, but physics is also concerned with the very small world of the atom as well as with some quantities of very large magnitude, and so physicists introduce decimal multiples of the standard units. Some common prefixes and their meanings are as follows:

$$\begin{aligned} \text{mega-} &= 1{,}000{,}000 = 10^6 \\ \text{kilo-} &= 1000 = 10^3 \\ \text{deci-} &= 0.1 = 10^{-1} \\ \text{centi-} &= 0.01 = 10^{-2} \\ \text{milli-} &= 0.001 = 10^{-3} \\ \text{micro-} &= 0.000001 = 10^{-6} \end{aligned}$$

The introduction of decimal multiples of units certainly leads to a better situation than exists in the British system, where larger and smaller multiples of various units came into use through custom rather than through scientific planning. It is easier to convert 1.35 m into centimeters than to convert 1.35 yards into inches! However, the decimal system still presents certain difficulties to the nonscientist and beginning student, such as the following.

(1) In the mks system the meter is the basic unit of length, but the *kilo*gram (not the gram itself) is the unit of mass.

(2) When converting centimeters to meters we must divide the number of centimeters by 100, while when changing grams to kilograms we must divide by 1000. Thus 200 cm = 2 m, 200 gm = 0.2 kg.

(3) When a quantity is expressed in terms of a larger unit, its *numerical value is less* than when expressed in terms of the smaller unit, and vice versa. Thus a given length contains *more* centimeters than meters and a given mass *more* grams than kilograms.

(4) When working numerical problems we must first express all quantities in terms of their basic units in the same system before substitution in the appropriate formula. It is best to use the mks units (see Section 3–4 and Table 3–2); then convert the answer into other units, if desired.

EXAMPLE 1. Tables give 2.7 gm/cm³ for the density of aluminum. Express this in mks units.

Solution.

$$2.7 \frac{\text{gm}}{\text{cm}^3} = 2.7 \times \frac{1 \text{ gm}}{1 \text{ cm}^3} = 2.7 \times \frac{10^{-3} \text{ kg}}{(10^{-2}\text{m})^3} = 2.7 \times \frac{10^{-3} \text{ kg}}{10^{-6}\text{ m}^3}$$

$$= 2.7 \times 10^3 \text{ kg/m}^3.$$

EXAMPLE 2. At sea level the pull of gravity on a pound of butter is 454×980 gm-cm/sec^2. Express this force, which is called the *pound-weight*, in newtons.

Solution.

$$1 \text{ pound-weight} = 454 \times 980 \ \frac{\text{gm-cm}}{\text{sec}^2}$$

$$= 4.45 \times 10^5 \times \frac{(10^{-3} \text{ kg})(10^{-2} \text{ m})}{\text{sec}^2}$$

$$= 4.45 \text{ kg-m/sec}^2$$

$$= 4.45 \text{ newtons.}$$

3–6 Relations between British and mks units

If in the future we encounter problems or read articles in which scientific quantities are expressed in British units, we may easily convert to mks units by referring to Table 3–1.

Note that in Table 3–1 the *pound* is used in two different senses, that is, as a unit of *mass* and as a unit of *force*. A pound-mass and pound-weight are not the same thing. The former is used in daily life to measure a quantity of something, while the latter is used by engineers to measure forces such as weight, thrust of a rocket engine, tension in a cable, etc.

EXAMPLE 1. Convert 1 mile/hour into m/sec.

Solution.

$$1 \ \frac{\text{mi}}{\text{hr}} = \frac{1.61 \times 10^3 \text{ m}}{3600 \text{ sec}} = 0.447 \text{ m/sec} = 4.47 \times 10^{-1} \text{ m/sec.}$$

EXAMPLE 2. Convert a thrust of 1 ton into newtons.

Solution.

$$1 \text{ ton-wt} = 2000 \text{ lb-wt} = 8.9 \times 10^3 \text{ newtons.}$$

EXAMPLE 3. Find the mks equivalent of one foot times one pound-weight. This product is called a foot-pound (ft-lb.)

TABLE 3–1

1 inch = 2.54 cm = 2.54×10^{-2} m,
1 foot = 12 in. = 3.05×10^{-1} m,
1 mile = 5280 ft = 1.61×10^3 m,
1 pound-mass = 454 gm = 4.54×10^{-1} kg,
1 pound-weight = 4.45 newtons,
1 kilowatt-hour = 3.6×10^6 joules,
1 horsepower = 746 watts.

TABLE 3-2

Quantities	Symbols	Defining formula	mks units
Length	l, s, d	Fundamental quantity	m (meter)
Mass	m, M	Fundamental quantity	kg (kilogram)
Time	t	Fundamental quantity	sec (second)
Area	A	$A = l^2$	m^2
Volume	V	$V = l^3$	m^3
Speed	v	$v = s/t$	m/sec
Acceleration	a	$a = \Delta v/\Delta t$	m/sec^2
Momentum	μ	$\mu = mv$	kg-m/sec
Force	F	$F = ma$	n (newton)
Density	ρ	$\rho = m/V$	kg/m^3
Pressure	p	$p = F/A$	n/m^2
Work, Energy	W, E	$W = Fs$	joule
Power	P	$P = W/t$	watt
Period	T	$T = t$	sec
Frequency	f	$f = 1/T$	1/sec
Angle	θ	$\theta = s/r$	radian

Solution.

$$1 \text{ ft} \times 1 \text{ lb-wt} = 3.05 \times 10^{-1} \text{ m} \times 4.45 \text{ n}$$
$$= 1.36 \text{ n-m or joules.}$$

The ft-lb and the kilowatt-hour are units of work or energy.

3-7 Summary

In Table 3-2 are listed the mechanical quantities defined in this chapter, their symbols, the formulas defining derived quantities, and the respective mks units.

It may seem that this chapter contains too much material to memorize all together. This is because the chapter is essentially one containing part of a physicist's vocabulary. When learning a new language, one is soon confronted with the task of memorizing a considerable vocabulary; this task is accepted as necessary if one is to gain a working knowledge of the language. So it is in physics, except that we do not have to memorize everything at once, provided that we *understand* the definitions and *know where to find them*. The best way to learn any vocabulary is with repeated use. Problem solving helps in this regard.

PROBLEMS

1. Find in mks units the (a) area of a circle whose radius is 2 cm, (b) the volume of a rectangular box whose dimensions are $2 \times 3 \times 5$ cm, (c) the volume of a sphere whose radius is 20 cm.

2. Express 4000 miles (the earth's radius) in meters.

3. Express your (a) height in meters, (b) weight in kilograms.

4. Convert one foot per second into m/sec.

5. Explain why 1 kilowatt-hour $= 3.6 \times 10^6$ joules.

6. Express 1800 revolutions per minute (rpm) in mks units.

7. A ball moves down a trough and travels 6 cm in the first quarter second and 24 cm the first half second. Find the average speed, in m/sec, during the first and second quarters of a second.

8. In problem 7 find the acceleration in cm/sec² and in m/sec².

9. Find the force in newtons that will give a pound-mass an acceleration of 32.2 ft/sec². Is this force equal to the pound-weight?

10. Normal sea level atmospheric pressure is about 15 pounds-weight per square inch. Express this in mks units.

11. The gravitational constant G is defined by Eq. (1–1), i.e., $G = Fs^2/m_1m_2$. Find its mks units.

12. In mks units the magnitude of G is 6.67×10^{-11}. What would be its magnitude in terms of grams, centimeters, and seconds?

13. Compute the gravitational attraction between (a) two balls, each of 1 kg mass, whose centers are 10 cm apart, and (b) an electron of mass 9×10^{-31} kg and a proton of mass 1.67×10^{-27} kg which are 5×10^{-11} m apart (as in a normal hydrogen atom).

CHAPTER 4

The Experimental Method. Errors

4–1 The role of experiment in science

Modern science owes its progress to a combination of experimental and theoretical work. Each has been a stimulus to the other.

We can say that in the development of a science the starting point must be experimentation. We cannot speculate and theorize until we have observations to speculate about. These observations may be simply those of our everyday lives, from infancy on, or they may result from planned and controlled experiments. Gradually the facts observed become so numerous as to be confusing and hard to handle. Until we find some pattern or order in the accumulated data, we do not know in what direction to turn next. At this point one looks for a correlation between two or more quantities. These quantities must, of course, first be defined, as some were in the last chapter, giving us a working vocabulary. The observed relations between our concepts constitute the *rules of grammar* of our subject. While we saw that a self-consistent set of rules may be arbitrarily chosen in a branch of mathematics, in a subject such as physics we must take the rules as we find them from our observations; they are the *laws of nature*.

The Greeks observed the world around them and noted how nature behaved, yet they failed to discover any of what are now considered the fundamental laws of physics. Why was this so? The reason was that the Greeks just let events *happen* in the random and complicated way that events in nature always take place. They did not try to *control* the way things happened, because that meant doing something with their hands and manual labor was considered demeaning for educated Greeks of the upper class — it was "beneath" them. The Greeks did much thinking and arguing about the physical world, but they did very little real experimenting. The work of Archimedes, which led him to his famous principle about the loss of weight of a body in a fluid, was an exception. Aristotle, on the other hand, just looked about, noted that leaves fell faster than feathers and stones faster than leaves (Fig. 4–1), and then concluded that a heavier body always fell faster than a lighter one; had he tried to drop together two heavy objects, such as two stones of different weight, he would have been surprised to find that they fell at the *same* rate. Unfortunately Aristotle did not experiment.

The Romans excelled in engineering, but they were not interested in what we now call basic research. During Roman rule, Greek knowledge was cut off from the West.

FIG. 4–1.   Stones fall faster than leaves.

In the 12th century Greek scientific writings reached the West via the Moslems. The spark of learning was kept alive by the Church, which under Thomas Aquinas merged Greek scientific philosophy and Christian theology. Scholars were taught to accept without question the statements of Aristotle. These statements became authoritative dogma. They were not tested. Since Aristotle and Ptolemy had said that all the heavenly bodies revolve around our earth, that hypothesis (for that is what it was) had to be accepted without any suggestion of an alternative view if one did not wish to find himself in trouble with the Church. In such an atmosphere science could not advance.

Galileo is generally credited with introducing the experimental method that embodies the spirit of modern science. He lived around 1600 A.D. and physics as we know it today dates mostly from that time. Galileo not only experimented, but he performed *controlled experiments*. Let us see what this means.

4–2 Controlled experiments

A controlled experiment is one in which the experimenter controls all the factors which may affect the result and then deliberately varies one such factor at a time. In this way one can find out how the result of the experiment (the effect) depends on each of the factors (the causes) involved. It is obvious that if one allows simultaneous variations in several relevant factors, then it will be difficult to sort out the individual contributions which each variation made toward changing the result of the experiment. Let us take an example.

Consider a stretched steel wire or string supported by two bridges (points of support) that are a distance l apart. Let the force pulling the string taut be F. (Fig. 4–2). The string when plucked will vibrate with a particular frequency f. Now if one simultaneously loosens the steel string (decreases F) and shortens the distance l, the frequency f may either increase or decrease, depending on how much one loosens and how much one shortens the string. Just loosening a violin string lowers its pitch and just shortening the vibrating length raises the pitch. To sort out these two effects one should (1) keep l constant and vary F, and then (2) keep

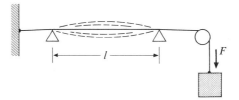

FIG. 4-2.   A vibrating string.

F constant and vary l, noting each time the variation in the frequency f. One will then discover that f is directly proportional to the square root of F and inversely proportional to l, that is,

$$f \propto \frac{\sqrt{F}}{l},$$ (4-1)

or

$$f = k \frac{\sqrt{F}}{l},$$ (4-2)

where k is independent of F and l. Suppose that F and l are each halved; will the frequency go up or down? (It will go up. Why?) Or suppose that F is increased to four times its original value and l is doubled, how will f be affected?

Experimental investigation of vibrating strings may be further extended by varying the diameter of the string. To do this properly one should compare the frequencies of two strings of *equal length l* which are under the *same tension F*, but which have different diameters. Note that on musical instruments, thick strings give notes of lower frequency than do thin strings. All else being the same, the frequency is inversely proportional to the diameter d, so that we may write

$$f = k' \frac{\sqrt{F}}{ld},$$ (4-3)

where k' is independent of F, l, and d.

The experimental investigator of vibrating strings would seek to find out whether the frequency depends on any other factors besides F, l, and d. He would finally discover that f also depends on the density ρ of the substance of which the wire is composed and that

$$f = \frac{k''}{ld} \sqrt{\frac{F}{\rho}},$$ (4-4)

where $k'' = 1/\sqrt{\pi}$, so that k'' is a universal constant for *all* vibrating strings. With this much information in hand, physicists would usually feel that a theory is called for to explain the dependence of f on F, l, d, and ρ and why k'' equals $1/\sqrt{\pi}$. How such a theory is constructed will be explained in the next chapter.

In everyday life we frequently lose sight of all the factors that must be controlled if we are to draw scientific information and valid conclusions from experiments. A person may alter (1) his diet, (2) the amount of sleep he gets, and (3) the amount of exercise he does, with the result that he feels better. To what should he credit his greater well-being? It would be unscientific and risky for this man to claim either that all the factors altered were equally important, or that one was particularly effective. Similarly, scientific claims should not be made by a tobacco company about the effect of altering the filtration in its cigarettes if at the same time the company alters by an unknown amount the strength of the tobacco used in the cigarettes. Only one factor at a time should be varied, and that by a measured amount.

The controlled experiment requires care and skill, but that is not all. The experimental physicist is confronted with the problem of sifting out the relevant factors. He must not only *control* but he must decide *what to vary*. One must acquire a method or *technique*, rather than experiment at random, and this requires intelligence and a knowledge of one's subject. Experiment 5 at the end of Chapter 5 illustrates the importance of technique and Experiments 2 and 3 at the end of this chapter are good examples of controlled experiments.

4–3 Empirical laws

We saw in the example of the vibrating string that by means of controlled experiments scientists have found a relationship between the frequency f and the tension F, length l, diameter d, and density ρ of a string, as stated by Eq. (4–4). Such a relationship, based purely on experimental evidence, is called an *empirical* relationship, or an *empirical* law. Empirical laws must be distinguished from those postulates or hypotheses made by the theoretical physicist, although such postulates are also often called "laws" (see Chapter 5). Empirical laws are only as good as the experimental observations on which they are based; they stand subject to contradiction when one uses them to guess the result of an experiment that has not been tried before.

As another example consider the stretching of a coiled spring (Fig. 4–3). With a steel spring that is not stretched too far, one will find that the stretching force F is directly proportional to the resulting elongation s, or

$$F = ks, \tag{4–5}$$

where k is constant for a given spring but varies from one spring to another. The statement of the above proportionality, or the statement that k is independent of s for a given spring, is often called *Hooke's law*. Now we know that rubber bands are quite stretchable and elastic, so we might be tempted to assume that Hooke's law also applies to the stretching of rubber bands, which Experiment 4 at the end of this chapter will show is not the case.

Three of the most famous empirical laws were discovered by the German scientist Johannes Kepler around 1600. Kepler had worked under the Danish astronomer Tycho Brahe. The latter throughout his life made painstaking measurements of the positions in the sky of the planets at various times of the year. Although Tycho Brahe worked before the telescope came into use, his sighting methods were accurate to better than one hundredth of a degree of arc. Tycho

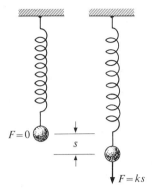

$F=0$

s

$F=ks$

FIG. 4-3. Stretching of a coiled spring.

Brahe accumulated a tremendous amount of data, which would be most confusing to anyone who saw it for the first time. Kepler had plenty of opportunity to study this data, and he sought to find some degree of order in it. As a result of his efforts he was able to show that all the information in the data could be summarized in three statements, or empirical laws, as follows.

I. Each planet moves in an elliptical orbit.

II. A planet moves in its orbit at a varying speed such that the line from the sun to the planet sweeps out equal areas in equal times (Fig. 4-4).

III. The square of the time a planet takes to make one trip in its orbit around the sun is directly proportional to the cube of the mean radius of its orbit.

These laws of Kepler describe *how* the planets move around the sun. The explanation, in terms of fundamental postulates, of *why* the planets move as they do was given later by Sir Isaac Newton. We shall come to this in a subsequent chapter.

Kepler's laws do not tell us the particular ellipses in which the planets move. The empirical law of Bode and Titus attempts to summarize this information in the statement

$$\overline{R} = 0.4 + 0.3 \times 2^{n-2}, \qquad (4\text{-}6)$$

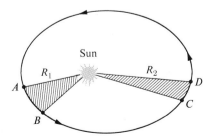

FIG. 4-4. Kepler's laws. The orbit of the planet is an ellipse. If the shaded areas are equal, the planet takes the same time to cover the distances *AB* and *CD*.

where $\overline{R}$ is the mean radius of a planetary orbit (taking that of the earth to be the unit of distance) and n is the planet's *number*, i.e., $n = 1$ for Mercury, $n = 2$ for Venus, $n = 3$ for Earth and $n = 4$ for Mars, while for the larger outer planets one must let $n = 6$ for Jupiter, $n = 7$ for Saturn, $n = 8$ for Uranus, etc. This law emphasized the gap between the inner and outer planets, since the planet for which $n = 5$ seemed to be missing. The search for the "missing" planet led to the discovery of the asteroids, small planetary bodies (the largest, Ceres, has a diameter of less than 500 miles) which circulate in orbits for which $\overline{R}$ is about 2.8 times its value for the earth's orbit. Note that in Eq. (4–6) $\overline{R} = 2.8$ when $n = 5$. The attempt is still being made to *explain* the Bode-Titus law in terms of the basic laws of physics.

4–4 The accuracy of a measurement

When one performs a controlled experiment in order to determine whether a quantity y depends on another quantity x and, if so, what the dependence and constant(s) of proportionality are, then one must ask the question: "How reliable are my experimental results?"

For example we might, as in experiment 3, time a pendulum whose length is 64 cm and arc of swing 25 cm and find that 25 oscillations take 40.2 seconds. Next we might change bobs, while trying not to vary the length of pendulum or the arc of swing, and we might then find that 25 oscillations take 39.8 seconds. We would immediately wonder whether the difference between the two times was significant and implied a dependence of the period of oscillation on the bob used. Here our conclusion would be based on two considerations, namely, (1) how accurately we could measure the two times and (2) how closely we could keep the other factors (length of the pendulum and arc of swing) under control, and hence constant. If our timing was only good to half a second, then the difference between 40.2 sec and 39.8 sec would not be significant. If we could not change bobs without altering the length, the change in time might be due to a change in length, because further investigation would disclose a dependence of period on length ($T \propto \sqrt{l}$); actually a 2% change in length would account for the 0.4 sec or 1% change in the time for the 25 oscillations.

It is evident that the experimental investigator must have a clear comprehension of the probable accuracy of his experiment and of the errors that may enter into it.

4–5 Sources of inaccuracy or error

Many kinds of error are involved in physical measurements. Errors have been classified in various ways, such as determinate versus indeterminate errors, systematic versus accidental errors, errors due to instruments versus errors due to the observer and his method of doing the experiment; these categories have been subdivided. The choice of classification is somewhat a matter of taste. As a complete study of errors is lengthy and involved, a simplification is necessary for our purposes. It is better to arrive easily at a fairly good understanding of the accuracy of an experiment than to undertake a detailed treatment of errors which is so complicated that it is never completed!

Inaccuracies in the results of an experiment may be due to the method chosen, the physical environment, the observer, and the equipment used. When one tries to estimate mathematically the possible error in one's results, one finds that the important distinction is whether errors are *systematic* or *random*; therefore, we shall adopt this classification.

4–6 Systematic errors

These include all inaccuracies that tend to be more in one direction than in the opposite one. Care and pains should be taken to reduce all such errors to the point where they are insignificant compared with the random errors.

(a) *Errors due to the method.* When one measures temperature with a gas thermometer [Section 3–2(d)], the result may be affected by the expansion of the glass bulb, by the fact that the neck of the bulb is out in the room, by moisture in the gas, by the fact that when the ice point was determined the ice bath was not exactly at the freezing point of water, and by the fact that the boiling point of water varies with the atmospheric pressure. If such sources of error cannot be eliminated, corrections for them should be made, although some of these corrections may turn out to be insignificant. We make a rough calculation of the magnitude of such corrections, forget the insignificant ones, and correct for the others.

(b) *Errors due to the environment* can only be reduced through proper control of such things as the temperature, humidity, noise background, vibration, stray electric or magnetic fields, etc. For this reason a laboratory may well have a carefully thermostated room, a soundproof room, vibration-free pillars, and an electrically shielded room.

(c) *Personal errors* are of many kinds. First there are *mistakes*, which may be due to carelessness, misreading a scale, lack of understanding of the equipment, faulty arithmetic, miscounting, etc. Mistakes *must* be eliminated through training and the use of sufficient intelligence and care, or otherwise the equipment used is too good for the experimenter! *Psychological* errors arise due to faulty senses (e.g., poor sense of pitch or color) and to the way one reacts to his environment. When timing an event one observer may tend to anticipate the signal and read too soon, while another person may react too late. In such cases the best procedure is to use several observers, eliminate the data of one who is obviously faulty, and treat the remaining data statistically (see next section).

(d) *Instrumental errors* of a systematic nature may be most important. Examples are: a warped or shrunken meter stick, a clock that always runs slow (or fast), a damaged electric meter that always reads low (or high), an instrument whose zero point is off, an inaccurate spring balance, etc. It is imperative to eliminate such sources of error by checking all questionable pieces of equipment against more reliable instruments. Faulty apparatus should be discarded, repaired, or calibrated and supplied with a table of corrections. Be alert and replace any piece of equipment that you suspect.

4–7 Random fluctuations and residual instrumental errors

Let us assume that errors due to method, environment, instruments, and ob-servers have been reduced to the point where they are either insignificant or of a completely random nature. By "random" we mean that they may be treated statistically, according to the laws of probability. These laws tell us that positive and negative fluctuations are equally probable, that large fluctuations are much less likely than small ones, that when the reading of a quantity is repeated the *mean* (average) of the readings is the most probable value of the quantity, etc. Other results of statistical theory will be mentioned presently.

(a) *Fluctuations due to the method.* These vary tremendously in importance. In Experiment 1 at the end of this chapter, two different methods of experimentally determining the value of π are described. In the first method one measures the circumference c and diameter d of several cylinders and then computes $c/d = \pi$. Since no cylinder can be made perfectly circular, the diameter of any one will vary and so will the computed value of c/d, but with well-constructed cylinders these fluctuations should be small. The second method of finding π, is a purely statistical one. Toothpicks are scattered at random over a large piece of paper on which parallel lines have been ruled just one toothpick length apart (Fig. 4–5). If N toothpicks are tossed and n of these fall so as to cross lines on the paper, then theory predicts that the most probable value of $2N/n$ is π. Suppose, however, that just *one* toothpick is tossed, so that n must be either 0 or 1, what will the result be? With $N = 1$, $n = 0$, $2N/n = \infty$, while with $N = 1$, $n = 1$, $2N/n = 2$. With one toothpick the experimental value of $2N/n$ and the true value of π (3.1416) are *bound* to differ by at least 36%! With two throws ($N = 2$), $2N/n$ might be ∞, 4, or 2, all of which differ from π by 27% or more. Only by tossing hundreds of toothpicks and then computing $2N/n$ can one expect to obtain a value close to that of π. This experiment has been programmed and given to an electronic computer which, in effect, proceeds to toss toothpicks at a rapid rate, computing $2N/n$ as it goes along; the computer's value for $2N/n$ was found to coincide with that of π more and more closely as time went on.

More familiar than the toothpick experiment is that of tossing coins. If one could always toss a coin in *exactly* the same manner, one could obtain "heads"

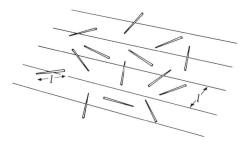

FIG. 4–5. Determination of π by the statistical method of tossing toothpicks onto a ruled paper.

every time or "tails" every time; but the tossing process, like the shuffling of cards, is supposed to involve so many variable factors that how the coin lands is purely a matter of chance. We may then apply statistical theory and predict that for a large number of tosses "heads" and "tails" should each turn up about 50% of the time.

One should realize that an element of chance enters into every experiment, but to a greater extent in some cases than in others. In the majority of experiments the fluctuations due to the nature of the method are small because one deals, not with the behavior of 2, 10, or 100 toothpicks or coins, but with the average behavior of perhaps 10^{23} atoms, molecules, electrons, etc. In such experiments statistical fluctuations due to other causes predominate.

(b) *Fluctuations due to the environment* are illustrated by the random variations in the temperature of a thermally controlled room, variations in the ordinary electric line voltage, rapid variations in the cosmic ray intensity or the activity of a radioactive source.

(c) *Fluctuations due to the observer.* After personal errors have been reduced to the point where they are equally likely to be positive or negative, they may be treated statistically. Such errors show up when the same measurement is repeated several times and the results vary in a manner that cannot be attributed to other causes. For example, if a person tries to estimate a reading to a tenth of a small scale division, he may sometimes guess a little high and sometimes a little low. There is certainly a limit to how accurately anyone can observe, and beyond this limit one must guess.

(d) *Residual instrumental errors.* Even after an instrument has been carefully calibrated it still cannot be used to measure a quantity to an infinite number of significant figures. The cost of apparatus rises so rapidly with its accuracy that a limit is soon reached. A rough but good rule to adopt is that *a scale is reliable to its smallest marked segment*, i.e., *to one division*, otherwise the manufacturer would divide the scale more finely. It is good practice to read a scale to the nearest half, fifth, or tenth, of a division, since such fractions *may* be sufficiently significant to increase one's accuracy, but do not rely on these fractions.

You will find that the measurement of many physical quantities involves making *two* readings of an instrument so as to obtain the *change* in a quantity, e.g., a rise in temperature or the change in the reading of a meter. Even the measurement of the diameter of a cylinder involves finding two points on a scale, points where a scale placed across the center of the cylinder meets opposite sides of the circumference. When two such readings taken on the *same scale* are to be subtracted, we must estimate each reading to half a division or better if we wish to keep the instrumental error in the difference of the two readings to within one division.

There are instruments such as weights, resistors, capacitors, standards cells, etc., which do not possess scales but have a calibrated value marked on them. The accuracy of such quantities should be specified by the manufacturer, or by the person who last calibrated the instrument. The indicated inaccuracy should be regarded as equally likely to be positive or negative. When we wish to determine the sum or difference of two weighings, it is best to add the possible errors in each weighing, since in one case the error might be positive and in the other case negative, or vice versa.

4–8 The accuracy of a single reading

One should not limit himself to a single reading of a quantity unless he has good reason to believe that subsequent readings would turn out to be the same. The best way to be sure of this is to try it! If readings are reproducible and systematic errors have been reduced to insignificance, then *take the possible error in the result to be the residual instrumental error r,* i.e., either one scale division or the value given on the instrument.

A numerical error in a quantity may be expressed as a *percent error* by dividing the numerical error by the quantity and multiplying by 100%.

EXAMPLE 1. A meter stick calibrated in millimeters (i.e., to 0.1 cm) is used to measure the stretch of a spring by mounting the stick behind the spring. Before loading, the reading of the end of the spring is 22.25 cm and, after stretching, the reading is 27.40 cm. Readings are reproducible. Find the stretch and the percent possible error in the result.

Solution. The stretch is 5.15 cm, good to one division of the stick, or 0.1 cm. Hence the

$$\text{stretch} = (5.15 \pm 0.10) \text{ cm.}$$

The percent possible error is

$$\% \text{ error} = \frac{0.1 \times 100\%}{5.15} = \text{about } 2\%.$$

EXAMPLE 2. The mass of a beaker is found to be 208.7 gm when empty and 462.9 gm when filled with water. Find the mass of the water and the percent possible error, given that each weighing is good to ±0.2%.

Solution. 0.2% of 462.9 is 0.9 and 0.2% of 208.7 is about 0.4. The mass of water is

$$(462.9 \pm 0.9) - (208.7 \pm 0.4) = (254.2 \pm 1.3) \text{ gm.}$$

The percent possible error is

$$1.3 \times 100\%/254 = 130\%/254 = 0.5\%.$$

Note the increase in percent error when the difference between two quantities is calculated.

EXAMPLE 3. The temperature of a beaker of water is measured with a thermometer graduated in degrees. At the start of the experiment the temperature read is 28.6°. After some ice has been allowed to melt in the water, the temperature read is 18.4°. Find the possible error in the computed temperature change.

Solution. The computed change in temperature is (10.2 ± 1.0) degrees, so that the possible error is 10%. Readings were estimated to 0.2°, but the thermometer was only good to 1°. Note that calling the percent error of, say, the first reading (1°/28.6°) × 100% = 3.5% is meaningless, since the zero mark on any but an absolute thermometer is arbitrary. Only the percent error in the temperature *change* has meaning.

4–9 The accuracy of the average of several readings

Suppose that we make six observations of some quantity and get numerical readings that are bunched closely together, e.g., 20.2, 20.1, 20.0, 20.3, 19.9, and 20.1. Would we not feel considerable confidence in our data and in taking the mean value of 20.1 as our answer? On the other hand, suppose that our six numerical readings were 22.2, 18.0, 24.2, 15.3, 23.0, and 17.9; how much confidence would we now feel in our readings or in their mean value of 20.1? Very little! For one thing, we can see that if we had omitted any one observation, then our mean value would have been quite different, while if we had taken a seventh reading, that also would probably have altered our mean value. Evidently what must be considered here are the fluctuations in the readings. The significance of these fluctuations is most easily evaluated by calculating the *average* or *mean deviation* $\overline{d}$. The deviation d for any one reading is here defined as the difference between the reading and the mean, with the smaller quantity being subtracted from the larger so as to make d come out positive. To obtain $\overline{d}$ one must average the deviations for all the readings, so that

$$\overline{d} = \frac{d_1 + d_2 + d_3 + \cdots + d_n}{n}. \tag{4-7}$$

The theory of probability tells us that, assuming no systematic errors, for a set of six readings ($n = 6$), 95% of the time the actual error in the mean will not exceed $\overline{d}$; henceforth we shall usually assume systematic errors eliminated and *regard $\overline{d}$ as our possible error due to random fluctuations*, provided that at least six readings are taken.

EXAMPLE. Take the two sets of data given at the beginning of Section 4–9. Compute the possible error in each case.

Solution. It is best to tabulate as in Table 4–1. For the first set of data $\overline{d} = 0.1$, and the random possible error is 0.5% of the mean. For the second set of data $\overline{d} = 3.0$, and the possible error is about 15% of the mean.

TABLE 4–1

Reading	Deviation	Reading	Deviation
20.2	0.1	22.2	2.1
20.1	0.0	18.0	2.1
20.0	0.1	24.2	4.1
20.3	0.2	15.3	4.8
19.9	0.2	23.0	2.9
20.1	0.0	17.9	2.2
Sum 120.6	0.6	120.6	18.2
Mean 20.1	0.1	20.1	3.03

In the first case it would seem very unlikely that the true value of the quantity being measured would actually lie above 20.2 or below 20.0, while for the other set 20.1 ±3.1 would seem to provide a liberal range of uncertainty.

4–10 The possible error in a combined result

Frequently the final result of an experiment is obtained by taking sets of observations of several different quantities and then adding, subtracting, multiplying, dividing, etc., the various mean values. For example, we might use Eq. (4–4) to compute the frequency f. Knowing the percent errors in our measured value of F, l, and d, respectively, how would we find the percent error in our computed value of f?

The important rules to remember when we wish to combine quantities are the following.

I. *When adding or subtracting quantities, add the numerical errors.*

II. *When multiplying or dividing quantities, add the percent errors.*

III. *When raising a quantity to the nth power, multiply the percent error in the quantity by n.*

IV. *When extracting the nth root of a quantity, divide the percent error in the quantity by n.*

EXAMPLE 1. Given $x = 200 \pm 2$, $y = 160 \pm 2$, $z = 2.00 \pm 0.05$. Find the possible error in $(x - y)/z^2$.

Solution. We have $x - y = 40 \pm 4$. The percent errors are 10% in $x - y$, 2.5% in z, 5% in z^2. Therefore the percent error in $(x - y)/z^2$ is $10 + 5 = 15\%$. We may write $(x - y)/z^2 = 10.0 \pm 1.5$.

EXAMPLE 2. Refer to Eq. (4–4). Suppose that our measurements give $F = (100 \pm 2)$ n, $l = (50.0 \pm 0.2)$ cm, $d = (50 \pm 2) \times 10^{-2}$ mm, and $\rho = (8.1 \pm 0.1)$ gm/cm^3. Compute the value of f from Eq. (4–4) and find its possible percent error.

Solution. First express all quantities in mks units. Thus $l = 0.500$ m, $d = 5.0 \times 10^{-4}$ m, $\rho = 8.1 \times 10^3$ kg/m^3. Also $F = 100$ n $= 100$ kg-m/sec^2:

$$f = \frac{1}{\sqrt{\pi}} \frac{1}{0.50 \text{ m} \times 5 \times 10^{-4} \text{ m}} \sqrt{\frac{100 \text{ kg-m/sec}^2}{8.1 \times 10^3 \text{ kg/m}^3}}$$

$$= \frac{4000}{\sqrt{\pi} \text{ m}^2} \sqrt{\frac{1}{81} \frac{\text{m}^4}{\text{sec}^2}}$$

$$= \frac{4000}{9\sqrt{\pi} \text{ sec}},$$

or about 250 waves are emitted per second.

The percent errors are 0.4% in l, 4% in d, 2% in F and 1.2% in ρ. One may take π to as many correct figures as desired so that its error may be neglected. Then the percent error in f is $0.4 + 4.0 + \frac{1}{2}(2.0 + 1.2) = 6.0\%$. We find $f = (250 \pm 15)$ per second.

4–11 The establishment of empirical laws

Now that we have seen how the reliability of a measurement may be evaluated, we return to the discussion of how experimental relationships (empirical laws) are established. As indicated earlier, this may involve the discovery that a certain quantity does not change in value when the value of another quantity is varied, or it may involve the discovery of a functional relationship between two quantities.

(a) *Establishment of a relationship of independence between two quantities.* Suppose that we want to determine whether the time of 25 swings of a pendulum is independent of the arc of swing, or whether the time for a stone to fall from rest through 20 ft is independent of the size of the stone, or whether the ratio of the circumference to the diameter of a cylinder is independent of the size of the cylinder. How would we proceed? In the case of the pendulum, we could take six readings of the time with one arc and six readings with the same bob and a larger arc. For each set of conditions we would find the mean time and the mean deviation. Then we would compute the possible error in each case. Only if the mean times for the two arcs differed by *more* than the sum of the possible errors should we definitely conclude that altering the arc of swing did affect the period of the pendulum.

Mean times of (40.2 ± 0.2) seconds and (39.8 ± 0.2) seconds should be regarded as possibly the same, within the accuracy of the experiment, since the two times might both be 40.0 seconds. On the other hand, (40.4 ± 0.2) seconds and (39.8 ± 0.2) seconds should not be regarded as the same.

The equality of two measurements made under different conditions may frequently be established by a *null method*, that is, a method in which *no effect* indicates equality. If little or no effect is expected, one may replace the measuring device with a much more sensitive detector. For example, two pendulums of equal length but with different bobs, could be set in motion together and an electrical device could be used to detect whether or not the two bobs continued to swing in synchronism.

Galileo used the null method in his famous experiment on falling objects. He dropped (legend says from the Leaning Tower of Pisa) a small and a large stone together and visually compared their rates of falling. Crude though Galileo's technique may now seem, it was truly scientific, and it led him to the discovery of some important properties of the physical world. Such experiments help us to see more clearly *how* nature behaves.

What were the results of Galileo's experiment? Did the two stones hit the ground simultaneously? A wise scientist would qualify his answer. Consider the following simple experiment. We hold a small stone in one hand and a large stone in the other; the larger one certainly feels heavier, so should it not fall faster? Now we release the stones simultaneously and see if they do or do not hit the floor with a single thud. We might then substitute a ball of paper or cork for one of the stones. When we do this sort of thing, we can be considered experimental scientists. It is experiments of this sort that lead students to speculate about the meaning of their results; this is the spirit of modern science — a spirit that is necessary to appreciate the study of physics.

TABLE 4–2

s	t
s_1	t_1
s_2	t_2
s_3	t_3
s_4	t_4

(b) *Establishment of a relationship of proportionality between two quantities.* Galileo was too good an investigator not to want to find out more about the nature of free fall than just whether two stones fell at the same rate. He could see that the speed of a falling object increased and he wondered whether it increased in proportion to the distance or the time. Since the time of fall was short (under 3 sec) and since methods of timing available to him were not nearly as precise as they are now, Galileo ingeniously hit upon the plan of "diluting" gravity by observing the motion of a ball rolling down an inclined plane (see Experiment 7 at the end of Chapter 6). Galileo proved that in such an experiment the distance traversed was proportional to the square of the time. From this he reasoned that the speed gained was proportional to the time. Varying the inclination of the plane did not alter the type of proportionality but only the constant involved. Galileo then argued that this type of proportionality should hold for free fall, since the latter corresponds to the fall down a plane whose inclination has been increased to 90°.

Suppose that we want to prove that the distance s through which a stone falls in the time t is proportional to some power, call it the nth, of t, so that

$$s = kt^n, \tag{4–8}$$

where k is the constant of proportionality. We would also like to find experimentally the values of n and k. We might start by choosing a measured distance s_1 and taking several readings of the time of fall; the mean value of the times will be called t_1, and we can compute its possible error. This one pair of readings of s and t will not tell us the values of either n or k, so we must choose another value of s, say s_2, and measure the corresponding value t_2 of t. Let us suppose that we do this for at least four different distances of fall. Our data may now be presented most clearly in tabular form, as in Table 4–2. Should we average the values of s in Table 4–2 and find their mean and mean deviation? This would be useless because we know that the values of s are not supposed to be the same, while in the case of t we strongly suspect that the times increase with s, and so are not constant either. We should average values of a quantity only when we have reason to believe that the values vary only because of random fluctuations. At this point we should look carefully at our data and do a little thinking. Remember that more often than not the relationships found in nature are simple ones. In the case of the free-fall experiment, we should observe immediately that (1) t increases with s, and (2) t does not increase as rapidly as s does. This means that if an equation such as

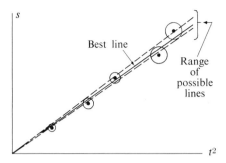

F<small>IG</small>. 4–6. Graphing experimental data so as to show possible errors.

Eq. (4–8) exists, n must be positive and greater than unity ($n > 1$). The simplest possibility is that $n = 2$, or that s is proportional to t^2. Let us write

$$s = kt^2. \tag{4–9}$$

In Section 2–7 we discussed the advisability of seeking a straight line graph. Thus in this case we should plot s against t^2. If we can find a straight line that will fit our points, then Eq. (4–9) is verified and the slope of our line will be k. We shall see later that theoretically k should equal $\frac{1}{2}g$, where g is the acceleration due to gravity. Therefore the determination of k may be used to find g experimentally.

We must return to the subject of possible errors. Since no measurements are perfectly accurate, we cannot expect the points on our graph to lie *exactly* on one line. If the points do not fall on a line, how can we tell whether this is because of errors or because we have assumed the wrong functional relationship? The answer to this question lies in consideration of the possible errors in our data.

After all our data have been plotted, we surround each point with a circle or rectangle whose size indicates the possible error. Then we can take a straightedge and easily see whether or not a line may be drawn that will pass through some part of each circle or rectangle associated with our experimental points. If we find that many lines may be drawn, the range in slope of these lines will indicate the possible error in the constant of proportionality (see Fig. 4–6). In this way we would, in the free-fall experiment, arrive at the possible error Δk in k. Our best value for k would be that given by the line that best fitted our experimental points.

The graphical method of establishing a proportionality relationship is to be preferred over a purely numerical one. A graph quickly gives a comprehensive picture of the results. In the example just discussed, it is better to determine k graphically rather than by averaging our values of s/t^2, (see Section 2–7).

(c) *Empirical graphs.* There are some experiments whose data are such that one cannot recognize any simple functional relationship between two of the measured quantities. For example, if we take a meter stick, drill holes in it at various points x meters from the center, and then put a nail horizontally through one of the holes, we will find that the stick can swing about the nail with a certain period T. By changing the nail to different holes we will get values $T_1, T_2, T_3, \ldots$ for T corresponding to the values $x_1, x_2, x_3, \ldots$ for x. The functional relationship between x and T is sufficiently complicated to make it difficult to discover experimentally. In such a case we might just as well plot T against x and see what sort of curve we obtain. Later, when a theory has been furnished, we could plot the theoretically predicted relationship on the same graph and compare the experimental and theoretical curves. A close fit would mean that the theory had been verified experimentally. In case the reader is curious as to the actual relationship in the case of the meter stick experiment, it is as follows:

$$x T^2 = \frac{4\pi^2}{g}\left(x^2 + \frac{1}{12}\right), \qquad (4\text{--}10)$$

where x is the distance in meters from the center of the stick to the point of support, T is the period in seconds, and $g = 9.8\text{m/sec}^2$. This is not a formula to memorize, because it does not represent a fundamental law of nature and because it only applies to a very special situation. Physicists either (1) learn how to derive an equation such as (4–10), or (2) they remember where they can look it up if they need it.

4–12 The need for humility in science

The experimental method has proved to be most fruitful; it has enabled us to see how the physical world behaves and what we can and cannot do with it. It is no wonder that there have been times when scientists have felt too certain of their results, or when the general public has accepted the statements of scientists as absolute truth, without the shadow of a doubt.

As measurements have become more refined and precise, physicists have been able to measure quantities such as the speed of light, or the wavelength of a spectral line, to another and yet another significant figure, but never to an infinite number of such figures. We have seen that a physicist should repeat measurements several times, compute the mean value of the quantity (call it K) that he is trying to measure, and estimate the accuracy of his result. He should issue a statement such as: "The best obtainable value of K is 6.25 and the chances are 19 out of 20 that the true value lies between 6.22 and 6.28," or "the best obtainable value of K is 6.25 and the chances are 50–50 that the true value lies between 6.24 and 6.26." Some modern weathermen have emulated the physicist in this respect and accompany their forecasts with statements about the reliability of their predictions.

Of course scientists feel much more certain about some things than they do about others. They are not likely to quote the odds in favor of finding that a stone released at rest will fall, although there is actually, according to Heisenberg's uncertainty principle, a very *small* chance (far less than one in a billion billion) that the stone will noticeably rise before it falls. For practical purposes in our daily lives we may *count* on the falling of the stone. On the other hand, suppose that preparations are being made to launch a rocket toward Mars. The scientists in charge of the project would feel far from certain that their projectile would hit its target.

Frequently a scientist must hedge in his answers because he is asked to solve problems in which not all the controlling factors are specified. If someone asks "What is the speed of sound in air?," the correct answer is not "1120 feet per second," but something like "It varies with temperature, but is roughly 1100 feet per second," or "It is (1087 ± 1) feet per second at 0°C and increases as the square root of the absolute temperature." To the question "Is air a good conductor of electricity?" a physicist might reply "Not usually, but the conductivity of air is greatly increased by radiation or an electric discharge."

We shall see in the next chapter that the theories proposed by scientists are speculations based on hypotheses. Therefore the theoretical physicist should also avoid being dogmatic. Of course a theory must explain known facts, but whether it will lead to new discoveries only time will tell. Theories should not be labeled "right" or "wrong," but rather "useful" or "useless."

Thus in both theory and experiment nothing is certain. Therefore a scientist should make his claims with modesty, and the public should understand the reservations pertaining to such claims.

PROBLEMS

1. A pendulum swings through a small arc, and 25 oscillations are timed six times. The six readings are 40.6, 39.4, 40.2, 39.6, 40.6, and 40.2 sec. (a) Find the mean deviation and the percent possible error due to random fluctuations. (b) If the timer runs 1 % fast, what is the total possible error in the mean?

2. The pendulum in problem 1 is made to swing through a larger arc, and the times for 25 oscillations are found to be 41.4, 42.2, 41.2, 43.2, 40.8, and 41.4 sec. Find the mean, the mean deviation, and the total possible error.

3. Show whether or not the data in problems 1 and 2 indicate a definite dependence of the period of a pendulum on the length of the arc of swing.

4. In an experiment on the stretching of a rubber band, the applied force is increased in steps of one newton. The length of the rubber band is successively 0.125, 0.132, 0.142, 0.158, 0.178, 0.194, and 0.198 m. (a) Find the successive stretches. (b) Plot the accumulated stretch against the accumulated applied force. (c) If you could measure each length to 0.004 m, would you say that your graph could be a straight line and that the rubber band obeyed Hooke's law?

5. Plot a graph of the theoretical curve given by Eq. (4–10). For what value of x is T a maximum?

6. Explain why a meter stick with a scale good to ±1 mm is a poor instrument to use when measuring the diameter of a tube or cylinder that is obviously not more than 1 cm across.

7. A certain meter has 200 divisions and readings are good to one division. What would be the instrumental error in computing a deflection covering (a) full scale, (b) half scale, and (c) a fifth of the scale?

8. Suppose that you measure A and B and find $A = (212 \pm 2)$ gm and $B = (108 \pm 1)$ gm. Find the percent error in the computed value of (a) $A + B$, (b) $A - B$. What conclusion can you draw from your answers?

9. Refer to Eq. (4–2). Suppose that you have found by measurement that $f = (320 \pm 1)$ vibrations/sec, $F = (40.0 \pm 0.4)$ newtons, and $l = (0.400 \pm 0.002)$ m, find the value of k and the percent error in its determination.

10. Four coins are tossed. What are the odds in favor of getting (a) no "heads," (b) "heads" once, (c) "heads" twice? (d) If you repeated the experiment ten times, would you expect these odds to be fulfilled? Explain.

11. By measuring the circumference and diameter for each of six cylinders, a student obtains the following values for c/d: 3.148, 3.163, 3.154, 3.147, 3.160, and 3.146. Find the actual percent error in the mean and the percent mean deviation. Give reasons why the actual error may, as here, exceed the mean deviation.

EXPERIMENT 1

DETERMINATION OF π
(Possible Error versus Actual Error)

Object: To use the measurement of π to learn about the meaning and determination of error in experimentation.

Problem: To determine π experimentally one need only measure the diameter d and circumference c of a cylinder. Then since $c = \pi d$, we have

$$\pi = \frac{c}{d}. \tag{1}$$

As there is an experimental limit to how accurately one can measure c and d, the calculated value of π will be correct only up to a certain figure. Experience shows that it is good practice to repeat a measurement several times and then average the values found. This average or *mean value* is more reliable than any single value. Furthermore, the *mean deviation* of the single values from the mean value is a measure of the *possible error* in the averaged value. Large deviations suggest an unreliable result, small deviations convey confidence in the answer. Therefore we will make ten calculations of π, using a different cylinder each time, and then calculate the mean deviation. Suppose, for example, that we get the following ten values of π; then the mean and mean deviation would be found as shown:

π	Deviation
3.122	0.029
3.164	0.013
3.184	0.033
3.106	0.045
3.122	0.029
3.134	0.017
3.202	0.051
3.156	0.005
3.172	0.021
3.148	0.003
Sum = 31.150	0.246 = Sum
Mean = 3.151	0.025 = Mean deviation = possible error

Percent Error: It is customary to express errors in percent.

$$\% \text{ possible random error } = \frac{\text{Mean deviation}}{\text{Mean value}} \times 100\%.$$

In the above example we get

$$\frac{0.025}{3.151} \times 100\% = 0.8\% \text{ possible random error.}$$

Actual Error: In research one may not know the correct answer, but only that it should not differ from the mean measured value by more than the possible error. In this, as in some of the other lab experiments, the correct value is known or given and the *actual error* may be computed. It should be less than the possible error. In our example

$$\text{Measured value of } \pi = 3.1510$$
$$\text{Correct value of } \pi = 3.1416$$
$$\text{Actual error} = 0.0094$$
$$\text{Percent actual error} = \frac{0.0094}{3.1416} \times 100\%$$
$$= 0.3\%$$

Procedure:

Measure c and d for six or more different cylinders. Compute the mean value of c/d. Find the percent possible random error and percent actual error for *your* determination of π. Should the latter exceed the former, look into and discuss possible *systematic* errors.

Alternative Method of Measuring π: A quite different way of measuring π involves throwing sticks on a ruled surface and counting what fraction cross a line. (The lines must be ruled one stick length apart.) Then

$$\pi = \frac{2}{\text{Fraction crossing a line}}. \tag{2}$$

Toss 100 toothpicks or matches on a suitably ruled surface. Compute π from (2). What actual error did this method yield? How does the accuracy of this second method compare with that of the first method? Repeat, using 400 or more sticks.

EXPERIMENT 2

THE INVESTIGATION OF FREE FALL
(Aristotle versus Galileo)

Object: To determine experimentally how the time it takes a body to fall depends on (1) the mass or weight, (2) the material, and (3) the distance fallen.

Problem: Aristotle argued that since a large stone is heavier than a small one, the large stone will fall faster. Galileo claimed that experimentally a large and a small stone fell at almost the same rate. You are to determine which of these famous men was right, and then you are to investigate free fall as thoroughly as possible. Before stating a conclusion, you must consider the possible error in your measurements. For example, if the time of fall of one object is measured as 1.2 ± 0.2 sec and that of a second object as 1.3 ± 0.2 sec, then you must conclude that within the limits of your measurements no difference in rates of fall was *proven* (though it may have been suggested). Two measurements such as 1.0 ± 0.1 and 1.3 ± 0.1 are definitely different. Thus you see that you should repeat each experiment several times (say five times), so as to obtain the possible error. Of course good timing technique should be developed so as to reduce your errors.

Procedure:

Step 1. In five trials find the time it takes a small stone of 500 gram weight to drop a given distance of at least 15 feet. Repeat for a larger stone or weight. Was Aristotle or Galileo right?

Step 2. In five trials find the time it takes a pingpong ball or a ball of light paper to fall the same distance. Now who was right, Aristotle or Galileo? How would you explain the results of Step 1 and Step 2?

Step 3. Time how long it takes the heavy stone or weight to fall through two other distances, and measure all three vertical distances that you used. Call the distance s and the time t. Plot whichever of the following will give a straight line graph: s against t, s against t^2, s against $\sqrt{t}$, s against $1/t$, etc. How does s depend on t? What is the constant of proportionality? Why were you told to use the *heavy* stone or weight in this last part?

EXPERIMENT 3

THE PERIOD OF A PENDULUM
(The Experimental Method)

Object: To illustrate the experimental method by finding how the period of a pendulum depends on various factors.

Problem: In experiment 2 we let objects fall freely under the pull of the earth's gravitational attraction and found $s = kt^2$, where s was distance and t time. The factor k should have been around 16 ft/sec^2. The formula $s = kt^2$ may be derived from Newton's laws, and this theory predicts that k should equal $g/2$, where g is the acceleration produced by gravity, namely about 32 ft/sec^2. This marks one of the many successes of Newtonian theory.

In the present experiment an object swings on the end of a string. Gravity makes the object fall and then its momentum carries it up to where it stops and falls back. Obviously the *period T*, or time of a complete cycle (over and back), must depend on g. But before we can find out how T depends on g we must investigate whether T depends on any other factors. What might these factors be? They are (1) the mass of the bob, (2) the length of the arc or swing, and (3) the length of the string. Following the true experimental method, we vary only one such factor at a time so that we can see what the dependence on each factor is.

Procedure:

Step 1. Using a string of 64 cm length (measured from the support to the *center* of the bob) find the time of 25 swings through a small arc (20 or 25 cm in all). Repeat four more times and determine the mean value of T and the possible error.

Step 2. Varying the arc. Repeat Step 1, but with a larger arc of 50 cm or more. Within your possible errors, is a dependence of T on the length of arc established?

Step 3. Varying the bob. Repeat Step 1 with a bob of different mass, but with the same length of string and the same arc. Within your possible errors, is a dependence of T on the mass of the bob established?

Step 4. Varying the length of the string. Repeat Step 3 (new bob, small arc) but for a string length of (a) 100 cm, (b) 32 cm. How does T depend on the length l? Plot whichever will give a straight line: T against l, T against l^2, or T^2 against l, and find the constant of proportionality (which Newtonian theory says should be $4\pi^2/g$).

EXPERIMENT 4

HOOKE'S LAW
(A Law of Limited Range)

Object: To investigate the relationship between stretching force and the resulting stretch, in order to determine if there is any "law" relating these quantities.

Problem: We may always define a new quantity as the ratio of two quantities already defined. So let us define the elastic constant k of a spring as the ratio of force F to the stretch s resulting from F. Then

$$k = F/s. \tag{1}$$

Now this definition does not make k a constant or assign to it any other properties. If we observe experimentally that k has the property of being constant for a given spring over a range of applied forces, then we will have established an empirical law for this spring. Such a law was discovered by Hooke for springs or straight wires of steel, brass, etc., and it is known as Hooke's law.

We shall see that Hooke's law has a limited range of applicability. It does not hold for many materials, even ones that are readily stretched, and for steel the law holds only up to a certain limit, called the "elastic limit." Our problem is to investigate the relationship between s and F for (a) a steel spring, and (b) a rubber band.

Procedure:

Step 1. Fasten the steel spring to the support and hook onto the lower end of the spring the hanger for slotted weights. A meter stick is mounted behind the hanger. Measure the length of the spring and record the height of a certain point on the hanger.

Place a 100-gram weight on the hanger and record the new height of the reference point on the hanger. Continue this process until eight 100-gram weights have been added. [*Note:* When adding a weight release it slowly and don't drop it onto the hanger.] Plot the stretch s against the weight causing it. Did the spring obey Hooke's law throughout your test? When it did obey Hooke's law; what was the constant value of k in gram-weight/cm?

Step 2. Repeat Step 1 for the rubber band, only continue carefully adding weights until you break the band. If after adding a weight you observe a creeping elongation, wait a minute or so before reading the hanger position. If you do not have enough 100-gram weights, carefully remove five and add a 500-gm weight in their place.

Plot s against F for the rubber band. Note whether any portion of the graph is a straight line; if so, for this portion determine k from the slope, that is, take

$$k = \Delta F/\Delta s, \tag{2}$$

where Δs means a small change in s and ΔF a small change in F. Does Hooke's law apply at all to a rubber band?

Which stretched more easily, the steel spring or the rubber band? Which stretched the greatest fraction of its original length?

CHAPTER 5

The Theoretical Method.
Laws, Hypotheses, and Theories

5–1 Theorizing

We all theorize from time to time. For example, suppose that when you get in your car you find that it will not start. You immediately ask yourself what the trouble might be. Perhaps it is something that you can fix yourself, or, if not, you would at least like to be able to give a garage man, when you call him, some idea of what he should bring. So you make a guess as to the cause of your trouble; let us say that you suppose it has something to do with your battery. In science a guess of this sort is called an *hypothesis* or *postulate*.

The next step in the development of a theory is to reason from the hypothesis, to deduce from it certain consequences. The first such consequence must be what has been already observed experimentally. In the example about the car your guess about the battery will certainly explain why your car will not start. But of course there are many other possible reasons for this and you want to find the right one. Therefore you now *test* your hypothesis by considering some of its other consequences that may be checked experimentally. If your car trouble is in the battery, then what other symptoms should you look for? One would be that the horn and the lights should not work either; if testing shows that this is so, you will begin to feel more certain that your trouble really is connected with the battery and not with the ignition switch or the self-starter. Your next step might be to take a look at the battery. Perhaps you would find that the battery cable had been eaten away by acid, or that the cable was loose and not making a firm electrical connection. If the trouble is not in the cable, you might make the additional hypothesis that the battery is "run down." From this new guess you may deduce further consequences which may be tested experimentally, given the proper tools or equipment. One test would be to check the density (or specific gravity) of the solution in the battery, using for this purpose an instrument called a "hydrometer." Another test would be to use a voltmeter to find out whether or not the battery is supplying the proper voltage. If you do not have the necessary instruments or the experimental "know-how" to use them, you must call for expert help. But when a mechanic comes he will simply continue the method outlined above until he feels reasonably sure that he knows what your trouble is. If he is a good mechanic, he will make several tests of his hypotheses before he subjects you to the cost of expensive new parts and labor. Probably we have all experienced instances in which experts have guessed wrong. Physicists too have made some poor guesses in the past, and their theories have been superseded later on by better theories.

Our example pertaining to trouble in starting your car is like many others in our daily lives. Radio and television repair men solve their problems in the same way; so do doctors. The theoretical method is also used in what are termed the social sciences. We are familiar with efforts on the part of a government to diagnose and attempt to cure a sick economy. In physics, however, the theoretical method is particularly successful because it can be applied to problems from which complicating factors have been eliminated and in which the cost of a bad guess is not measured in terms of human lives or the livelihood of the guesser. On the other hand, when a physicist makes a poor hypothesis that leads nowhere, he may retard the progress of science or encourage people to waste money in the construction of some device whose design is based on unsound principles.

5–2 The purposes of a theory

From the last section we see that a theory involves making one or more hypotheses and then deducing the consequences. These consequences must include the facts that we already know. Thus the first aim of a theory is to *explain*, in terms with which we are familiar, the cause and effect relationship between our hypotheses and these facts. We look upon theories as aids in our understanding of the way in which our world behaves. For example, in the 18th and 19th centuries it was popular to propose a *mechanistic* explanation for many nonmechanical phenomena. The internal energy associated with the temperature of a body was attributed to the random motion of molecules, sound was explained in terms of a to-and-fro motion of particles in the transmitting medium, and Newton showed that even light *might* (he made it clear that this was only a guess) be pictured as a stream of particles that are attracted toward a denser medium, such as glass. These theories appealed to people because everyone was familiar with the motion of balls and other ordinary objects, and so they enabled everyone to visualize, as it were, what happens in nature when water is heated, when sound is transmitted, and when light passes from air into glass. Such theories represent a description of an invisible or otherwise not easily recognizable experience in terms of better known phenomena.

Mechanistic theories were later supplemented by what are called *field* theories. We shall consider fields in more detail later, but here we may note that the concept of a field and the hypothesis that fields exist around mass particles and electric charges makes what is called "action at a distance" seem more understandable and plausible to many people. For example, the law of gravitation states that the sun attracts the earth, i.e., exerts a force on the earth, even though practically empty space intervenes between the two bodies. The action of the sun on the earth cannot be explained in terms of such familiar actions as the pushing or pulling of some object with the aid of rods or ropes. How, then, does the sun exert a force on the earth? According to field theory we say that around the sun there exists a gravitational field, that such a field will exert a force on any mass situated in the

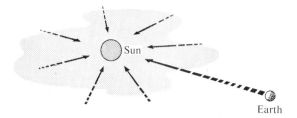

FIG. 5–1.   The earth is attracted toward the sun by the sun's gravitational field.

field, and that, since the earth is located in the sun's field, a force acts on the earth
(Fig. 5–1). Note that such an explanation does not say *why* gravitational fields
exist, but it may seem easier to picture the sun's pull on the earth in terms of a
field. The force of the field may be visualized as arising right where the earth is
located, just as the pull of a tugboat on a barge is considered to act on the barge
at the point where the towrope is attached.

The formation of a theory frequently involves the mental construction of an
associated *model*. The sun's gravitational field may be pictured in terms of lines
(they are called lines of force) radiating out in all directions away from the sun
(Fig. 5–1). Of course such lines do not really exist. Another famous example
of a physicist's model is the planetary model of the atom, which is associated with
the Bohr theory of the hydrogen spectrum. In his theory (Section 17–4) Bohr
adopted a model of the atom which was first proposed by Rutherford. According
to this model, an atom consists of a positive core called the nucleus, surrounded
by circulating negative charges called electrons (Fig. 5–2). The nucleus is supposed
to contain nearly all of the mass of the atom. An electron is attracted to the nucleus
of its atom by an electrostatic force which varies inversely as the square of the
distance of separation, but the electron does not fall into the nucleus because it is
supposed to be circling around it at sufficient speed to maintain a fixed orbit,
just as does an earth satellite in the earth's gravitational field of attraction.
Note that this whole model bears a very close analogy to our solar system, although
the scale is vastly different and the attractive force is of different origin in the two
cases. The nucleus is the atom's sun; the electrons are its planets or satellites.
Since we are all rather familiar with drawings and descriptions of our solar system,
we can immediately form a mental picture of Rutherford's atom. However, no
one has ever *seen* an atom with its nucleus and circling electrons, and such a system
may not really exist. In fact, other atomic models have been proposed, and currently Rutherford's model is not taken too seriously.

While the explanation of physical phenomena in terms with which we are more
familiar is a worthwhile objective for a theory, it is not the most important goal
from the physicist's point of view. To a physicist a theory is not successful unless
it is *fruitful*, that is, the theory should enable one to deduce certain consequences
which were not previously known but which, upon experimental testing, are found
to be actual properties of our physical world. In this respect physical theories are
far more than a process of diagnosing and explaining the cause of some effect;

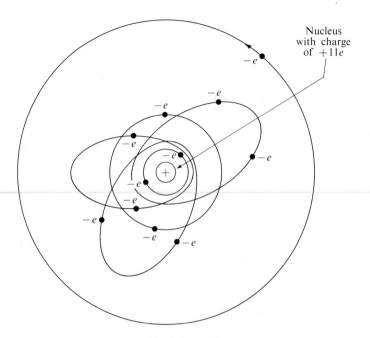

FIG. 5–2.   Model of the sodium atom.

the main purpose of constructing a physical theory is to use it as a means of making new discoveries.

This is also true of models. The planetary model of the atom suggested many things, such as the possibility of removing an electron from a normal neutral atom. What should we expect to have left if a negatively charged electron is taken away from a system in which the positive and negative charges originally balanced? Should not the resulting system be positively charged? It is found that atoms seem to become what are called *positive ions* in just this way. Atoms that gain extra electrons become *negative ions*, and, since unlike charges attract (Chapter 12), a positive ion and a negative ion may come together to form a molecule of a very stable compound, as in the case of common salt (NaCl), in a crystal of which the sodium atoms have lost electrons to the chlorine atoms (Section 18–9). Here the model leads us on into chemistry.

After many of the consequences of a theory have been developed, it is often found that quite a number of interesting facts about nature have been discovered. For a student to learn all of these facts just for their own sake is not justified unless the facts must be recalled repeatedly because they are associated with a branch of physics in which one is specializing. Generally speaking, memorization of too many facts leads to confusion rather than understanding, and memorized information is easily forgotten if not continually used. It is best to learn the basic hypotheses and to *understand* the deductions that follow when these are presented, then it will be an easy matter to refresh one's mind about a certain topic by looking it up again whenever there is a need to refer to it. In this connection the association of a model may be of much help, because models serve as a framework on which many facts may be hung. The planetary model of the atom, for example, is a most valuable one in this respect. In the so-called *periodic table* of the chemical elements, the elements are arranged in rows and columns. For all the elements in a given column the atoms have similar arrangements of their outermost electrons. From a knowledge of what these arrangements are, one can quickly figure out most of the physical and chemical properties of all the elements. Thus we shall find that the elements lithium (Li), sodium (Na), potassium (K), rubidium (Rb), and caesium (Cs) are located in the first column of the table. These are the elements called the alkalis in whose atomic models we should picture (Fig. 5–2) one electron circling around outside of all the others. Would it not seem likely that an isolated outermost electron could be easily detached, leaving behind a negative ion? This supposition should remind us of the fact that sodium atoms readily become negative ions and that the alkali elements in general have this property, which is the basis of their chemical behavior. Because alkali atoms will readily donate an electron to another atom that can accept it, the alkali elements are said to have a *valency* of one. The important thing is to be able to deduce this once we are shown the periodic table. Since we are not working in chemistry, it is not necessary to memorize the valencies of the elements, nor is it even necessary to memorize the periodic table, because it is reproduced in most books on either general or atomic physics, or chemistry.

5–3 The role of mathematics in physical theory

The new predictions of a physical theory are usually obtained in the form of mathematical relations between observable quantities. We shall call these relations *derived laws*. How are they attained? Let us consider the steps involved.

The first step after choosing the hypotheses and possible model for a theory is to express the hypotheses in the form of mathematical equations. Since some of the hypotheses in physics cannot be fully expressed except in terms of higher mathematics, a more advanced study of physics necessitates learning the theory of the calculus, differential equations, vector and tensor analysis, etc. In fact, Newton *invented* the calculus because he found that he could not express his law of motion properly except as a differential equation! However, we shall see that the fundamental laws of physics may be expressed in an understandable, if not in their most general, form without the calculus. When the complete mathematical expression of a fundamental law involves higher mathematics, this form will sometimes be given for the sake of completeness and to satisfy the curiosity of those readers who may wish to further their study of physics.

The next step in developing the consequences of a theory is to combine the equations expressing hypotheses with others of a similar nature and with ones expressing definitions of derived quantities. With the aid of mathematical manipulation, certain variables are eliminated and the derived relations obtained. Here, of course, facility with mathematics is a great help.

ILLUSTRATION. Let us see how Newton derived the relation between the gravitational constant G, the mass M of the earth, the radius R of the earth, and the acceleration due to gravity, g.

Solution. Newton first postulated the law of gravitation, namely, that between a body of mass m and another of mass M a distance s apart there exists a force of attraction F, given by

$$F = G \frac{mM}{s^2}, \qquad (5\text{--}1)$$

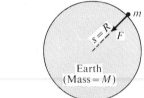

where G is a universal constant (Fig. 5–3). Newton showed that a sphere will attract an outside body just as would a concentrated object of the same mass located at the center of the sphere.

FIG. 5–3. Attraction between the earth and a body on its surface.

Equation (5–1) therefore applies to an object of mass m located on or near the earth's surface, for which s equals R, the earth's radius. Newton next assumed that in the relation "force equals mass times acceleration" ($F = ma$), the mass of the body will be a constant property of the body and the same as the mass m that appears in Eq. (5–1). He therefore wrote

$$F = ma \qquad (5\text{--}2)$$

and reasoned that, since the force in this case was that due to gravity, he could substitute Eq. (5–1) for F. This gave him the equation

$$\frac{GmM}{R^2} = ma. \qquad (5\text{--}3)$$

Since, Newton postulated, gravitational mass and inertial mass are the same, the m's on the two sides of Eq. (5–3) may be regarded as identical and hence can be canceled out. Equation (5–3) then reduces to

$$\frac{GM}{R^2} = a. \qquad (5\text{--}4)$$

Newton recognized a as the acceleration produced by gravity on a body falling freely near the earth's surface; this is the acceleration we now designate by the symbol g. With g substituted for a, Eq. (5–4) becomes

$$\frac{GM}{R^2} = g, \qquad (5\text{--}5)$$

which is the desired *derived* relation.

Let us see how much useful information may be obtained from Eq. (5–5). This will illustrate the fruitfulness of Newton's theory and hence the value of his original hypotheses.

First, Eq. (5–5) enables us to compute the mass M of the earth quite accurately. It is easy to measure g, directly or indirectly (see Experiments 2 and 3), and G

may be determined by the Cavendish method (Experiment 11, Chapter 8). The radius of the earth is well known from measurements of the earth's curvature. Therefore in Eq. (5–5) we may solve for M, the only unknown.

Second, we may calculate from Eq. (5–5) the variation in g with altitude. At sea level R is about 4000 miles. At an elevation of 5280 ft (one mile) R will have increased by only one part in 4000, or by

$$\frac{1}{4000} \times 100\% = \frac{1}{40}\% = 0.025\%,$$

while the percent increase in the *square* of R will be twice that, or 0.05%. Hence at an altitude of 5280 ft, g should be 0.05% less than at sea level. Actually g is more affected by variations in latitude and in the density of the rocks in the earth's crust.

A third application of Eq. (5–5) is to use this equation to compute the acceleration of free fall near the moon's surface. In this case we must consider M to be the moon's mass and R to be the moon's radius. However, G will have the same value; according to Newton's hypothesis, G is a universal constant. For the moon, M is about $\frac{1}{80}$ and R is $\frac{4}{15}$ as large as for the earth. Now let us compute the value of g on the moon. (This sort of proportionality problem is encountered frequently in physics, and is easily solved once the general method of solution is known.) The value of g should be between $\frac{1}{5}$ and $\frac{1}{6}$ of its value on the earth. The reasoning is as follows. If M is reduced by a factor of $\frac{1}{80}$, so will g be reduced by this factor; but if R is reduced by a factor of $\frac{4}{15}$, g will at the same time be *increased* by a factor of $1/(\frac{4}{15})^2$ or $\frac{225}{16}$. Thus, altogether, g is altered by the factor $\frac{225}{1280}$, which is between $\frac{1}{5}$ and $\frac{1}{6}$.

A very famous derived law is the following:

$$E = mc^2. \tag{5–6}$$

This is derived in the theory of relativity from the basic postulates of that theory (Section 16–21). Here E stands for the energy associated with the mass m of an object, and c is the speed of light in vacuo. We shall not derive Eq. (5–6) at this point, but simply point out that this consequence of relativity theory was entirely unsuspected when the postulates of the theory were first proposed. However, this consequence has been verified experimentally in many important ways, such as (1) the mass (inertia) of an atomic particle increases rapidly when it is given sufficient energy to bring its speed up to a little less than that of light, and (2) a nuclear reaction in which the matter present loses mass is also a reaction in which there is a loss (release) of energy.

5–4 What does the failure of a theory signify?

A poorly constructed theory, one based on bad "guesses," may explain the known facts all right, but it will not prove fruitful. This was the case with the geocentric theory of Ptolemy and Aristotle which postulated that the sun and planets revolve about the earth. This theory should not be labeled "wrong" because it *did*, and still does, explain the apparent motions of the heavenly bodies. We now prefer the heliocentric theory, which supposes that the planets go around the sun, because this theory is much simpler, because it is based on hypotheses of wide scope, and because it has enabled people to make such correct predictions as the occurrence of eclipses and the existence of the outermost planets.

However, even our best theories have been found to lead us to incorrect consequences. As far as we know, a perfect theory never has been, and probably never will be, discovered. Let us consider, then, what it means for a theory to make a wrong prediction.

In the first place, if a theory has predicted certain consequences, say A, B, C, D, E, all of which have been experimentally verified, and if the theory also predicts another consequence F which is not found to agree with the observed facts, then the theory is to a certain extent erroneous. However, one must remember that the failure of the theory in respect to F does not nullify its value in explaining A, B, C, D, and E. For the latter the theory is as good as ever, and it need not be suddenly scrapped. Newton's theory of mechanics (Newtonian mechanics) still explains all the mechanical phenomena observed in everyday life, although it does not explain the consequences of Eq. (5–6). This equation is based on Einstein's theory of mechanics (relativistic mechanics); but since this theory is much more complicated than Newton's, physicists still prefer to use Newtonian mechanics when they can, which is whenever one does *not* have to deal with speeds close to that of light. Newton's theory is in many instances a good approximation to the "truer" theory of Einstein.

The second important point in regard to the failure of a theory is that this very failure is itself an important discovery, and usually it heralds a new advance in physics. After a theory has been found to predict successfully several new things, physicists continue to explore its consequences and in their hearts there is likely to be hidden the hope that they will perform an experiment that turns out differently than the theory predicts.

When a theory has failed in some respects, physicists do one of two things, namely, (1) they try to correct the old theory by modifying or adding to its postulates, or (2) they start anew by forming a fresh and completely different theory. The modified, or the new, theory will have additional consequences, which in turn may be investigated experimentally until eventually the newer theory may also meet with failure. Thus the process goes on and science progresses. We may indicate this progression schematically as follows:

Experiment → Theory 1 → Experiment → Theory 2 → Experiment → ....

Note the interplay between experimental and theoretical work that is necessary if science is to advance. Although some physicists have marked mathematical ability and prefer theoretical work, while others can do things better with their hands and like experimental investigation, it is important that one who desires to be a good physicist should be somewhat familiar with both kinds of work. The theoretical worker must be able to visualize tests of his theories that may be carried out practically, and the experimental investigator will enjoy his work much more if he understands the theory that he is trying to prove or disprove.

5–5 What are some of the great theories in physics?

The discussion of the great theories of physics will take up most of the remainder of this book. These theories and their hypotheses or postulates constitute the backbone of physics, and to such a framework the various facts of physics may be appended if and when desired. In such an approach one learns the most fundamental and important ideas and relationships first.

As an outline of what follows and what constitutes the main body of physics, the theories to be discussed will be listed; they are:

(a) The theory of Newtonian mechanics.
(b) The theory of thermodynamics.
(c) Kinetic theory.
(d) Wave theory.
(e) Electromagnetic theory.
(f) The special theory of relativity.
(g) Quantum theory.
(h) The theory of the periodic table and valence.

One could add to the above list, but as it stands it will lead us into all of the branches of physics: mechanics (a), heat (b and c), sound (d), light (d, e, and f), electricity and magnetism (e), and atomic physics (g and h). The theory of the nucleus and that of the elementary particles will be omitted because these theories are still in the stage of growth and revision, but some attention will be given to the structure of nuclei and how energy may be obtained from them, and the known elementary particles will be described and listed for ready reference in case they are encountered in other reading.

5–6 Fundamental and restricted laws

The great laws of physics are those that express principles or relations which are independent of the specific properties of certain materials or objects. These laws will therefore be called our *fundamental laws;* they must be distinguished from those *restricted laws* which apply only to certain materials and only under a limited range of conditions. By their nature, fundamental laws are not derivable from anything else; they are our starting points in the various branches of physics. They are often arrived at by the inductive method, in which one seeks that general principle which will explain the greatest number of specific facts. In such cases, fundamental laws are not wild guesses. On the other hand, the postulates of the quantum theory and of relativity were bold, inspired guesses, differing radically from previous beliefs. It is said that when Planck first made his quantum postulate he could hardly believe it himself, although from it he was able to derive for the first time an important empirical (experimentally observed) law whose explanation had been attempted unsuccessfully by others.

Restricted laws are usually first discovered experimentally, so that they are initially empirical laws. Physicists generally believe that such laws follow from the fundamental ones provided that one has complete information about the structure of the material or medium involved. When such information is not directly available, one must make further guesses in the form of *postulates about the structure of matter*. For example, in kinetic theory one assumes a gas to be composed of hard elastic spheres in random motion. Such hypotheses are not as universal in scope as are our fundamental laws, but, like all postulates, they must explain known facts and they should lead us to new discoveries. In the process of establishing a theoretical basis for an empirical law, other laws are often deduced as well. These *derived laws* are really theorems that come out of the theory. They may be universal in scope (e.g., the conservation of momentum, $E = mc^2$, etc.), or they may be restricted to certain media or situations (e.g., the formula for the velocity of a wave in a string).

The various "laws" (principles, hypotheses, postulates, theorems) of physics may be classified as follows.

(1) *Fundamental laws or principles:* hypotheses or postulates of a general nature (e.g., the law of gravitation).

(2) *Restricted laws:* empirical relationships of limited applicability (e.g., Hooke's law of elasticity).

(3) *Postulates about the structure of matter:* educated guesses (e.g., the postulates of kinetic theory, the theory of solids, atomic structure, etc.).

(4) *Derived laws:* relationships discovered mathematically from (1), (2), and (3).

5–7 What are the fundamental laws of physics?

Since the fundamental laws (postulates, principles, etc.) are by far the most important, we should keep them clearly in mind at all times. In the remainder of this book, a chapter will be devoted to each of these laws in turn; it is hoped that they will stand out in the reader's memory, uncluttered by too much factual information.

The following fifteen fundamental laws (they will be designated by Roman numerals) summarize what we now know about the way our physical world behaves:

    I. Newton's law of motion (or "second law").
    II. Newton's law of action and reaction (or "third law").
    III. Newton's law of gravitation.
    IV. The conservation of energy principle.
    V. The degradation of energy principle (or second law of thermodynamics).
    VI. Huygens' principle of wave propagation.
    VII. Coulomb's law of electrostatic force.
    VIII. Ampere's law of magnetic force.
    IX. Faraday's law of electromagnetic induction.
    X. Maxwell's law of magnetoelectric induction.
    XI. The relativity principle.
    XII. The quantum principle.
    XIII. Pauli's exclusion principle.
    XIV. The conservation of matter principle.
    XV. The law(s) of nuclear force.

This list is certainly not complete. New fundamental laws will probably be discovered in the future. It is also quite possible that a unifying theory may show that two or more of the laws listed may be combined or treated as applications of a still more comprehensive principle. Einstein and Heisenberg have worked on this problem.

5–8 The role of constants in physics

The examples of physical laws that have been given show that such laws express a constancy, or a relationship between previously defined quantities. Frequently the relationship takes the form of a simple proportionality, such as the statement "y is directly proportional to x^2, or $y/x^2 = k$, where k is a constant of proportionality independent of x. Sometimes the relationship is more complicated, as in the case of the Bode-Titus law, Eq. (4–6). Evidently, constants play an important part in physics. Many quantities are defined and introduced, such as k above, just because they are constant in value. This was discussed in Chapter 3. Let us now review the types of constants encountered in physics from the point of view of their relation to physical laws.

(a) *Constants associated with certain media.* Examples are the elastic coefficients of various solids and liquids, the index of refraction of a transparent medium, and the specific resistance of a metal. The statement that any one such quantity is constant is one of our *restricted laws*, because such statements apply only to certain media and then only within a limited range. The values of such constants vary from medium to medium, so that these constants are in no sense fundamental or universal. However, they are sufficiently important to have their values measured and listed in tables.

(b) *Constants associated with certain objects* include the stiffness constant k of a spring, the resistance of a piece of wire, the inductance of a coil, and, of course, the mass of a body, Except for mass, these constants are also associated with limited or restricted laws, such as Hooke's law for a spring and Ohm's law for resistors. The constancy of mass, however, is different. Newton postulated as a *universal law*, applicable to all bodies, that the mass of a given body is constant. Of course the value of mass varies from object to object, but Newton's law appears to hold for any given amount of matter for which the speed is well under that of light.

(c) *Universal constants.* A universal constant has the same value whenever it is encountered. The magnitude of its value depends only on the system of units in terms of which it is expressed and not on such factors as temperature, pressure, velocity, chemical combination, etc. The constants associated with *universal laws* must be of this type.

If the law of gravitation, Eq. (1–1), is a universal law, as is postulated, the constant of proportionality in it must be a universal constant. Thus our first constant of this type is G, the *gravitational constant*.

Two similar universal constants are k_e, *the constant of proportionality* in Coulomb's law for the electric force between static charges, and k_m, the *pro-*

portionality constant in Ampere's law for the magnetic force between current elements or moving charges.

Related to the second law of thermodynamics and the definition of absolute temperature is *Boltzmann's constant k*, whose size determines the average thermal energy of an atom or molecule per degree above absolute zero.

The quantum principle states that the ratio of the amount of energy in a unit (photon, quantum) of light energy to the frequency of the light is a universal constant *h* called *Planck's constant*.

The relativity principle states that *c, the speed of light in vacuo*, is a universal constant, because *c* is the same for all wavelengths and is independent of the motion of the source or that of the observer.

Another universal constant is *e, the smallest unit of electrical charge*, and the magnitude of the charge on the electron and on the proton.

There are also certain classes of objects such that the objects in a given class are indistinguishable and possess common specifications. Thus all electrons have the same rest mass $m_e = 9.1 \times 10^{-31}$ kg and all protons have a rest mass 1836 times that of an electron. Most oxygen atoms have a mass almost 16 times that of a proton, and so on. The ratios of atomic and molecular masses may be determined from a study of chemical combining weights, while the rest mass of the electron and that of the proton have been observed through physical experiments. The chemist's table of atomic weights is essentially a listing of relative atomic masses, based on an arbitrary scale which takes the average mass of an oxygen atom to be exactly 16 chemical mass units (cmu). The chemist says that the *atomic weight w* of oxygen is 16 cmu, while the physicist calculates that the mass of an oxygen atom is about 16×1836 times the rest mass of an electron, or $16 \times 1836 \times 9.1 \times 10^{-31}$ kg, so that

$$1 \text{ chemical mass unit} = 1.67 \times 10^{-27} \text{ kg.} \tag{5-7}$$

Suppose that the atomic mass of an atom is 1 cmu (as it very nearly is for hydrogen), then the mass of such an atom is 1.67×10^{-37} kg and it will take

$$N_0 = \frac{1}{1.67 \times 10^{-27}} = 6 \times 10^{26} \tag{5-8}$$

such atoms to make up a kilogram of the substance. Since the atomic weight of oxygen is 16 cmu, one would have to take 16 kg of oxygen in order to obtain the same number (N_0) of oxygen atoms (Fig. 5–4). The number of atoms in w kilograms of any element of atomic weight w is always N_0; this is called *Avogadro's number*. If two or more atoms have combined to form *molecules* of a substance and if w is now the sum of the atomic weights of the atoms comprising each molecule (this is called the *molecular weight*), then w kilograms of the substance constitute what is termed a *kilogram-mole*. A kilogram-mole of any substance will also contain 6×10^{26} molecules. This important number is usually listed with the universal constants mentioned earlier, but one should remember that the reason why a mole of any substance contains the *same* number of particles is

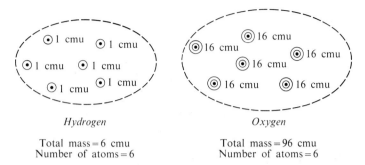

Hydrogen

Total mass = 6 cmu
Number of atoms = 6

Oxygen

Total mass = 96 cmu
Number of atoms = 6

FIG. 5–4. Avogadro's law: Masses proportional to the atomic mass contain equal numbers of atoms.

because of the way a mole is defined and not because of any physical law. The truly physical constants in this and the preceding paragraph are the masses of the electron, proton, oxygen atom, etc. The value of Avogadro's number is simply the reciprocal of $\frac{1}{16}$ of the mass of an oxygen atom, or approximately the reciprocal of the mass of the proton.

Other constants have been introduced, such as the Rydberg constant in spectroscopy, the Faraday constant in electrochemistry, the Compton wavelength in x-rays, and the gas constant R in kinetic theory, but all of these constants are simply related to the ones which we have previously mentioned. Thus

Rydberg constant (for hydrogen): $R_H = 2\pi^2 k_e^2 m_e e^4 / h^3 c$,

Faraday's constant: $F = N_0 e$,

Gas constant: $R = N_0 k$.

In Appendix 2 there is a table listing the values, in the mks-°K-coulomb system, of the universal constants mentioned above. Note that $k_e/k_m = c^2$, a relation first noticed by Maxwell, who then reasoned that very likely there exists a relationship between electricity, magnetism, and light.

In Appendix 3 there are certain other useful data, such as the acceleration due to gravity at sea level and latitude 40°, the speed of sound in air at 0°C, and the freezing point of water at a pressure of 1 atmosphere. Since the acceleration due to gravity varies with altitude and latitude, the speed of sound with the medium and its temperature, and the freezing point of water with pressure, none of these quantities is a constant, but in the range of everyday experience their values do not vary much from the values listed.

Many of the experiments in this book are devoted to measuring the constants listed. Since our attention is going to be directed to the fundamental laws, we should know how the values of the universal constants in these laws are determined. Better still, we should measure them. The suggested methods are:

G with the Cavendish experiment (Experiment 11, Chapter 8),

k_e with the Coulomb balance (Experiment 17, Chapter 12),

k_m with the Ampere balance (Experiment 18, Chapter 13),

Boltzmann's constant k from the gas law and size of a molecule (Experiment 24, Chapter 18),

Planck's constant h with a photocell (Experiment 23, Chapter 17),

Speed of light c with rotating mirror (Experiment 15, Chapter 11),

Charge on electron e by electrolysis (Experiment 19, Chapter 13),

Mass of electron and/or proton by magnetic deflection (Experiment 20, Chapter 13).

5–9 Pure mathematics contrasted with theoretical physics

In Chapter 1 we touched on the subject of how a mathematician builds a branch of mathematics by inventing a self-consistent set of definitions and postulates. We may now note the fundamental difference between theoretical physics and pure mathematics.

The postulates of theoretical physics must agree with the way nature is observed to behave. The mathematician is not restricted by the empirical laws of nature; his theories do not have to explain observed facts, nor do they have to result in new experimental predictions. A mathematician plays intellectual games; to him the important thing is that the game should be interesting. It may, or it may not, be useful. Let us take an example.

The rules of arithmetic give us a branch of mathematics that is applicable to daily life. When we make rules such that $2 + 3 = 5$, we ensure that our symbols 1, 2, 3, etc., can be taken to correspond to numbers of apples, pounds, feet, etc. Now consider a different kind of arithmetic in which there are only two numbers, 0 and 1, and the rules are $0 + 0 = 0$, $0 + 1 = 0$, $1 + 0 = 0$, $1 + 1 = 1$, $0 \times 0 = 0$, $0 \times 1 = 1$, $1 \times 0 = 1$, $1 \times 1 = 1$. This system may be represented by the following two diagrams or matrices:

	0	1
0	0	0
1	0	1

	0	1
0	0	1
1	1	1

Operation $+$ Operation $\times$

The rules are self-consistent, but at first sight this system does not seem to make much sense or to have any practical application. Actually, however, this system is most useful in connection with switch circuits. An electronic tube, such as a vacuum tube, and a transistor are essentially electrical valves (the British call radio tubes "valves") which regulate an electric current. If a voltage source is connected to such a device, current may or may not pass; just as in the case of a switch, an electronic tube or transistor may be considered to be either "on" or "off." If a tube, or any combination of tubes, allows current to pass, we may say that it is in State 1, which we shall represent by the symbol "1." Similarly, if the system does not let current pass, we shall say that it is in State 0, designated by the symbol "0." The symbols $+$ and $\times$ here do not represent the usual operations of addition

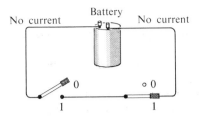

FIG. 5–5. Switches in series $(1 + 0 = 0)$.

and multiplication; perhaps it would be better to use instead some other symbols, such as s and p, but to a mathematician this point is not important. The symbols $+$ and $\times$ are defined by stating what operations they perform; in the present case their definitions are given by the two matrices above. Remember that a mathematician, and not nature, determines what these rules are to be. The rules given do, however, correspond to certain physical operations with electronic tubes and transistors. The operation $+$ corresponds to putting tubes in series, while $\times$ corresponds to putting them in parallel. In Fig. 5–5, we see two switches placed in series; each switch has two positions, open and closed, or "0" and "1." Current can only pass through the combination when *both* switches are closed, so in this case our rules for the operation $+$ apply. In Fig. 5–6, we see two switches in parallel, and in this case current can pass whenever *one* of the switches is closed; in this case our rules for the operation $\times$ apply. So we see that this branch of mathematics, which may at first seem strange, does find an important application after all.

Such well-known games as ticktacktoe, checkers, chess, etc., may be regarded as branches of mathematics. Mathematicians have spent much time investigating the properties of such games, that is, whether there are perfect ways of playing them, whether a game played perfectly will always end in a draw, etc. If there are too few perfect ways of playing, these ways soon become too obvious; in this case the game's inventor must make his game more complicated by adding additional rules. For example, ticktacktoe may be made into a better game by extending it to three dimensions. Variations of chess that apply to cylindrical and doughnut-shaped boards have been invented, but, since chess is a rather intricate game to begin with, its variations are not likely to meet with popular acclaim.

At this point the reader should review in his mind the similarities and the differences in the ways in which physicists and mathematicians theorize.

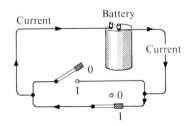

FIG. 5–6. Switches in parallel $(1 \times 0 = 1)$.

PROBLEMS

1. Imagine that you have some specific illness. Describe how your doctor might diagnose your trouble.

2. Imagine that your radio has some specific trouble, and describe how an expert would go about finding the trouble.

3. Find the ratio of the value of g on Mars to its value on earth, given that the radius of Mars is one-half and its mass one-eighth that of the earth.

4. How much energy in joules is associated with a mass of one kilogram? $(c = 3 \times 10^8$ m/sec)

5. An electron of charge e will experience a force eE due to an electric field E and a force evB when moving with speed v across a magnetic field B. What mathematical relation must hold true when both an electric and magnetic field are present, and the force due to one cancels that due to the other?

6. After an electron has been accelerated through a potential difference of V volts, its speed v is given by the relation $\frac{1}{2} mv^2 = eV$, where m is the electron's mass. This equation is a statement of the conservation of energy principle; combine this equation with the one derived in problem 5 and obtain an expression for e/m in terms of E, B, and V, quantities which are easy to measure experimentally.

7. According to the law of friction, the force of friction between a block of wood and the table on which the block rests is doubled when the weight of the block is doubled. (a) Is the law of friction empirical? (b) Is it a fundamental or a restricted law? Explain. (c) What constant appears in this law? Is it a universal constant?

8. Why is the melting point of ice not a universal constant?

9. Suppose that the operation "$+0$" means that you do not touch a certain off-and-on toggle switch, while the operation "$+1$" means that you press the switch once. Construct the addition table and its matrix for this situation.

10. Since electronic computers employ tubes that may be "on" (1) or "off" (0), computations by such computers are based on a *binary system*, according to which $0 + 1 = 1$, $1 + 1 = 10$, $10 + 1 = 11$, $11 + 1 = 100$, $100 + 1 = 101$, $101 + 1 = 110$, etc. In the binary system, 9 becomes 1001, since $9 = 1 \times 2^3 + 0 \times 2^2 + 0 \times 2^1 + 1 \times 2^0$, while 25 becomes 11001, since $25 = 1 \times 2^4 + 1 \times 2^3 + 0 \times 2^2 + 0 \times 2^1 + 1 \times 2^0$. (a) Express $225 (= 9 \times 25)$ in the binary system. (b) Find the rules of multiplication that will make 1001×11001 equal to your answer in (a); what must 0×0, 0×1, 1×0, and 1×1 each equal? (c) Try another example of your own choice.

11. (a) How would you extend the game of ticktacktoe to three dimensions? (b) How should the game be played in one dimension if it is always to end in a draw?

EXPERIMENT 5

STACKING BLOCKS
(An Example of How Science Advances)

Object: To learn from a simple experiment how a scientist goes about his work of discovering new knowledge.

Problem: Given five identical blocks (preferably meter sticks), each of length l, stacked one over the other at the table's edge; what is the greatest displacement over the edge of the table that you can give the top block, and what is then the displacement of each block relative to the one under it?

Procedure:

Step 1. Developing good experimental technique. Find the best systematic procedure. Should you start by displacing the bottom block or the top block? Get all the blocks out over the edge of the table as far as you can.

Step 2. Collecting the data. For maximum displacements, measure the successive relative displacements. Repeat.

Step 3. Looking for correlations in the data, or an empirical law. Express each relative displacement as a decimal fraction times l. Do these decimals suggest any simple common fractions such as $\frac{1}{2}, \frac{1}{3}, \frac{1}{4}$, etc.? Now write the total displacement of the top block as the sum of simple fractions times l. Does this series seem to approach a limit (converge) as one adds more and more terms? If you plot each successive fraction against the number of the block to which it applies, what kind of curve do you obtain?

Step 4. Finding the postulates for a theory. We now want to make some general assumption(s) from which we can deduce (explain) the relationships found in Step 3. The postulate here involves the center of mass of the blocks above the nth block. The center of mass of these $(n - 1)$ blocks is at a point whose x-coordinate is the average of the x-coordinates of these blocks. Thus for the first two blocks, the center of mass is half-way between their centers. How is the center of mass point related to the front end of the nth block?

Step 5. Deducing the empirical relationship. Show that your answer to the last question in Step 4 explains the relations found in Step 3.

Step 6. Applying the theory to new situations. Can you think of another experimental result that the above theory will also explain?

CHAPTER 6

Newton's Law of Motion

6–1 Galileo's famous experiments on motion

The medieval scholastics who followed in the path of Aristotle argued about the causes of motion, postulating that heavy "earthy" objects, such as stones, sought their most "natural" state, namely one of rest in the lowest possible position. This hypothesis was not wrong, for it explained many facts, but it led nowhere.

Galileo pointed out that it was better to study motion itself before trying to discuss the causes of motion. In so doing he developed the modern experimental method.

Mention was made in Chapter 4 of Galileo's work on falling bodies. While he was too keen an observer not to notice that a light object did not fall *quite* as fast as a heavier one, he also observed that the variation in the time of fall was much less than the variation in the size or weight of the object; for dense, heavy objects there was little difference in rate of fall. Galileo realized that the fact that the rates of fall were nearly the same was more significant than the fact that they differed slightly. He sensed that in an idealized situation where the effect of the air could be considered negligible, the rates of fall would be *exactly* the same. Although those who followed Galileo developed vacuum pumps and with them came much closer to creating an actual airless condition, Galileo did not have to wait for this to happen before drawing his conclusions. By combining *thought experiments* with fact he saved much time. This method has been useful ever since, but only to those who can supply the necessary thought!

In his inclined plane experiments Galileo observed that hard spheres rolled straight down an inclined plane in such a manner that, for a given inclination, the gain in speed Δv during the time interval Δt was *nearly* constant (see Fig. 6–1). The ratio $\Delta v/\Delta t$ seemed to be an important and interesting quantity, and he therefore proposed to give it a name by calling it the *acceleration a*. He was the first to introduce this scientific definition of acceleration, a concept that had previously been only vaguely associated with motion at varying speeds.

Since by definition $a = \Delta v/\Delta t$, then for linear motion

$$\Delta v = a \, \Delta t \qquad (6\text{–}1)$$

represents the change in velocity of a body, during the time Δt, due to a constant acceleration a. If such a body starts from rest, then in t seconds it will acquire a velocity given by Eq. (6–1). The Δ symbol means "change in," and it may be dropped for convenience if the body starts from rest when we start counting time

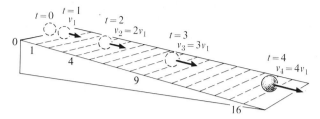

FIG. 6–1. Constant acceleration of a sphere rolling down an inclined plane.

and attains the speed v at the time t, so that $\Delta v = v$ and $\Delta t = t$; we may then write

$$v = at, \tag{6–2}$$

where v is the velocity gained from rest in a time t under constant acceleration a. If the initial velocity is zero and the final is at and the change is at a uniform rate, then the *average velocity* $\bar{v}$ is the arithmetic mean, or

$$\bar{v} = \frac{0 + at}{2} = \tfrac{1}{2}at. \tag{6–3}$$

The definition of $\bar{v}$ in terms of distance and time is

$$\bar{v} = \frac{s}{t}, \tag{6–4}$$

where s is the distance traversed in the time t. Let us equate the two expressions for $\bar{v}$; the result is

$$\frac{s}{t} = \tfrac{1}{2}at, \qquad s = \tfrac{1}{2}at^2. \tag{6–5}$$

It was in this way that Galileo realized that when a body is accelerated from rest, at constant acceleration, s is proportional to t^2, or $s \propto t^2$ (see Fig. 6–1). He also showed that if $s \propto t^2$, then the acceleration must be constant, or $\Delta v \propto \Delta t$.

Galileo rolled balls up and down planes at various inclinations. It was easy for him to see that the acceleration of a downward-rolling ball and the retardation of an upward-moving one decreased in magnitude as he made the slope of the plane less. He then raised the question of what the motion would be if the plane were *very smooth* and *exactly horizontal*. He answered this question by saying that the acceleration would be zero and that an object rolling or sliding on such a plane would move with constant velocity as far as the plane extended.

Of course Galileo could not eliminate friction entirely or be sure that a certain plane was exactly horizontal, but he could picture such a plane in his mind and conjecture about the behavior of a body on it. Here we see another example of the *thought experiment*, in which one mentally sets aside extraneous factors and concentrates on the point at issue, which in this case is how a body would move under the action of no force. Galileo was aware of the existence of friction and its retarding effect on motion along a horizontal plane, but he could see that as friction was reduced, the moving body kept on going for a longer and longer time. He realized that it took a force, such as friction, to stop the body, that is, change its state of motion. He thus arrived at the concept of *inertia*, or the tendency of a body to keep going when no force acts on it.

6–2 The concept of force

Before the time of Galileo, scientists regarded force as a push or pull that was needed to keep a body moving. It was obvious that a steady force had to be applied to a plow, a boat, or a cart on level ground, just to maintain steady motion. But how can a force produce only steady, unaccelerated motion in the case of the cart, while in the case of a falling body, or a ball rolling down a plane, the force (pull) of gravity produces constant acceleration? The resolution of this paradox is to introduce the concept of *friction*, or to be more exact, *moving friction*, as a force opposing motion. We must then say that when a cart is being pulled along level ground there are *two* horizontal forces in opposite directions acting on the cart, namely the forward pull of what we call the *applied force* and the backward drag of friction. What is the effect of these two forces together? We observe that the effect of friction is opposite to that of the applied force. Let us therefore define the *net force* acting on the cart as the difference between the two opposing forces and let us postulate that it is this net force that we must consider to be the effective force in place of the applied force in the idealized case of motion without friction. Then if friction just balances the applied force, the *net* or *unbalanced force* is zero, and we know from Galileo's work that with no force the acceleration is zero. So for a cart in steady motion the applied force must just balance friction. Since friction increases with speed, a greater applied force is required to maintain a high speed than a low speed.

We see from the above that the direction of a force is important. Thus force must be regarded as a quantity having both *magnitude* and *direction*. Such a quantity is called a *vector*. The rules for adding vectors in general will be explained in Section 6–6, but until then we shall assume that we are dealing with forces that are in the *same direction*, in which case they are added numerically, or in the *opposite direction*, in which case the numerical difference represents the effective force. In Section 6–7 we shall discuss the concept of the *component* of a force in a direction other than that of the force itself. For present purposes we may consider such a component to be the projection of the force on a line in the chosen direction, or the part of the force effective in that direction.

When a body rolls down a relatively smooth inclined plane, the acceleration is due to the pull of gravity. Since this pull is found to be vertically down toward the center of the earth, the part of the pull effective down the plane and hence the net force down the plane must decrease as the slope of the plane is made less (Fig. 6–2). But the acceleration also decreases with decreasing slope. Therefore, when constructing the concept of force, it would seem reasonable to associate net force with acceleration. The greater the acceleration of a given body the greater must be the net force acting on that body.

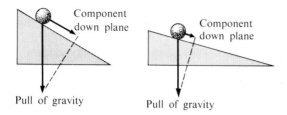

FIG. 6–2. The component of gravity down a plane decreases with decreasing inclination of the plane.

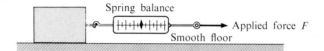

FIG. 6–3.   Acceleration on a smooth floor.

Is the net force acting on a body directly proportional to the resulting acceleration? We could define force so as to make this true, but there would then arise the question of whether this definition would be compatible with our intuitive conception of force in terms of push and pull. Push and pull are usually measured with elastic springs that return to their original length when released. Let us then try accelerating a body along a smooth horizontal surface and, as we do so, let us measure the force with a spring balance (Fig. 6–3) and the acceleration by measuring s and t in Eq. (6–5).

First imagine that we pull the body by attaching it to a spring balance and pulling the spring horizontally at such a rate that the reading stays constant. The applied force F_1* must then also be constant. We record s and t and compute the acceleration $a_1 = 2s/t^2$.

Next suppose that we take a second spring balance and hook it to the test body in place of the first spring. When the acceleration is again a_1 we make a mark F_1 to indicate where the pointer must be on the scale of this second spring when it produces the same acceleration. Let us assume that it takes the same force F_1 to produce the same acceleration a_1 of a given body.

Next let us stretch a third spring by attaching in opposition to it (1) one of the other springs stretched to the mark F_1, (2) both of the other springs, each stretched to the mark F_1. If we use steel springs that always return to the same length under the same physical conditions, we will find that in (2) the stretch of the third spring is twice what it is in (1). By our rule for the addition of forces, the net force F_2 in (2) is the sum $F_1 + F_1 = 2F_1$. Hence this rule is in accord with the spring definition of a force scale, according to which force is taken proportional to the stretch it produces in a spring.

---

* The symbol F will stand for the magnitude of a force, **F** for its magnitude and direction.

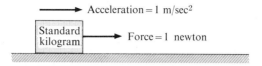

FIG. 6–4.   Definition of the unit of force.

Finally we attach the third spring to our test body and pull it at such a rate that the spring reads the same as in (2) above. The force is then $F_2 = 2F_1$. We record the resulting acceleration a_2. We find $a_2 = 2a_1$. Similarly, if we make $F_3 = 3F_1$, we find $a_3 = 3a_1$, etc. We thus conclude that

$$F \propto a. \tag{6–6}$$

We may then think of force in terms of the acceleration it will impart to a body. We could measure force by measuring this acceleration, only we would find that the ratio of F to a depends on the test body, so that we would have to adopt a standard test body. This is just what is done when we take as the *standard kilogram* a certain piece of platinimum kept in Sèvres, France, with replicas in the bureaus of standards of other countries. For this standard kilogram we take the constant of proportionality in Eq. (6–6) to be unity (Fig. 6–4). This defines our *unit of force* (see Chapter 3). If a force F imparts an acceleration of x meters per second to a standard kilogram, then F has a magnitude of x newtons.

But what is the constant of proportionality in Eq. (6–6) when the test body is not a standard kilogram? The answer to this question involves Newton's concept of *mass*.

6–3 The concept of mass

As has been stated several times, the ratio of the applied force F to the resulting acceleration a was found by Newton to be a property or characteristic of a given body. This constant ratio is called the *mass* (strictly speaking, the *inertial mass*) of the body. Let us see how one might in a logical manner arrive at Newton's conclusion.

Suppose that a net force F imparts an acceleration a_1 to a standard kilogram and an acceleration a_2 to an unknown mass m; than we have $F = 1 \times a_1$ newtons for the standard kilogram. Let us *define* m by setting $F = ma_2$ newtons for the unknown mass. If we equate the two expressions for F, we have

$$m = \frac{a_1}{a_2} \times 1 \text{ kilogram}$$

as our definition of the unknown mass. In general, if the same force F is applied successively to bodies of mass m_1 and m_2, respectively, and the corresponding accelerations are a_1 and a_2, then, by our definition of mass,

$$\frac{m_1}{m_2} = \frac{a_2}{a_1}. \tag{6–7}$$

Note that the less the acceleration the greater the mass, because Eq. (6–7) is an *inverse* proportionality. It is for this reason that mass should be associated with *inertia*. The bigger m the smaller a and the harder it is to start the body in motion, or to slow it down once it is moving. Mass measures the reluctance of a body to change its state of motion or rest.

We see that the mass of any body may be measured by comparing its acceleration under a given net force F with the acceleration of a known mass under the same force F. However, something is implied in this definition, namely, that it does not matter what the magnitude of F is. This assumption amounts to a postulate about the way the physical world behaves and this postulate will be discussed in the next section. Meanwhile let us see what the relation is between mass and (a) quantity of matter, (b) volume of matter, and (c) weight.

(a) *Mass versus quantity of matter.* Is mass a measure of the quantity of matter in a body? The answer to this question is "very nearly so." For a long time the two concepts were regarded as synonymous. In fact, in everyday life a pound of butter or a kilogram of cheese represents to a customer in a grocery store a definite quantity of an item of food.

When a substance changes its state, as when ice melts, the mass does not measurably change. Compressing a gas without letting any enter or leave the vessel does not alter the mass of the gas. In both of these cases the number of atoms or molecules remains constant. It was pointed out in Chapter 4 that for each chemical element, the atoms all have a definite mass so that two kilograms of, say, lead must contain twice as many atoms as does one kilogram of lead. Thus for a given chemical substance, mass is proportional to the number of atoms or molecules of the substance. The proportionality constant depends on the atomic or molecular weight of the substance.

Since the mass of an atom is practically the mass of its nucleus, and since nuclei are composed of neutrons and protons of almost equal mass, the mass of *any* object is very nearly proportional to the total number of neutrons and protons in the object. Actually the mass of a proton is 0.14% greater than that of a neutron, so that the ratio of neutrons to protons slightly affects the value of the proportionality constant relating mass to number of nuclear particles or *nucleons*, as neutrons and protons are called. The constant is approximately 1.67×10^{-27} kg per nucleon.

According to the theory of relativity, the mass of an object should vary with its total energy content. A hot metal ball should lose mass as it cools down and so should a car when it slows down. However, for ordinary objects such variations in mass are far too small to be observable. Only in nuclear reactions, which involve much larger changes in energy, and in the case of particles moving close to the speed of light, can we measure a change in mass not associated with a change in the number of nucleons. In the fusion of hydrogen nuclei to form helium the mass decrease is only a few parts in a thousand. Hence if we exclude the case of particles moving at speeds greater than a twentieth that of light, we may say that the mass of any object is very nearly proportional to the number of neutrons and protons in the object.

(b) *Mass versus volume.* The density ρ of a substance was defined in Chapter 3 as the ratio of the mass m to the volume V, that is, $\rho = m/V$, or

$$m = \rho V.$$

Obviously mass is proportional to volume only when the density ρ is a constant. Only for a given liquid or solid, within a limited range of temperature and pressure, is this true. Since ρ varies from substance to substance, a cubic centimeter of, say, lead will not have the same mass or contain the same number of nucleons as will a cubic centimeter of aluminum.

(c) *Mass versus weight.* Weight is defined as the force of gravitational attraction acting on an object due to the celestial body on or near which the object is located. Gravitational forces will be discussed more fully in Chapter 8, but we have already seen in earlier examples of this force, for example, Eq. (1–1), that it is proportional to the product of the masses and inversely proportional to the square of their distance of separation. Thus weight (a) depends on the location of a body, and (b) at a fixed location is proportional to the mass of the body. For practical purposes, the two pans of a balance are near enough together to be "in the same location" so that when the weights on the two sides balance we may take the masses on each side to be equal. We thus use weighing as an easy method of *comparing* an unknown mass with a known mass. However, one should remember that weight is a *force*, not a mass.

6–4 Newton's law of motion. Fundamental Law I

According to our definition of net force,

$$a \propto F \tag{6–6'}$$

for a given object, and according to our definition of mass,

$$a \propto \frac{1}{m} \tag{6–7'}$$

for a fixed force. When combined, these two relations become

$$a \propto \frac{F}{m}. \tag{6–8}$$

When $m = 1$ kg and $a = 1$ m/sec^2, $F = 1$ newton, by definition of the newton. So in this case the proportionality factor in (6–8) is unity. But is it *always* unity? Newton *postulated* that the constant of proportionality in (6–8) is always the same, so that if we choose its value to be unity in one situation, we must always assign to it that value. We then write

$$a = \frac{F}{m},$$

$$F = ma. \tag{6–9}$$

We shall not be able to choose unity as the value of all of the universal constants that we shall encounter. We could do so here because we were free to define the unit of force; if, however, the units for F, m, and a had all been previously defined, then we would have to determine the constant of proportionality experimentally.

Newton's postulate that the constant of proportionality in (6–8) is always the same is equivalent to postulating that the mass m of a body is independent of its acceleration a and of the net force F that is producing this acceleration. What is assumed is that for *any* given object F and a are proportional. It is true that (6–6) was used to define a scale of forces, but this was in terms of only *one* test body. How do we know that if another test body had been used, then (6–6) would give us the *same* scale of forces? Newton made the hypothesis that a consistent scale of forces and masses could be estabiished by combining (6–6) and (6–7).

Actually, Newton stated his principle in terms of *momentum* rather than acceleration. In Chapter 3 momentum μ was defined (in magnitude) as mass times velocity, or

$$\mu = mv.$$

If during acceleration the velocity changes by Δv, i.e., from $v_1 = v$ to $v_2 = v + \Delta v$, and m is constant, then the change in momentum will be

$$\Delta\mu = m(v + \Delta v) - mv = m\,\Delta v.$$

If we substitute for Δv from Eq. (6–1), we have

$$\Delta\mu = ma\,\Delta t, \qquad ma = \frac{\Delta\mu}{\Delta t}.$$

If we substitute this in Eq. (6–9), we get

I. $$F = \frac{\Delta\mu}{\Delta t}, \tag{6–10}$$

or *the net force equals the time rate of change in the momentum imparted to a body by the net force.* This is *Newton's law of motion* and our *Fundamental Law I.*

In relativistic mechanics, m is no longer constant and $\Delta\mu$ is not equal to $m\,\Delta v$, so that Eq. (6–10) is not equivalent to Eq. (6–9). In this case it is Eq. (6–10) that is still valid and not Eq. (6–9). Implied in Eq. (6–10) is the postulate that if, in the relation

$$F \propto \frac{\Delta\mu}{\Delta t},$$

we make the constant of proportionality unity for a given test body, then it will be unity for *any* body.

6–5 Weight

Weight was defined as the force of gravitational attraction. A force is measured by the acceleration it imparts to a mass m. For a body that is allowed to fall freely the acceleration due to gravity is called g. Then from Eq. (6–9), since $a = g$

when F = weight,

$$\text{Weight} = mg. \tag{6-11}$$

In the mks system weight is measured in newtons. Near sea level g varies from 9.78 m/sec² at the equator to 9.83 m/sec² at the poles. At a place where $g = 9.80$ m/sec², the force of gravity on a mass of one pound, a force called the *pound-weight*, is

$$1 \text{ pound-weight} = 0.454 \text{ kg} \times 9.8 \text{ m/sec}^2$$
$$= 4.45 \text{ newtons},$$

since one pound = 454 gm = 0.454 kg. Where $g = 9.8$ m/sec² the weight of a kilogram will be $1 \times 9.8 = 9.8$ newtons, while on the moon, where $g = 1.67$ m/sec², the weight of a kilogram will be only 1×1.67 newtons.

We see from the above that weight varies with location, but mass does not.

In connection with space technology, one often encounters the term *weightlessness*. This is taken to mean that there is no counterforce to oppose whatever gravitational force acts on a body. A so-called "weightless" person near the earth is still acted on by the earth's gravitational pull; therefore he must be falling toward the earth with the acceleration g. Thus a person who falls freely from a bridge is "weightless" during his fall. A "weightless" person is not subject to the upward push of something, such as the floor or a chair, that supports his weight, but he still has weight in the sense in which we have defined it.

EXAMPLE. How fast must an elevator accelerate downward if it is to support half of the weight of an occupant?

Solution. Let m be the mass of the occupant. Then his weight is mg newtons down, and the upward push of the elevator floor against the person's feet must be $mg/2$ newtons up. The net force F acting on the person is

$$F = mg - mg/2 = mg/2 \text{ down.}$$

We now use Newton's law of motion and obtain

$$F = \frac{mg}{2} = ma, \qquad a = g/2.$$

The occupant of the elevator might be described as "half weightless."

6–6 Addition of forces. Concept of a vector

It must be remembered that the F in Newton's law of motion is the net or unbalanced force acting. A problem arises concerning how F is to be computed when two or more forces in different directions act on a body.

It was implied in the definition of force that forces in the *same direction* are added numerically. When forces act along the same line but in *opposite directions*, the

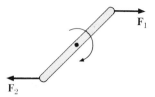

FIG. 6–5. A couple, or a pair of equal and opposite forces that are not colinear, will produce rotation.

acceleration *a* is such as to indicate that if forces in one direction are taken as positive, then forces in the opposite direction must be considered negative.

Newton realized that there are situations in which forces are equal in magnitude and opposite in direction and yet their combined effect is not zero because they do not have a common line of action. Such a pair of forces, called a *couple*, exerts a *torque* on the body which tends to make the body rotate or twist (Fig. 6–5). In general, when a body moves through space its *center of mass*, or point about which it will balance in any plane, follows some path, while the body may simultaneously rotate about axes through its center of mass. The motion is described as a combination of *translational* motion of the center of mass and *rotational* motion about the center. The theory of rotational motion is more complicated than that of translational motion, and when the two types of motion are combined, the theoretical treatment is still more difficult. It seemed to Newton that it would be best to start with the simpler situation of pure translational motion. He reasoned that actual bodies are a conglomerate system of tiny particles (we now call them atoms) and that the motion of a body such as a wheel is simply the sum of the motions of its particles. This approach has proved highly successful and may be studied in books on analytical mechanics. Here the important point is Newton's concept of a *particle*. A particle is regarded as an idealized small body, still possessing a finite amount of mass, but so small that all forces acting on it must act at practically the same point. We need consider, then, only the translational motion of a particle. Large bodies behave like particles when all the forces acting are directed along lines that pass through the center of mass* of the body.

Suppose that two forces, each equal in magnitude to *F*, act *at right angles* on a small body or particle of mass *m* (Fig. 6–6). What will be the magnitude and direction of the resulting acceleration? A simple test will show that the direction of the acceleration is midway between that of the two forces, or at an angle of 45° with each. Careful measurement will show that the combined effect of the two forces is the same as that due to a single force of magnitude $\sqrt{2}F$ acting in the direction of the acceleration. We call the force that combines the effect of two or more forces the *resultant* **R** of these forces. In this case the magnitude of **R** is

$$R = \sqrt{F^2 + F^2}.$$

* The position of the center of mass is such that each of its coordinates has a value that is the average value of that coordinate for all the mass particles in the body.

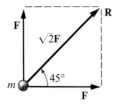

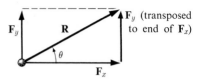

FIG. 6–6. Addition of two equal forces acting at right angles to one another.

FIG. 6–7. Addition of unequal forces acting at right angles.

In general it is found that when forces F_x and F_y act at right angles on a particle, the resultant **R** has the magnitude

$$R = \sqrt{F_x^2 + F_y^2} \tag{6–12}$$

and the effective direction of **R** is as shown in Fig. 6–7, for which

$$\cos \theta = \frac{F_x}{R} \quad \text{and} \quad \sin \theta = \frac{F_y}{R}. \tag{6–13}$$

From this figure we see that **R** may be obtained by considering F_x and F_y as having direction as well as magnitude and plotting them graphically end to end; the line connecting the beginning of F_x with the end of F_y represents **R** in direction and relative magnitude (because of the Pythagorean theorem).

When any number of forces act in various directions, **R** may still be found graphically by adding the individual forces end to end (Fig. 6–8). From the way in which force was defined, forces and accelerations must add in the same way. So do velocities; for example, if an airplane headed north is flying at 120 mph relative to the air and there is a cross wind of 50 mph toward the east, the ground speed of the plane will be

$$\sqrt{120^2 + 50^2} = 130 \text{ mph},$$

and relative to the ground the plane will be traveling east of north.

Altogether there are quite a few physical concepts that have both magnitude and direction and add as do forces. We call such quantities *vectors*, as contrasted with quantities that have only a magnitude and are termed *scalars*. When we wish to emphasize the directional property of a vector we may put an arrow above it,

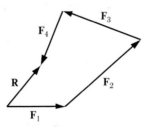

FIG. 6–8. Addition of several forces.

e.g., $\vec{F}$; in print the custom is to use *bold-face type* to distinguish vectors, as we started to do in connection with the resultant vector **R**. We used the symbol R to designate only the *magnitude* of the vector **R**. Examples of vectors are force, acceleration, velocity, momentum, and gravitational, electric and magnetic fields. Examples of scalars are mass, time, speed (the magnitude of a velocity), density, work, energy, difference of potential, pressure, temperature, etc. While length is a scalar, a displacement is a vector.

To specify a vector one must state (a) its magnitude and units, and (b) its direction, as we did when stating that a wind was 50 mph toward the east.

EXAMPLE. The following forces are to be added: F_1 in the positive x-direction (to the right), F_2 in the positive y-direction (up), and F_3 in the negative y-direction (down). The magnitudes are: $F_1 = 40$ n, $F_2 = 80$ n, $F_3 = 50$ n.

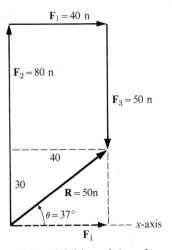

FIG. 6–9. Addition of three forces.

Solution. Since F_2 and F_3 are opposite, we subtract F_3 from F_2 and say that

$$\mathbf{F}_2 + \mathbf{F}_3 = 80 - 50 = 30 \text{ n up.}$$

Since the sum of F_2 and F_3 is at right angles to F_1, F_x, we consider this sum to take the place of F_y in Eq. (6–12). Let

$$\mathbf{R} = \mathbf{F}_1 + \mathbf{F}_2 + \mathbf{F}_3.$$

Then the magnitude of **R**, designated by R, is

$$R = \sqrt{40^2 + 30^2} = 50 \text{ n.}$$

The magnitude of the resultant is 50 newtons. The angle θ between **R** and x-axis is given by

$$\cos \theta = F_1/R = \tfrac{40}{50} = 0.8$$

(see trigonometry, Chapter 2). The angle whose cosine is 0.8 is about 37°.

The magnitude and direction of **R** may also be found graphically with the aid of a ruler and graph paper. We might conveniently adopt a scale of 1 cm = 10 n, or 1 cm = 5 n. The order in which vectors are added makes no difference; thus in Fig. 6–9 we see that $\mathbf{F}_2 + \mathbf{F}_1 + \mathbf{F}_3 = \mathbf{R}$.

6–7 The components of a vector

We have seen that when two forces, $\mathbf{F}_x$ in the x-direction and $\mathbf{F}_y$ in the y-direction, act together on a particle the result is the same as though the force **R** alone acted, where **R** has the magnitude

$$R = \sqrt{F_x^2 + F_y^2},$$

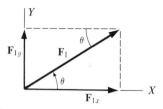

FIG. 6–10. Components of a vector.

and the angle θ between **R** and the x-axis is given by

$$\cos \theta = F_x/R, \quad \text{or} \quad \sin \theta = F_y/R.$$

We may turn this analysis around and say that a force **R** acting in the direction making an angle θ with the x-axis will have the same effect on a particle as will the force $F_x = R \cos \theta$ acting in the x-direction and the force $F_y = R \sin \theta$ acting in the y-direction. The rule for vector addition shows that $\mathbf{R} = \mathbf{F}_x + \mathbf{F}_y$, because $\mathbf{F}_x$ and $\mathbf{F}_y$ added graphically end to end give the vector **R**. The projections of a vector along the principal axes are called the *components* of the vector.

When the vectors to be added are *oblique* to one another, the graphical method requires the use of a protractor to measure the angles; this may introduce considerable error. In this case a purely *analytical method*, based on the use of trigonometry tables, is preferable.

The trigonometric method resolves each vector into its horizontal and vertical components (Fig. 6–10). Consider the first vector $\mathbf{F}_1$. The horizontal component F_{1x} of $\mathbf{F}_1$, or the projection of $\mathbf{F}_1$ along the x-axis, is

$$F_{1x} = F_1 \cos \theta_1, \tag{6–14a}$$

where θ_1 is the acute angle between $\mathbf{F}_1$ and the x-axis.* Similarly, the vertical component F_{1y} of $\mathbf{F}_1$ is

$$F_{1y} = F_1 \sin \theta_1. \tag{6–14b}$$

Since $\mathbf{F}_1 = \mathbf{F}_{1x} + \mathbf{F}_{1y}$ (added vectorally), we may replace each vector to be added with its two components and proceed to add the respective components rather than the original vectors. If the vector directions fall in any quadrant, horizontal components may be regarded as positive when to the right, and negative when to the left, and are quickly added to give the horizontal component R_x of the resultant. Vertical components may similarly be added to give the vertical component R_y of the resultant, and finally R may be found by combining R_x and R_y. Thus we write

$$R_x = F_{1x} + F_{2x} + \cdots, \tag{6–15}$$

---

* Since the direction of a component is implied in its definition, we shall usually be concerned only with its magnitude.

calling *any component* to the *right positive* and *any* to the *left negative*, and

$$R_y = F_{1y} + F_{2y} + \cdots, \tag{6-16}$$

calling *any component up positive* and *any down negative*, and

$$R = \sqrt{R_x^2 + R_y^2}. \tag{6-17}$$

The acute angle θ between **R** and the *x*-axis is given by

$$\cos \theta = \frac{R_x}{R}, \quad \text{or} \quad \sin \theta = \frac{R_y}{R}. \tag{6-18}$$

EXAMPLE. A force of 40 n to the right is to be added to one of 20 n in a direction to the left and down at an angle of 45° (Fig. 6–11).

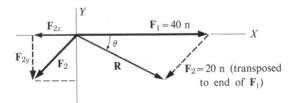

FIG. 6–11.   Addition of two oblique forces.

Solution. For the first force we have $\theta_1 = 0°$,

$$F_{1x} = 40,$$
$$F_{1y} = 0.$$

For the other force $\theta_2 = 45°$, $\cos 45° = \sin 45° = 0.707$. Then

$$F_{2x} = -20 \times 0.707 = -14.14,$$
$$F_{2y} = -20 \times 0.707 = -14.14.$$

The component F_{2x} is negative since it is to the left; F_{2y} is negative because it is down. It is helpful to list the components in tabular form, as in the following table.

Force	Horizontal or *x*-component	Vertical or *y*-component
F_1	40.00	0
F_2	−14.14	−14.14
R	+25.86	−14.14

Thus $R_x = 25.86$ and $R_y = -14.14$, so that

$$R = \sqrt{(25.86)^2 + (-14.14)^2} = \sqrt{669 + 200} = 29.5.$$

From Eq. (6–18),

$$\cos \theta = \frac{25.86}{29.5} = 0.873, \qquad \theta = 29.2°.$$

The resultant is 29.5 n. It is to the right (because R_x is positive) and down (because R_y is negative) at an angle of about 29° from the horizontal. Graphical addition is shown in Fig. 6–11. Experiment 8 (at the end of this chapter), on the force table, will illustrate further the addition of vectors.

Since so many physical quantities are vectors, the further one goes into the theories of physics, the more advisable it is to study the properties of vectors. A mathematical theory called *vector analysis* was developed by the American physical-chemist J. W. Gibbs. He devised not only the rules we have used for adding vectors, but also rules for subtraction, two kinds of multiplication, differentiation, and integration of vectors. Since he had physical applications in mind, Gibbs chose his rules so that they would correspond with the actual behavior of vector quantities in physics.

Some physical quantities, particularly those associated with crystals (called *tensors*), are a step more complicated than vectors. Such quantities will be avoided in this book. It is better to *understand* a little physics than to be acquainted with a lot!

6–8 The special case of statics

When a body continues to remain at rest, it is said to be in a state of *static equilibrium*.

If a particle remains at rest, then its acceleration and its rate of change of momentum are zero. From Newton's law of motion, Eq. (6–9) or Eq. (6–10), the net force **F** must be zero.* This in turn means that (a) the components of **F** must each be zero and (b) the sum of the forces acting on the particle must form a closed polygon, since the resultant **R** = 0. Conversely, if the forces acting add up to zero, then **F** = 0, **a** = 0, and a particle at rest will remain at rest.

The conditions for the static equilibrium of a particle may be summarized as follows.

The forces up must equal the forces down, and those to the right must equal those to the left; when the forces acting are added graphically, they must form a closed polygon.

---

* Equations (6–9) and (6–10) are really vector equations, $\mathbf{F} = m\mathbf{a}$ and $\mathbf{F} = \Delta\mu/\Delta t$, since force, acceleration, and momentum are vector quantities.

These theorems were derived from Newton's law of motion by applying it to this special case of equilibrium. Newton summarized this special case in what is frequently termed his *first law of motion* (our Fundamental Law I is then called Newton's second law of motion), which states that *a particle not acted on by a net force will remain at rest or move in a straight line at constant speed.* The latter part of this statement is illustrated by a car moving at constant velocity, in which case the applied forward force is exactly balanced by the backward drag of frictional resistance. Let us consider an illustration of the rules of static equilibrium.

EXAMPLE. A boy sits in a swing supported by a rope 15 ft long. The boy and swing together weigh 240 n (about 54 pound-weight). A man pulls the boy out a distance of 12 ft from the vertical. Find the tension (pull) that the rope must supply and the pull exerted by the man.

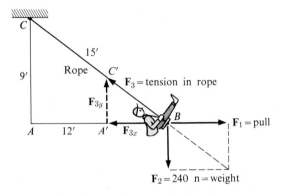

FIG. 6–12.   Vector diagram of a boy in a swing.

Solution. In Fig. 6–12, B represents the boy, BC the rope, F_1 the pull by the man, F_2 the weight of the boy and swing, and F_3 the tension of the rope. Triangle ABC is a right triangle whose sides are in the ratio $3:4:5$, so that $AC = 9$ ft.

The only oblique force is F_3, and it may be resolved into components F_{3x} and F_{3y}, as shown. Since the force triangle $A'BC'$ is similar to the distance triangle ABC, we have

$$\frac{F_{3x}}{F_3} = \frac{AB}{BC} = \frac{12}{15} = 0.8,$$

$$F_{3x} = 0.8F_3;$$

F_{3x} is to the left (negative). Similarly $F_{3y} = 0.6F_3$ and F_{3y} is up (positive).

Since F_1 is the only force to the right and F_{3x} the only one to the left, our equilibrium conditions tell us that

$$F_{3x} = 0.8F_3 = F_1.$$

Since F_{3y} is the only force up and $F_2 = 240$ n is the only force down, we have

$$F_{3y} = 0.6F_3 = 240 \text{ n}$$

$$F_3 = 400 \text{ n}.$$

From $F_1 = 0.8F_3$ we find that

$$F_1 = 320 \text{ n}.$$

The components of the forces and of their resultant **R** may be listed in tabular form, as follows.

Force	x-component	y-component
F_1	320 n	0
F_2	0	−240 n
F_3	−320 n	+240 n
R	0	0

Note that the pull exerted by the man in this example is greater than the weight of the boy and swing; also, the rope must support a tension of 400 n, which is one and two-thirds times the weight. Calculations of this sort are important to engineers and architects, who must determine how strong a supporting beam, girder, column, etc., must be.

6–9 Linear motion

If a body continues to move in the same direction, then any acceleration **a** and the net force **F** causing this acceleration must be in this direction or its opposite. Here we may drop vector notation.

Suppose that there is an applied force F_1 and an opposing force F_2 (usually due to friction), then

$$F = F_1 - F_2. \tag{6–19}$$

From Newton's law of motion in its most general form, Eq. (6–10), we have

$$\Delta\mu = F\,\Delta t = (F_1 - F_2)\,\Delta t \tag{6–20}$$

for the change in momentum in the time Δt.

From the nonrelativistic form of Newton's law of motion, Eq. (6–9), we have

$$ma = F = F_1 - F_2$$

$$a = \frac{F_1 - F_2}{m}. \tag{6–21}$$

If F_1 and F_2 are constant with time, a will also be constant, and then Eqs. (6–2) and (6–5) will apply. Suppose, however, that F_1 is constant but that F_2 (the frictional resistance) increases with the speed v, i.e., $F_2 = kv$, where k is a constant; in this case the acceleration will decrease as the speed of the body approaches that limiting value for which $F_1 = F_2$. The limiting speed v_l is given by $kv_l = F_1$, or

$$v_l = \frac{F_1}{k}. \tag{6–22}$$

There are important physical situations in which the net force F is a function of the displacement of the body. For example, when a spring is stretched by an amount s beyond its equilibrium length, a body attached to the end of the spring will be pulled toward the spring by a force $F = -ks$; here k is a constant of the spring and the minus sign means that F is opposite to the displacement s. In this case Eq. (6–9) becomes

$$ma = -ks. \qquad (6\text{–}23)$$

In Eq. (6–23), s varies with time, and so a is not constant. The type of motion described by this so-called *equation of motion* can be properly computed only with the aid of the calculus, but a good deal may be learned from Eq. (6–23) without using the calculus. Thus suppose that the body is given an initial shove in the positive x-direction so that $s = x$; then x will increase and a will become increasingly negative. A large negative acceleration or positive deceleration will eventually bring the body to a stop and then start it moving back faster and faster. After x becomes negative, a will become positive and the backward motion will be slowed down, halted and reversed. The motion will be *oscillatory* with maximum speed at $x = 0$. This particular type of periodic motion that results when $F = -ks$ is called *simple harmonic motion*. The swing of a pendulum bob is another illustration of such motion.

6–10 Motion in two or three dimensions

Since force and acceleration are both vectors, we should, when the motion is not linear, write Eq. (6–9) as a *vector* equation, namely,

$$\mathbf{F} = m\mathbf{a}. \qquad (6\text{–}24)$$

This states that m times the vector $\mathbf{a}$ equals the vector $\mathbf{F}$. Two vectors cannot be equal, i.e., one and the same, unless they have the same x-components, the same y-components, and the same z-components. So in three-dimensional space, Eq. (6–24) is equivalent to three scalar equations, namely,

$$F_x = ma_x, \qquad F_y = ma_y, \qquad F_z = ma_z. \qquad (6\text{–}25)$$

Each of these scalar equations represents the one-dimensional motion discussed in the last section. We may then analyze motion in, say, the xy-plane as a combination of horizontal and vertical motion, *each going on independently of the other*. Galileo realized this point in his analysis of the motion of a projectile.

ILLUSTRATION. *Projectile motion.* A projectile is launched with an initial upward velocity v_{0y} and an initial horizontal velocity v_{0x} (Fig. 6–13). Neglect air resistance and find the resultant motion.

Solution. The only force to be considered is the weight mg which is downward (negative). Therefore we have

$$F_x = 0, \qquad F_y = -mg.$$

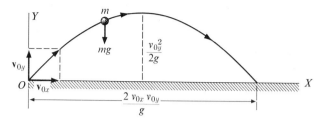

FIG. 6–13.   Motion of a projectile.

In this case Eqs. (6–25) become

$$0 = ma_x, \qquad -mg = ma_y.$$

The first equation tells us that the horizontal acceleration is zero (since m is not zero) and hence the horizontal velocity will remain unchanged and equal to v_{0x}. The second equation tells us that $a_y = -g$, which means that the vertical acceleration and resulting motion is the same as it would be if the body were hurled *straight up* with the initial speed v_{0y}.

What will happen to an object that is thrown vertically upward with an initial velocity v_{0y} and a constant downward acceleration g? From Eq. (6–1) we see that its upward velocity will decrease by $g \, \Delta t$ in the time Δt, so that after v_{0y}/g seconds its upward velocity will be zero. Thus $t_{up} = v_{0y}/g$. After this time the object will start to fall, just as any object will that is released from rest. After another v_{0y}/g seconds it will have acquired a *downward* velocity of v_{0y} and will have returned to its starting point. At every point on its downward path it will have the speed it had at the same point while rising. But an object falling from rest for a time $t_{down} = v_{0y}/g$ will, according to Eq. (6–5), travel a distance

$$s = \tfrac{1}{2} g t_{down}^2 = \tfrac{1}{2} v_{0y}^2/g.$$

We may now summarize by saying that the object will rise to a height of $v_{0y}^2/2g$ and be in the air for a time $t_{up} + t_{down} = 2v_{0y}/g$.

Returning to the projectile, we note that the horizontal velocity v_{0x} will carry it through a horizontal distance $v_{0x}(2 \, v_{0y}/g) = 2v_{0x}v_{0y}/g$, which is the *range* on level ground.

If we call the origin of coordinates ($x = 0$, $y = 0$) the starting point of a projectile, the coordinates of its position after the time t are given by

$$x = v_{0x}t, \qquad y = v_{0y}t - \tfrac{1}{2} g t^2.$$

The $v_0 t$ terms represent distances traveled due to the initial velocity components, while the $-gt^2/2$ term represents height lost due to gravity. Can you derive the equation for y from the definitions of average velocity and time? [See the method by which Eq. (6–5) was derived.] Elimination of t between the x and y equations leads to the equation

$$y = \frac{v_{0y}}{v_{0x}} x - \frac{1}{2} \frac{g}{v_{0x}^2} x^2,$$

which is the equation of a *parabola* with a vertical axis. This equation also represents the path or *orbit* of the projectile (Fig. 6–13). Therefore we may say that, if air resistance is neglected, the path of a projectile is a parabola.

6–11 The meaning of the derivative

We have considered problems in which the net force, and hence the acceleration, are given, and one wishes to find the resulting motion of an object. Experimentally one frequently reverses this procedure by *measuring the position* of the object at various times; the displacement s is then known as a function of the time, and one wishes to find the velocity and acceleration at any time t. The relation between s and t may always be plotted graphically, but, if possible, one tries to find an empirical formula that expresses the relationship.

Let us then suppose that the displacement s may be expressed as a given function of the time t. Mathematicians state this as $s = f(t)$, where $f(t)$ means "a function of t." Now, for purposes of illustration, let us take a specific example and assume

$$s = bt^3,$$

where s is in meters, t in seconds, and

$$b = 2 \text{ m/sec}^3.$$

(Note that the units for each side of the equation are the same, namely meters.) The particular problem that we shall try to solve is to find the *instantaneous* speed v at the time $t = 3$ sec.

In Chapter 3 the average speed v for a certain time interval was defined as the ratio of the distance traveled to the time taken. If the time interval taken is a small one, which we shall call Δt, and if the small distance traversed in this time is called Δs, then the ratio $\Delta s/\Delta t$ will represent the average speed during the short time interval Δt. Suppose that Δt is the smallest time interval of any significance, say 0.1 sec, then $\Delta s/\Delta t$ is the mean speed for that 0.1 sec. By letting Δt approach zero ($\Delta t \to 0$), $\Delta s/\Delta t$ is made to approach a value corresponding to v at the time t about which the interval Δt is taken. We express this symbolically as

$$v = \underset{\Delta t \to 0}{\text{Limit}} \left(\frac{\Delta s}{\Delta t} \right), \qquad (6\text{–}26)$$

or *instantaneous speed is the instantaneous time rate of change of the distance traveled* from some reference point. This concept is called the *derivative of s with respect to t* and is designated as *ds/dt, so that ds/dt* is just an abbreviation for the right-hand side of Eq. (6–26). We may then write

$$v = \frac{ds}{dt}. \qquad (6\text{–}27)$$

Let us return to our specific example. In Table 6–1 are listed (for $s = 2t^3$) some corresponding values of t and s, grouped about $t = 3$; from the right toward

TABLE 6–1

t	s				
0	0				
1	2				
2	16				
2.5	31.25				
3	54	$\dfrac{\Delta s}{\Delta t} = \dfrac{54.5}{1} = 54.5$	$\dfrac{112}{2} = 56$	$\dfrac{248}{4} = 62$	$\dfrac{432}{6} = 72$
3.5	85.75				
4	128				
5	250				
6	432				

the left the ratio $\Delta s/\Delta t$ has been computed for $\Delta t = 6 - 0 = 6$, $\Delta t = 5 - 1 = 4$, $\Delta t = 4 - 2 = 2$, and $\Delta t = 3.5 - 2.5 = 1$.

It is evident that in this example the value of $\Delta s/\Delta t$ does depend on the size of the interval taken for Δt, even though $t = 3$ lies in the middle of each interval. As $\Delta t \rightarrow 0$ we see that $\Delta s/\Delta t$ decreases, at first rapidly, then more and more slowly. What is the limiting value of $\Delta s/\Delta t$ as $\Delta t \rightarrow 0$? It is exactly 54.

If we plot a graph of s against t we get a curve such as that in Fig. 6–14. Referring to Section 2–7 we see that $\Delta s/\Delta t$ is the average slope of the curve over the interval Δt. (In the present graph s takes the place of y and t that of x.) As Δt is made smaller and smaller, this average slope approaches that of the tangent to the curve at $t = t$, or the slope of the curve itself at that point. We may thus say that

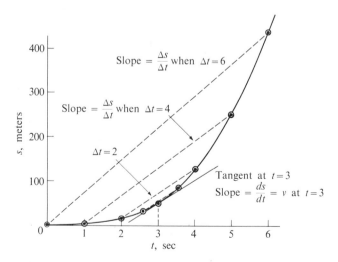

FIG. 6–14. Relation between average slope, slope of tangent to curve, and the derivative.

the slope of the curve at any time t represents the instantaneous speed at this time. Thus by plotting s against t we may always compute the instantaneous speed v at any time by measuring the slope of the graph for that value of t.

The concept of the derivative is fundamental to all branches of physics. The important idea to grasp is that of the limiting value of the ratio of the corresponding changes in two related quantities. It does not matter what the quantities are called; they might be x and y instead of t and s, but if y changes by Δy when x changes by Δx, then

$$\frac{dy}{dx} = \underset{\Delta x \to 0}{\text{Limit}} \left(\frac{\Delta y}{\Delta x}\right) \qquad (6\text{–}28)$$

is the *derivative of y with respect to x*.

Referring to the definition of acceleration, we see that

$$a = \frac{dv}{dt}. \qquad (6\text{–}29)$$

PROBLEMS

1. If a car accelerates from 10 mi/hr to 60 mi/hr in 20 sec, what is its average acceleration? Express your answer in terms of (a) mi/hr-sec, (b) mi/hr-min, (c) mi/hr^2, and (d) mi/sec^2.

2. A body falls from rest with a constant acceleration of 9.8 m/sec^2. Find the (a) speed at the end of each of the first five seconds, (b) the average speed during each of the first five seconds, (c) the distance traveled during each second, and (d) the distance fallen from rest after 1, 2, 3, 4, and 5 sec.

3. A body moving at a speed of 20 m/sec is given a constant acceleration. In the next two one-second intervals it travels 22 and 26 m, respectively. Find (a) the acceleration and (b) the distances traveled in the third and fourth seconds after the acceleration began.

4. A net force F is found to give an acceleration of 6 m/sec^2 to a 5-kg object and an acceleration of 2.4 m/sec^2 to an object of mass m. (a) Find F and m. (b) What definition did you use in each calculation? (c) Did you assume Newton's law of motion and, if so, how?

5. A net force of 0.4 n is found to give a mass m an acceleration of 0.12 m/sec^2, while a net force F gives the same mass an acceleration of 0.30 m/sec^2. (a) Find F and m. (b) Did you assume Newton's law of motion and, if so, how?

6. Explain the statement, "Newton's law of motion may be used to define the unit of force and the concept of mass."

7. Approximately how many nucleons (nuclear particles) are there in a kilogram of matter?

8. The pull of gravity varies inversely as the square of the distance from the *center* of the earth. Take $g = 9.8$ m/sec^2 at sea level, for which the earth's radius is about 4000 miles. Compute g at an altitude of (a) 4 miles (top of Mt. McKinley), (b) 100 miles, (c) 4000 miles.

9. Refer to the last problem and determine the weight in newtons of a 75-kg man at (a) sea level, (b) on Mt. McKinley, (c) at an altitude of 4000 miles.

10. (a) Find the horizontal and vertical components of each of the following forces: $F_1 = 100$ n to the right and up at an angle of 45° with the x-axis, $F_2 = 150$ n to the left,

$F_3 = 50$ n to the right and down at an angle of $45°$ below the x-axis. (b) Add respective components and find the resultant of these three forces. (c) Check by graphical addition.

11. A 5-kg picture is supported by a 1-m wire which passes over a hook. Each end of the wire is fastened to the picture near one of its upper corners. The points where the wire is attached are 0.6 m apart and each is 0.5 m from the hook. Find the pull exerted by each end of the wire on the picture.

12. A car is stuck in the mud. A man fastens a taut rope from the car's axle to a tree 20 ft away. He lifts the midpoint of the rope one foot, thereby exerting a lifting force of 222 n (50 pound-weight). Find the tension in the rope, which is the effective pulling force on the car.

13. A 400-gm block rests on a horizontal table. Find the acceleration under applied forces of 1, 2, 3, and 4 n, if in each case the frictional drag is 1 n.

14. What opposing force of magnitude F will bring a body of mass m to rest in a time Δt if the initial speed of the body is v? Compute F in newtons and pound-weight for a 2000-kg car going 29 m/sec (about 60 mi/hr) which must be stopped in 4 sec.

15. Suppose that for a 400-gm object the frictional resistance is proportional to the speed and that for an applied force of 40 n the limiting speed is 5 m/sec. (a) Find k in Eq. (6–22). (b) Find the frictional resistance and acceleration when the applied force is 60 n and $v = 2$ m/sec. (c) Find the acceleration when $F = 60$ n and $v = 7.5$ m/sec. (d) Find the acceleration when $F = 60$ n and $v = 10$ m/sec.

16. An 80-kg man stands on platform scales in an elevator. What will the scales read if the acceleration of the elevator is (a) zero, (b) 0.98 m/sec^2 up, (c) 0.98 m/sec^2 down? [*Note:* the scales really read in terms of kilogram-weight units, 1 kg-wt being equal to 9.8 n.]

17. The period of oscillation of a spring is $2\pi\sqrt{m/k}$. Show that this expression has the units of time and that, apart from the formula, you would expect the period to increase as m gets larger and to decrease as the spring constant k gets larger.

18. A ball is thrown vertically upward with an initial speed of 14.7 m/sec. Find its velocity and position after 0.5, 1.0, 1.5, 2.0, 2.5, and 3.0 sec, respectively.

19. A baseball is thrown across a horizontal distance of 30 m (about 100 ft) and in its path it rises and falls 2.5 m. Find the ball's initial velocity components and speed.

20. The distance s through which a body falls from rest in t seconds is given by $s = \frac{1}{2}gt^2$. By means of the derivative concept, as given in Section 6–11, find expressions for v and a (a) at the time $t = 2$ sec, (b) at any time t.

EXPERIMENT 6

THE SPEED OF SOUND
(Measurement of Constant Velocity)

Object: To measure the speed of sound in air, using the reflection property of waves and the formula defining velocity.

Problem: When a velocity v is constant, it may be defined as distance traveled (s) divided by the time taken (t), or

$$v = s/t.$$

We shall time how long it takes sound to travel from the observer to a wall and back. Then s is twice the distance to the wall; this may be measured with a tape.

To find t the observer claps his hands at a gradually increasing rate, listening for the echoes. When the echo from one clap arrives at the instant of the next clap, the echoes will be blotted out. Therefore, when the observer reaches a clapping rate for which the echoes disappear, he should try to continue this rate steadily while his partner times 100 claps. The time between successive claps will then be t.

Procedure:

Step 1. Select a large flat wall that will serve as a reflector of sound waves. The face of a domitory or gymnasium are possibilities. You must back away about 150 ft (50 paces) from the wall so as to make t large enough and the clapping rate a reasonable one. Greater distances are desirable if the echoes can still be detected. Measure the distance to the wall with a tape.

Step 2. Develop the proper clapping technique and rhythm. Then make five runs in each of which your partner(s) time 100 clap intervals. One partner should count "0, 1, 2, 3, . . . , 100." Average and find the mean deviation. The percent mean deviation will be your possible error, in both 100 t and t itself. Add any possible percent error in measuring s that you deem reasonable. This will give the possible error in your value of v, which you compute from the formula $v = s/t$.

Step 3. If you want to determine your actual error, look up the speed of sound in a book. Since it depends on the air temperature, you should record the outdoor temperature. If conditions are good, this experiment may be done with sufficient accuracy to enable one to measure the air temperature by computing at what temperature the accepted value and the measured value are the same.

Step 4. Explain why you timed 100 clap intervals rather than one, five, or ten intervals.

EXPERIMENT 7

BALL ROLLING DOWN A TROUGH
(Accelerated Motion)

Object: To study motion under constant acceleration.

Problem: When bodies fall freely they experience a constant acceleration of about 32 ft/sec², or 9.8 m/sec². Newtonian theory predicts this and experiment confirms it. This acceleration is too large for easy measurement, so we dilute gravity, as it were, by letting a ball roll down a plane of slight inclination. We thus obtain a much smaller acceleration.

We shall measure the gain in velocity of our ball in a given time t. Then from the definition of acceleration we have

$$a = \text{Gain in velocity}/t.$$

The time t will be small (much less than 1 sec) because we want to compute a for a number of intervals in order to see whether or not it is a constant.

The gain in velocity in a time interval t will be the mean velocity in one such interval minus the mean velocity in the next previous interval, and mean velocity is defined as distance traveled divided by the time t.

So we shall measure successive distances traveled in a time t and then, of course, we must find t. We shall find t by measuring 25 t, as in Experiment 4.

Procedure:

Step 1. Support one end of a curved trough about two centimeters above a table. Chalk the ball and release it at the side of the upper end. The ball will oscillate back and forth as it rolls down. The time of each complete oscillation is our t.

Measure and record distances between successive maxima of the chalk track, first on one side and then on the other.

Step 2. With the trough flat on the table release the ball from the side and time 20 or 25 complete oscillations. Repeat this timing several times, average and find the possible error. What was your value of t?

Step 3. Divide each distance measured in Step 1 by your time t. This will give you the mean velocities in each interval.

Step 4. Compute the acceleration a between each pair of successive intervals. Is it constant? Average all your values of a and obtain the mean deviation in them.

Step 5. Can the mean deviation in Step 4 be accounted for in terms of possible errors in measurement? If so, your results indicate constant acceleration, otherwise not. You found the possible error in t in Step 2. The rest of your experimental error is in the measuring of the distances in Step 1. Estimate whether you could measure the distances to within 1, 2, 3, 4, or 5 mm and then find the resulting possible error in your computation of a typical (say the fourth) gain in velocity. Express this as a percent error and add it to the percent error in t. Compare with the mean deviation in a found in Step 4 and draw your conclusions.

EXPERIMENT 8

THE FORCE TABLE
(Vector Addition and Static Equilibrium)

Object: To observe how vectors add and to verify the conditions for static equilibrium.

Problem: If two or more vectors are laid off end to end, each with its proper magnitude and direction, then the vector connecting the beginning of the first with the end of the last vector is, by *definition*, the sum of the vectors considered. If the sum is *zero*, the vectors when added should form a *closed polygon*.

According to Newton's first law, if an object such as a ring is stationary (in equilibrium, we say), then the sum of the forces acting on the ring must be zero. When added graphically the forces should then give a closed polygon. Any failure to do so must be attributed to experimental error.

What errors may arise? First there are errors in finding a set of forces that will experimentally produce equilibrium. Due to friction, some variation in one force is possible without producing a noticeable effect. This source of error must be investigated. Second, errors may arise in the plotting of the polygon with ruler and compass; such errors may be minimized with care, or they may be avoided by adding the vectors *analytically*, that is, with the aid of mathematics rather than ruler and compass. We may check Newton's first law analytically by seeing whether the sum of the *x*-components and the sum of the *y*-components are both zero.

Procedure:

Step 1. To find the error due to friction, put a 500-gm weight on one string and a 500-gm weight on another opposite string. Find how much extra force is needed to move the ring noticeably when (a) weights are added gently to one side, (b) when the table is tapped as weights are added to one side.

The largest amount you can add without detectable motion of the ring is the instrumental error per 1000 grams due to friction. Decide on and use consistently either the jarring technique or the other.

Step 2. Set two 500-gm weights at 120° apart. Find the third force (magnitude and direction) that will give equilibrium.

Step 3. Find the force to balance 300-gm weight at 0°, 400-gm weight at 90°.

Step 4. Find the force to balance 200-gm weight at 0°, 100-gm weight at 90°, and 100-gm weight at 180°.

Analysis 1. Graphic. Add the force in Step 2 by the ruler and compass method. Do you get a gap rather than a closed polygon? If so, measure the gap and compute what force it represents. Try to justify this experimental error. Repeat for each of the other two sets of forces (Steps 3 and 4).

Analysis 2. Analytic. Find the components (*x* and *y*, or east and north) of each force used. Make a chart for Step 2, another for Step 3, and a third for Step 4. In each case see what the *x*-components add up to and what the *y*-components add up to. Did you verify Newton's first law within your possible errors?

CHAPTER 7

Newton's Action-Reaction Law

7–1 Introduction

In the last chapter we commenced with a study of motion itself, apart from its causes. Speed, velocity, and acceleration were defined and from these definitions we developed expressions that related distance (*s*), speed (*v*), acceleration (*a*), and time (*t*). These relations followed just from the definitions of the quantities involved and the arbitrary assumption of conditions typifying a certain kind of motion, such as motion under constant acceleration. We were discussing a branch of mechanics called *kinematics*.

Chapter 6 continued with a discussion of the causes of various types of motion. We saw that a constant net force results in a constant acceleration, and that a net force of zero results in motion under constant velocity. The relation between force, mass, and acceleration was summarized in Newton's law of motion. This law was based on numerous experimental observations and the assumption that it will also apply to future experiments of various kinds. This law thus stands as our first fundamental postulate about how our physical world behaves. The branch of mechanics that is concerned with the relation between force and motion is called *dynamics*.

To complete his theory of mechanics, Newton found that he needed another fundamental postulate which is quite independent of his law of motion. This new law is frequently called "Newton's third law of motion," but we shall identify it as *Newton's action-reaction law*, since our title will always remind us of the subject with which this law is concerned. The importance, in fact the necessity, of this law in mechanical theory is not always apparent, as it is frequently tacitly assumed, but illustrations will be given that should clarify its meaning.

7–2 Newton's action-reaction law. Fundamental Law II

This law may be stated as follows.

When two objects interact, the force exerted by the first on the second (the action) is equal in magnitude and opposite in direction to the force exerted by the second on the first (the reaction).

If we label the action $\mathbf{F}_{12}$ and the reaction $\mathbf{F}_{21}$, then the law may be expressed mathematically as

II. $$\mathbf{F}_{12} = -\mathbf{F}_{21}. \tag{7–1}$$

This is our *Fundamental Law II*.

To illustrate the action-reaction law let us consider some familiar examples.

EXAMPLE 1. *A pushing force.* If a person pushes his finger down against the top of a desk with a force of magnitude F, the desk will push up against his finger with a force of the same magnitude.

EXAMPLE 2. *A pulling force.* If one pulls out on a hook in the wall, he will feel a force on his arm toward the wall. The strength of the action and reaction may be measured by hooking the bottom ends of two spring balances together, attaching the top of one spring balance to the hook and grasping the top of the other in his hand (Fig. 7–1). If you try this experiment you will see that the two spring balances read the same. You should next disconnect the first spring from the wall and let a friend hold its far end so that you are pulling against one another. Again the readings will be the same.

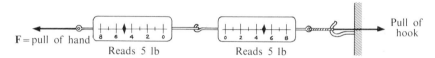

FIG. 7–1.   Action and reaction measured by two spring balances.

EXAMPLE 3. *A supporting force.* Suppose that one holds a child in his arms. He will feel the child's body pushing downward against him. The child, however, will feel an upward lifting force exerted by the person holding him.

EXAMPLE 4. *Gravitational attraction.* The earth attracts the moon and the moon attracts the earth. The pull of the moon on the earth gives rise to the tides. Similarly, a falling apple is pulled down by the earth's gravitational attraction, and at the same time the earth is attracted toward the apple. To an outside observer the apple and earth would appear to move toward each other, but because of its much greater mass (inertia) the earth would be seen to gain speed *much* more slowly than would the apple.

The above examples all illustrate one important aspect of the action-reaction law, namely that *the action and corresponding reaction never act on the same body.* For this reason a force acting on a body is not nullified by the reaction to this force, since the reaction does not act on the body in question. Thus in Example 4 the apple is only acted on by the pull of the earth, and so the apple is not in equilibrium but is being accelerated. A body can be in equilibrium only if all the forces acting on the body add up to zero.

Another important point to note is that an action cannot exist without a reaction. Action and reaction always appear as a pair of forces. If one disappears, the other does also. This means that an object cannot exert a force unless there is some other object present upon which this force may be exerted, for without the other object a reaction could not arise. One cannot push against empty space! If one pushes or pulls against a fixed object such as the floor or wall, the reaction certainly continues as long as does the action. But what will happen if one pulls an easily moved object such as a toy wagon? In this case the force of the pull may easily exceed the retarding force of friction, and so there will be a net forward force on the wagon which will cause it to be accelerated. The wagon will soon acquire a velocity equal to that with which one wishes (or is able) to pull it, and as it does so the person pulling the wagon will unconsciously reduce the force of his pull until it is just enough to balance the retarding force. Throughout the process he will experience the reaction of the wagon against his hand, but this reaction will also vary, being greatest while the wagon is accelerating and much less when its speed is constant. In other words, the reaction will at each moment be equal and opposite to the instantaneous value of the action.

If one pushes against a wall, he will slightly deform the wall, causing a large number of its atoms to be crowded ever so slightly closer together. The displaced atoms will repel each other strongly (another example of action and reaction). Only the atoms touching his finger will exert the reaction against him, but the effect of his pushing action is transmitted into the wall through the internal interactions between its atoms.

When a force is exerted that accelerates an object, the reaction that is experienced will again be felt at the points of contact with the object. However, the reaction in this case results not from deformation but from the inertia of the object. In the last chapter we saw that the inertia of a body is measured by its mass.

Since action and reaction occur together as a pair of forces, should one of the forces in such a pair always be labeled the "action" and the other the "reaction"? The answer to this question is "No." When the forces are due to interactions between inanimate objects, such as molecular or planetary bodies, neither F_{12} nor F_{21} in Eq. (7–1) is more the action or the reaction than is the other. The force F_{21} is the reaction to F_{12}, and F_{12} is the reaction to F_{21}. However, when one of the forces is exerted by an animate being as the result of a mental decision by this being, then it seems natural to call this force the action, even though this distinction carries no physical significance.

In this chapter the word "action" is used to imply that a force is exerted against something. Physicists also give the word a second meaning, particularly in connection with the quantum theory (Chapter 17), where action is identified with the concept of energy multiplied by time. However, this second meaning will not be used before Chapter 17.

7–3 The physical explanation of ocomotion

Locomotion furnishes many interesting, even surprising, examples of the action-reaction law.

EXAMPLE 1. *Walking.* While a person stands on the floor, the only external forces acting on his body are (1) a downward force *mg*, called his weight, which is due to the earth's gravitational pull, and (2) the force exerted by the floor against his feet (Fig. 7–2). This second force is *not* the reaction to his weight, rather it is the reaction to the force which he exerts through his feet against the floor. If he is standing still, the net force

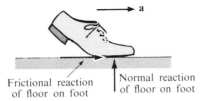

FIG. 7–2.   Reactions exerted by a floor on the shoe of a man walking.

acting on him must be zero, and so the two forces acting on him then actually are equal and opposite. However, when he commences to walk, he is being accelerated forward, which means that a net external force in the forward direction must act on his body. This forward force is supplied by the floor, whose total action on him is now both upward and forward. To make the floor supply a forward push, one must push backward on the floor. One does this with his feet, counting on friction (here it is *static friction*) to prevent his feet from slipping. It is then through the friction between the feet and the floor that one obtains the desired forward force. To realize the value of friction just imagine the difficulty of walking on very smooth ice.

EXAMPLE 2. *Jumping*. Since jumping involves an initial upward acceleration it can only occur when there is a net upward force acting on the jumper. In the previous example weight was balanced by the upward reaction of the floor. How could we ensure that the upward push of the floor would exceed our weight?

It was pointed out that the push of the floor on a person is not the reaction to his weight, but to the force exerted by his feet against the floor. Therefore, to cause the push of the floor on him to increase, he must increase his push against the floor; this is what we do when we bend our knees and then suddenly straighten them as we jump. The action and reaction between our feet and the floor now exceed our weight in magnitude (Fig. 7–3).

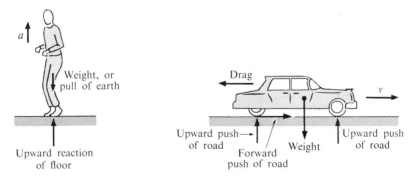

FIG. 7–3.   Man jumping: the upward   FIG. 7–4.   Forces acting on an automobile.
reaction of the floor exceeds his weight.

EXAMPLE 3. *Traveling by car*. Let us consider only the external forces that act on an automobile as it accelerates. These forces (see Fig. 7–4) are the following: (1) the weight, acting down, (2) the upward force exerted by the road on the tires, (3) a backward drag due to air and road resistance, and (4) a forward horizontal force exerted by the road on the rear wheels. If the car is accelerating, the fourth force must exceed the third. Through the action of the motor, the wheels are caused to push back harder on the road, thus causing the road to supply the required forward thrust to the car. Here again the action and reaction are of a frictional nature and so dependent on the nature of the surfaces in contact.

In the case of a wheel rolling on soft ground, the ground becomes depressed under the wheel, and the wheel is continually trying to roll up out of the depression. In this case the ground, at the forward point of contact with the wheel, exerts a *backward* force on the wheel and hence on the car. This force must not be confused with frictional force that opposes skidding and pushes the car forward. The backward force on a rolling wheel is simply an additional drag on the car; note that it was referred to in (3) as the "road resistance."

EXAMPLE 4. *Traveling by boat.* The forward force acting on a boat is supplied by the water against the blades of the oars or propeller. The harder an oar pushes against the water in a backward direction, the harder the water pushes forward on the oar, which is part of the boat.

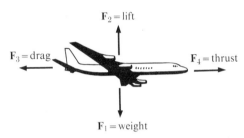

FIG. 7–5.   Forces acting on an airplane.

EXAMPLE 5. *Flying.* An airplane is acted on by four external forces (Fig. 7–5), as follows: (1) the weight F_1 down, (2) the lift F_2 up, the drag F_3 backward, and the thrust F_4 forward. To each of these there is an equal and opposite reaction exerted *by the plane* on its surroundings. Since F_1 is exerted on the plane by the earth, its reaction is the gravitational pull of the plane on the earth. The reaction to F_2 is a downward push against the air, the reaction to F_3 is a forward drag on the air, and the reaction to F_4 is a backward push against the air.

If the plane is in equilibrium, that is, if it is flying horizontally at constant velocity, then $F_2 = -F_1$ and $F_4 = -F_3$. But the plane may be climbing, in which case F_2 must exceed F_1, or the plane may be accelerating, in which case F_4 must exceed F_3. Since action and reaction are always equal and opposite and act on different bodies, F_1 obviously cannot be the reaction to F_2, or F_3 the reaction to F_4.

As man's progress in flying has carried him to higher altitudes he has found the air to be less and less dense. Since one cannot push against empty space, one cannot expect to obtain a forward thrust from it. Hence, man has turned to rocket engines in which gases are pushed out backwards, thus resulting in a forward thrust on the vehicle by the expelled gas.

EXAMPLE 6. *Space travel.* Above the earth's atmosphere a vehicle will be acted on by the gravitational forces due to the heavenly bodies, of which only one or two may have a significant effect. The rocket principle may be used to create additional forces, but fuel supplies are limited on a prolonged space trip, and so rockets must be used mainly for guidance and for take off and landing. If only the net gravitational force acts, it will cause a space ship to be accelerated in the direction of that net force. We shall see in the next chapter that this acceleration is welcome if it is just what is needed to keep the vehicle in the desired orbit, as is the case for earth-circling satellites.

7–4 Application of Newton's laws to physical systems

In the last chapter we discussed the motion of a particle or single body under the action of one or more forces. In this chapter we have investigated the inter-actions between bodies. We are now ready to solve problems involving the motions of two or more bodies that are connected in some way to form what is called a *system*.

The action-reaction law applies to the internal forces that arise between the parts of a system. Newton's law of motion may be applied to the system as a whole or to any part that one wishes to *isolate* mentally from the rest of the system. When one isolates part of a system, the action(s) of the rest of the system on this part must be taken into account, but how the rest of the system produces such action(s) need not be considered.

EXAMPLE 1. Two blocks, each having a mass of 1 kg, are connected by a light in-extensible string and placed on a smooth horizontal table (Fig. 7–6). A force $F_1 = 19.6$ n to the right is applied to the right-hand block and a force $F_2 = 9.8$ n to the left acts on the other block. We wish to find the acceleration of the system (the two blocks), when the string is taut, and the various actions and reactions.

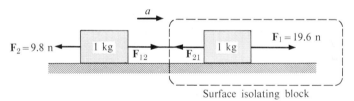

FIG. 7–6.   Acceleration of two connected blocks.

Solution. Since one block cannot be accelerated without the other, we must take the mass m of the system to be 2 kg. The net force F acting on the system from outside is $19.6 - 9.8 = 9.8$ n to the right. Hence the acceleration a of the system will be

$$a = \frac{F}{m} = \frac{9.8 \text{ n}}{2 \text{ kg}} = 4.9 \frac{\text{m}}{\text{sec}^2}$$

to the right, according to Newton's law of motion.

The reaction to F_1 will be a force of 19.6 n to the left exerted by the right-hand string against the agent supplying the force F_1. The reaction to F_2 will be 9.8 n to the right, exerted by the left-hand string against the source of F_2.

Consider now only the first block, i.e., let us isolate it (see dotted line in Fig. 7–6). Two horizontal forces act on the block, namely F_1 to the right and a force F_{21} in the opposite direction due to the string running to the second block. The acceleration of the block is 4.9 m/sec². Application of Newton's law of motion to the first block alone (for which m is only 1 kg) tells us that

$$19.6 \text{ n} - F_{21} = 1 \text{ kg} \times 4.9 \text{ m/sec}^2$$
$$F_{21} = 19.6 \text{ n} - 4.9 \text{ n} = 14.7 \text{ n}.$$

This is also the magnitude of the reaction F_{12} of the first block on the second. One may further say that the connecting string between the blocks is under a *tension* of 14.7 n.

For the second block we have two applied forces, F_{12} and F_2, which oppose each other; the net horizontal force acting on this block is 14.7 n $-$ 9.8 n $=$ 4.9 n to the right, which is just the force necessary to give the block the acceleration of 4.9 m/sec² to the right.

When a rigid body is accelerated the situation is, from a microscopic viewpoint, similar to the above example. The atoms of the body correspond to the blocks and the intermolecular forces to the interactions $F_{12} = -F_{12}$.

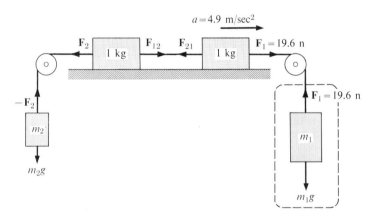

Fig. 7-7. Acceleration of two blocks caused by hanging weights.

EXAMPLE 2. Suppose that the forces F_1 and F_2 in the previous example are supplied by passing light strings from each block over pulleys to hanging weights (Fig. 7-7). What must the masses, m_1 and m_2, of the weights be?

Solution. Let us isolate the right-hand weight. It is acted on by a force $m_1 g$ down due to the pull of gravity and by a force of 19.6 n up, the reaction on it due to its action (through the string) on the first block. The acceleration of the weight is to be $a = 4.9$ m/sec² down. Newton's law of motion then tells us that

$$m_1 g - F_1 = m_1 a,$$
$$m_1 \times (9.8 \text{ m/sec}^2) - 19.6 \text{ n} = m_1 \times (4.9 \text{ m/sec}^2),$$
$$m_1 \times (4.9 \text{ m/sec}^2) = 19.6 \text{ n},$$
$$m_1 = 4 \text{ kg}.$$

For the left-hand weight the acceleration is 4.9 m/sec^2 up, so that this direction will now be taken as positive. The magnitude of the net force on m_2 is $F_2 - m_2g$. Therefore

$$F_2 - m_2g = m_2a,$$
$$9.8 \text{ n} - m_2 \times (9.8 \text{ m/sec}^2) = m_2 \times (4.9 \text{ m/sec}^2),$$
$$m_2 \times (14.7 \text{ m/sec}^2) = 9.8 \text{ n},$$
$$m_2 = 0.667 \text{ kg}.$$

Note that the weight of m_2 is $m_2g = 0.667 \text{ kg} \times 9.8 \text{ m/sec}^2 = 6.53$ n, which is only two-thirds of F_2. However, since m_2 is being accelerated upward, its reaction on the left-hand string is greater than its weight. Similarly, the weight of m_1 is $m_1g = 39.2$ n, while its reaction on the right-hand string is only half as much because its downward acceleration is $g/2$.

EXAMPLE 3. Let us find the horizontal interaction between the wheels of a locomotive and the tracks, and the interaction between the locomotive and the train of cars being pulled by the locomotive, given that the mass of the locomotive is m_1, that of the cars is m_2, the frictional drag on the cars is **f**, and the acceleration of the train is (a) **a**, (b) zero.

Solution. As the wheels of the locomotive are made to push back on the rails, the rails exert a forward push, which we shall call $\mathbf{F}_1$ on the wheels of the locomotive. This is the only forward force on the train as a whole and the only backward force is **f**. The magnitude of the net forward force is $F = F_1 - f$, and the mass to be accelerated is $m = m_1 + m_2$. Therefore we have

$$F = ma,$$
$$F_1 - f = (m_1 + m_2)a,$$
$$F_1 = f + (m_1 + m_2)a.$$

Let $\mathbf{F}_{12}$ represent the action of the locomotive on the following car. Let us isolate the cars and apply Newton's law of motion to them alone: we get

$$F_{12} - f = m_2a,$$
$$F_{12} = f + m_2a = F_1 - m_1a.$$

We see that when $a = 0$, $\mathbf{F}_1$ and $\mathbf{F}_{12}$ are just equal in magnitude to f, the drag that must be overcome, while during acceleration of the train F_1 and F_{12} are greater because of the inertia of the locomotive and cars.

Note the dual role played by friction in this example. The wheels of the locomotive must not skid in order that through friction the track may supply the forward force $\mathbf{F}_1$ to these wheels. However, as a result of friction the track exerts a backward drag on the wheels of the cars. Is friction a good thing or a bad thing? (Remember not to answer such questions with an outright "Yes" or "No.")

7–5 Collisions and explosions. The conservation of momentum

When two objects A and B meet in a collision they interact, that is, A exerts a force $\mathbf{F}_{AB}$ on B, and B exerts a force $\mathbf{F}_{BA}$ on A. Each of these forces may vary with time, but at any instant they must, according to the action-reaction law, be equal and opposite, so that

$$\mathbf{F}_{AB} = -\mathbf{F}_{BA}. \tag{7–2}$$

These two forces exist simultaneously for equal intervals of time. They may arise only at the moment of physical contact and last for a fraction of a second, as when two billiard balls collide, or they may originate when the approaching objects are far apart and exert gravitational or electrical forces on one another for a long period of time, as in the case of an astronomical collision. However, in any collision the momentum imparted to B by $\mathbf{F}_{AB}$ is equal and opposite to that imparted to A by $\mathbf{F}_{BA}$. Let us see why this is so.

In the last chapter we saw that Newton's law of motion was best expressed by Eq. (6–10), which in vector form is

$$\mathbf{F} = \frac{\Delta\mu}{\Delta t},$$

where $\Delta\mu$ is the change in momentum imparted to a body by a net force $\mathbf{F}$ acting for a time Δt. Here we are interested in the change in momentum, so we write the equation in the form

$$\Delta\mu = \mathbf{F}\,\Delta t. \tag{7–3}$$

The product of a force and the time the force acts represents the resulting change in momentum. Hence if a force $\mathbf{F}_{AB}$ acts on an object B for a time Δt, the momentum of B will change by

$$\Delta\mu_B = \mathbf{F}_{AB}\,\Delta t,$$

while if the force $\mathbf{F}_{BA}$ acts on object A for the same time Δt, the momentum of A will change by

$$\Delta\mu_A = \mathbf{F}_{BA}\,\Delta t.$$

From the action-reaction law $\mathbf{F}_{BA} = -\mathbf{F}_{AB}$, therefore

$$\Delta\mu_A = -\Delta\mu_B. \tag{7–4}$$

We may write this in the form

$$\Delta\mu_A + \Delta\mu_B = 0, \tag{7–5}$$

which states that the combined change in momentum of A and B due to $\mathbf{F}_{AB}$ and $\mathbf{F}_{BA}$ is zero. As this is true for all of the intervals that make up the time during which the bodies interact, we may say that during a collision in which the only forces acting are the action and reaction, the combined momentum of the system remains constant, having the same value after the collision as it had before the collision. In other words, *momentum is conserved*.

What has been said about collisions also applies to explosions. Suppose that through the release of stored energy a body breaks into two fragments A and B. While A and B are being torn apart and accelerated they must exert equal and opposite forces, $\mathbf{F}_{AB}$ and $\mathbf{F}_{BA}$, on each other, and these forces must exist for equal times. The reasoning above then tells us that here too

$$\Delta\mu_A = -\Delta\mu_B, \qquad \Delta\mu_A + \Delta\mu_B = 0.$$

Nor does it matter how many fragments are produced; the sum of the momentum changes will be zero.

A word of caution about signs is in order here. Momentum is a *vector* quantity, having the direction of the associated velocity. In one-dimensional problems, we may choose momentum in one direction, say to the right, to be positive, and then we must call momentum in the opposite direction (left) negative. In two-dimensional problems the momentum must be resolved into its components. If the motion is in the xy-plane, we must compute the net momentum in each direction before the collision or explosion; then the net momentum in the x-direction of A and B together must be conserved during the interaction. The same must be true of the net momentum in the y-direction.

In a collision or explosion, we may regard all of the interacting objects (A, B, etc.) as the parts of a *system*. The forces $\mathbf{F}_{AB}$ and $\mathbf{F}_{BA}$ may then be considered as internal interactions within the system. We have seen that these forces alone cannot change the momentum of the system. Therefore, if no external forces act on a system, its momentum will remain constant. Finally, if external forces act on a system but the sum (resultant) of these forces is zero, the momentum of the system will be conserved. This theorem is called the *conservation of momentum principle;* it is a derived law, derived from our first two fundamental laws, the law of motion and the action-reaction law.

FIG. 7–8.   A coupling collision.

EXAMPLE 1.   Two coupled freight cars, each of mass m, are moving with an initial speed v. The two cars collide and couple with three stationary cars, each of mass m (Fig. 7–8). What is the final speed of the five-car train?

Solution. Let v' be the final speed.

> Momentum before collision $= 2mv$.
>
> Momentum after collision $= 5mv'$.
>
> Momentum after collision $=$ momentum before, therefore,
>
> $$5mv' = 2mv,$$
> $$v' = 0.4v.$$

So if the two cars were traveling at 20 mi/hr, the five would move along at only 8 mi/hr.

EXAMPLE 2.   A 1-ton sports car runs head-on into a 5-ton truck. The truck driver survives and testifies that he was going 32 mi/hr before the accident and that after the collision he initially traveled at 10 mi/hr with the wrecked car on his hood. How fast was the sports car going?

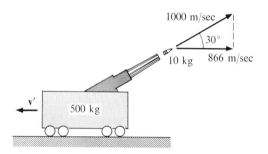

FIG. 7–9.   Recoil of a gun upon firing.

Solution. Take the direction of motion of the sports car as positive, that of the truck as negative. Let v be the initial speed of the sports car.

Momentum before collision $= [(1)v + 5(-32)]$ ton-mi/hr.

Momentum after collision $\quad = [(6) \times (-10) = -60]$ ton-mi/hr.

Momentum before collision $=$ momentum after.

$$v - 160 \; = -60$$
$$v = 100 \text{ mi/hr.}$$

EXAMPLE 3.   Calculate the horizontal recoil velocity of a 500-kg gun, mounted on wheels, that shoots a 10-kg projectile with a velocity of 1000 m/sec at an angle of 30° with the ground (Fig. 7–9).

Solution. Before the firing of the gun the total momentum of the system (gun plus projectile) is zero. After the explosion the projectile has a momentum of $10 \times 1000 = 10,000$ kg-m/sec in a direction making an angle of 30° with the gound. This momentum must be resolved into its horizontal and vertical components, as in Fig. 7–9. The horizontal component is $10,000 \times \cos 30° = 10,000 \times 0.866 = 8660$ kg-m/sec, and the upward component is $10,000 \times \sin 30° = 10,000 \times 0.500 = 5000$ kg-m/sec.

Since there was no upward momentum before the firing, that gained by the projectile must be compensated by an equal downward momentum imparted to the gun. If the gun is mounted on a firm support, this downward momentum is passed on to the earth.

Since there was no forward momentum before the firing, that gained by the projectile must be equal and opposite to that given to the gun. If the speed of recoil of the gun is v', we have

$$500v' = -8660,$$
$$v' = -17.32 \text{ m/sec.}$$

The negative sign means that the gun recoils backwards with a speed of 17.32 m/sec. This is just the *initial* speed of recoil; the gun may soon come to rest if it is allowed to move against a shock-absorbing bumper.

PROBLEMS

1. In a tug-of-war two boys pull on opposite ends of a rope and each exerts a force of 100 n (about 22.5 lb-wt). (a) What horizontal forces act on each boy? (b) What horizontal forces act on the rope? (c) Which of the above forces are action-reaction pairs?

2. A piece cut from the rope in problem 1 is hung vertically and made to support an increasing weight until it breaks. If the rope breaks when the mass tied to the end is 20 kg or greater, what is the breaking strength of the rope in newtons? Will the boys in problem 1 break the rope?

3. Suppose that in a tug-of-war the mass of each boy is 50 kg and that of the rope is 5 kg. Now suppose that one boy (Bill) increases his pull to 110 n, while the other boy (Dick) continues to exert a pull of 100 n on his end. (a) Find the acceleration of the system. (b) What horizontal forces act on each boy? (c) At the midpoint of the rope what is the tension or force of interaction between one half of the rope and the other half?

4. A skier climbs up a slope and then glides down it. (a) When is the frictional force of the snow on the skier directed up the slope and when is it directed down? (b) When is the frictional force on the skier in the direction in which he is going, and when is it in the direction opposite to his motion? (c) Must the frictional force be greater when going up or when going down and why?

5. Objects whose masses are 300 gm and 200 gm, respectively, are attached to opposite ends of a light string passing over a light frictionless pulley. Find (a) the acceleration of the system and (b) the tension in the string.

6. In problem 5 let the 200-gm object be replaced by a monkey whose mass is 300 gm (Fig. 7–10). Show that if the monkey and counterweight are originally at rest and the monkey starts to climb, then the counterweight will rise at the same rate as the monkey.

7. Suppose that three blocks, each with a mass of 1 kg, are connected by light strings and rest on a rough table, the frictional drag on each block being 2 n. Find the acceleration of the blocks and the tension in the strings connecting them together if an external horizontal pull of 9.8 n is applied to the first block.

8. Suppose that the first block in problem 8 is connected by a light string passing over a pulley to a hanging block of 1 kg mass. (a) Find the acceleration of the system and the tension in each connecting string. (b) Explain why this problem differs from the previous one even though the weight of the hanging block is 9.8 n.

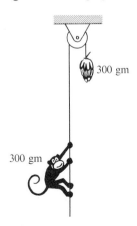

300 gm

300 gm

Fig. 7–10. Monkey climbing rope with counterweight.

9. If the mass of the earth is 81 times that of the moon, compare the acceleration, due to gravitational attraction, of the moon toward the earth with the acceleration of the earth toward the moon.

10. Show that if the only forces acting on two bodies are their mutual interactions and the bodies both start from rest, then the distances traveled by each are inversely proportional to the respective masses of the bodies.

11. A freight car of mass m moving at 20 mi/hr catches and couples with two similar cars that were moving at 5 mi/hr. Find the speed of the three cars just after coupling.

12. Repeat problem 11 for the case where the cars have the same original speeds (20 and 5 mi/hr) but are approaching one another.

13. A projectile whose mass is 50 kg is fired directly forward by an airplane whose mass without the projectile is 5000 kg. If the plane's original velocity is horizontal at 180 mi/hr and that of the projectile is 840 mi/hr, both relative to the earth, find the plane's speed after firing the projectile.

14. Two men, each of mass m, sit facing each other in opposite ends of a boat of mass $2m$. One man throws a ball of mass $m/40$ to the other man, who catches it. If the horizontal velocity of the ball is 80 ft/sec, what will be the velocity of the boat (a) while the ball is in the air, (b) after it is caught? (Neglect water and air resistance.)

15. A 20-kg bomb moving toward the north at 30 m/sec breaks up into a 16-kg fragment and a 4-kg fragment. The heavy fragment has a velocity of 50 m/sec to the west. Find the northward and eastward components of the light fragment and its resultant speed.

16. Suppose that a rocket emits 200 kg of exhaust each second from its rear and that the velocity of the exhaust relative to the rocket is 2500 m/sec. (a) What thrust in newtons will be developed between the rocket and its exhaust? (b) Express this thrust in pound-weight. (c) How much speed will the rocket gain per second when its mass is 20,000 kg and it is traveling vertically upward? [*Hint:* Do not neglect the weight.]

EXPERIMENT 9

COLLIDING CARS
(Newton's Laws—Meaning of Mass)

Object: To verify Newton's law of motion and action-reaction law and to see that the property of a body known as *inertia* is measured by its *mass*.

Problem: If two cars are connected by a stretched rubber band, then according to Newton's action-reaction law, the elastic must exert equal and opposite forces $\mathbf{F}_1$ and $\mathbf{F}_2$ on the two cars, or $|\mathbf{F}_1| = |\mathbf{F}_2|$.* If the cars have masses of m_1 and m_2, respectively, then Newton's second law tells us that the accelerations should be

$$a_1 = F_1/m_1 \quad \text{and} \quad a_2 = F_2/m_2,$$

so that, if $F_1 = F_2$, we should find that

$$a_1/a_2 = m_2/m_1.$$

Now since distance traveled from rest under a given acceleration is $s = \frac{1}{2} at^2$, in the same time the two cars should travel distances proportional to their respective accelerations, or inversely proportional to their respective masses. If we can verify this conclusion experimentally, then we shall have obtained experimental evidence supporting Newton's laws of motion.

Procedure:

Step 1. Weigh separately the two cars. Connect them with several elastic bands tied in series. Using the meter stick, separate the front ends 100 cm and then release cars simultaneously. Record the distance traveled by each before they collide. Repeat four times, invalidating any run in which motion is hampered by the slack elastic or is not parallel to meter stick.

Step 2. Repeat Step 1, first with 200 grams added to one car, then with 400 grams added. Do your results confirm Newton's laws within experimental error? Explain. What role did friction play?

---

* $|\mathbf{F}_1|$ means "magnitude of $\mathbf{F}_1$," or F_1.

CHAPTER 8

Newton's Law of Gravitation

8–1 What kinds of force exist in nature?

We have seen that Galileo investigated various types of motion, notably motion at constant velocity and motion under constant acceleration, while Newton described the relation between the motion of a body and the net force producing the motion. The next question to arise naturally concerned the origin of forces. Where do forces come from? Newton gave a partial answer to this question with his theory of gravitation.

The most common forces in everyday life are pushes and pulls and gravitational attraction. The explanation of pushes and pulls of muscular origin is rather complicated and involves an understanding of muscular structure, chemistry, and atomic physics. However, the physicist believes that ultimately such forces may be attributed to forces between atoms, which in turn may be resolved into electromagnetic forces. The physicist is really concerned only with the basic or fundamental types of force that exist in the physical world. We shall see, in the course of the book, that at present he recognizes the following fundamental types (see Fig. 8–1) listed in order of increasing strength:

(a) Gravitational forces between two masses (Section 8–5).

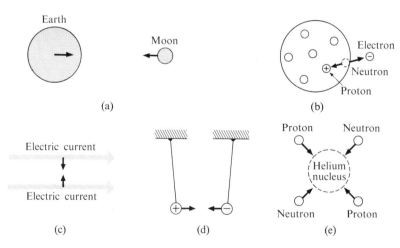

(a) (b)

(c) (d) (e)

Fig. 8–1. Fundamental types of force. (a) Gravitational force. (b) Beta decay. (c) Magnetic force. (d) Electric force. (e) Nucleon force.

(b) The so-called "weak" beta-decay forces involved in radioactive decay (Section 20–3).

(c) Magnetic forces between moving charges (Section 13–2).

(d) Electric forces between charges at rest (Section 12–2).

(e) The very strong forces between nuclear particles (Section 20–2).

It was the first of these five types of forces that Newton originally discovered or postulated.

It should be borne in mind that we still do not know *why* these forces exist. We merely postulate that they do exist and show that we may then explain varied phenomena in terms of them. It is possible that two or more of these forces may be explained in terms of a single, still more basic, postulate. Einstein and Heisenberg have attempted to do this in their unified field theories, but we do not expect ever to find an ultimate explanation, since man is not omniscient. For our purposes the important thing is to reduce chaos to order, that is, to explain many things in terms of a few hypotheses. As the number of fundamental hypotheses is reduced through generalization, simplicity is gained up to a point, but beyond that point it appears that the increasing complexity of the concepts and mathematics makes the subject more difficult for the ordinary mind to grasp. Just when this point is reached is a matter of personal opinion and taste. This book merely reflects the author's (and others') opinion as to what is the clearest way to describe how the world around us behaves. Time will undoubtedly alter this viewpoint.

8–2 An historical survey of planetary theories

The development of planetary theory has been referred to in previous chapters in order to illustrate the way science progresses. Let us review this development briefly.

In Greece during the 4th century B.C., observations of the night sky led Plato and Aristotle to postulate a theory to explain the apparent motions of the heavenly bodies. It best suited the Greek philosophy, or metaphysics, to assume at the start that the earth is the center of the universe and that the other bodies move around the earth in orbits of the most "perfect" (to them) shape, namely, circles. These initial hypotheses led to the necessity of also postulating a most intricate system of revolving spheres. The whole theory was unable to lead to new discoveries and when further observations were made, the theory had to be patched up by being made still more complicated. One Greek, Aristarchus (3rd century B.C.), did propose a heliocentric (sun-centered) system, but it was not popular, and he gave no quantitative calculations. Ptolemy of Alexandria in the 2nd century A.D. modified the Aristotelian theory by assuming motion in epicycles rather than in revolving spheres. Ptolemy postulated that a planet moved in a circle whose center moved in another circle and so on until one finally came to a circle whose center moved in a circle with the earth at its center (Fig. 8–2). This theory could be made to explain the observed facts, but it too was complicated and unfruitful.

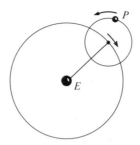

FIG. 8–2.   Example of epicyclic motion.

The Polish scientist Copernicus (1473–1543) revived the heliocentric theory and carried out the quantitative calculations that were necessary in order to show that his theory could be made to explain the known facts. He found that he too had to postulate a complicated system of circular motions which, though a little simpler than that of Ptolemy, was no better at correlating the facts and opening up new discoveries. The importance of the work of Copernicus was that it (1) challenged the dogmatic belief in Aristotelian science, (2) showed that more than one theory could successfully explain a set of known facts, and (3) paved the way for Newton's theory of gravitation.

We saw in Section 4–3 how Kepler (1571–1630) surveyed the more accurate observations of Tycho Brahe and found order in the data. Kepler described this order in his three empirical laws, which are as follows.

(1) Each planet moves in an elliptical orbit.

(2) A planet moves in its orbit at such a varying speed that the line from the sun to the planet sweeps out equal areas in equal times.

(3) The square of the time of revolution (period) is directly proportional to the cube of the mean radius of the planet's orbit.

While Kepler was carrying on his work in Germany, his friend and correspondent Galileo was eloquently defending the heliocentric theory in Italy. Galileo was the first to use the telescope to make astronomical measurements, and the results of his observations only added to the zeal with which he attacked the geocentric (earth-centered) theory and the scholastics who dogmatically defended that theory. He was eventually forced by the Inquisition to make a formal renunciation of the Copernican theory and to promise to discontinue making statements antagonistic to the Church. However, this did not change his beliefs.

Kepler's postulate of elliptical orbits made the heliocentric theory much simpler. Of course the "perfect" circle no longer played a part in the theory, but in place of several epicycles it was necessary to associate only a single ellipse with each planet. However, the theories of Ptolemy, Copernicus, and Kepler all correlated the observed facts and nothing more. Indeed we can still say today that the planets appear to move in the sky just as though their actual motions were those postulated by any one of the above theories. What has made Kepler's model the one now universally accepted by scientists is the work of Newton (1642–1727).

Newton *explained* Kepler's laws with his theory of universal gravitation. This theory took as its premises Newton's law of motion and a new fundamental law that Newton postulated, namely his law of gravitation. From these postulates Newton was able not only to derive Kepler's laws but also to explain many other things and to predict still others. We now say that it is gravitational attraction that keeps the planets from leaving the solar system, that keeps the moon in its orbit about the earth and Jupiter's moons moving around Jupiter, that makes objects fall toward the ground and gives us weight, and that accounts for the minute attraction observed between ordinary uncharged objects when a sensitive experiment is performed to measure this attraction. Without Newton's theory, we would not have artificial satellites, because no one would have thought them possible.

8–3 Centripetal acceleration and centripetal force

Newton showed (and we shall presently) that if an object is moving in a curved path, then the object is being accelerated toward the center of curvature of the path, regardless of whether or not the speed of the particle changes. This acceleration *toward* the center of a curved path is called *centripetal acceleration* $\mathbf{a}_c$ and we shall see that it arises because of the *change in the direction* of the body's motion, so that its velocity is not constant. Remember that velocity is a vector quantity and that it may change in magnitude, or direction, or both. Change in velocity $\Delta\mathbf{v}$ in a time Δt implies the existence of an acceleration

$$\mathbf{a} = \frac{\Delta\mathbf{v}}{\Delta t}. \tag{8–1}$$

This follows from the definition of acceleration, Eq. (3–7).

Since a small arc of any curve may be regarded as an arc of a circle, let us consider a particle moving in a circle of radius r with a speed v. At the point P in Fig. 8–3(a), the direction of motion will be along a tangent to the curve at P, so that the velocity $\mathbf{v}_1$ will be as shown. A short time Δt later the particle moving along the circle will reach Q, where its velocity $\mathbf{v}_2$ will be along the tangent to the curve at Q, as shown. We see that $\mathbf{v}_1$ and $\mathbf{v}_2$ have different directions. Let us assume that the speed does not change appreciably in the time Δt, so that $\mathbf{v}_1$ and $\mathbf{v}_2$ will have the same magnitude v.

The *change* in a quantity is what one must add to the original value of the quantity in order to obtain its new value. In Fig. 8–3(b), $\mathbf{v}_1$ and $\mathbf{v}_2$ have been transposed, with their original directions unchanged, to the point A that serves as a common origin for the two vectors. Since a vector is specified by giving its magnitude and direction, but not its point of origin, $\mathbf{v}_1$ and $\mathbf{v}_2$ are the same vectors in Fig. 8–3(a) and Fig. 8–3(b). We see that the vector labeled $\Delta\mathbf{v}$ added end-to-end to the vector $\mathbf{v}_1$ gives the vector $\mathbf{v}_2$, so that

$$\mathbf{v}_1 + \Delta\mathbf{v} = \mathbf{v}_2,$$
$$\Delta\mathbf{v} = \mathbf{v}_2 - \mathbf{v}_1. \tag{8–2}$$

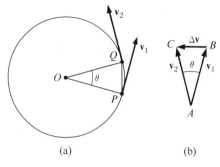

(a)

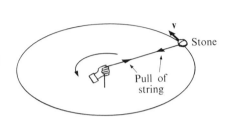

(b)

FIG. 8–3.   Centripetal acceleration.

FIG. 8–4.   Centripetal pull on a whirling stone.

Since v_1 is perpendicular to OP in Fig. 8–3(a) and v_2 is perpendicular to OQ, the angle θ between OP and OQ is also the angle between v_1 and v_2. The triangles OPQ and ABC are similar triangles because they both have two equal sides enclosing the same angle θ. This means that the third side of triangle ABC, which is Δv, must be perpendicular to the corresponding side PQ of triangle OPQ. A vector perpendicular to PQ at its midpoint will lie on a radius of the circle; therefore Δv must, for small values of θ, be directed *toward the center of the circle*.

In similar triangles corresponding sides are proportional; therefore

$$\frac{\Delta v}{v} = \frac{\overline{PQ}}{r}, \qquad \Delta v = \frac{v\overline{PQ}}{r}.$$

If θ is small, as we have assumed, $\overline{PQ}$ will very nearly equal the distance $v\Delta t$ that the particle moves along the arc of the circle in going from P to Q in the time Δt. If we set $\overline{PQ} = v\Delta t$, we have

$$\Delta v = \frac{v^2}{r} \Delta t,$$

$$a_c = \frac{\Delta v}{\Delta t} = \frac{v^2}{r}. \tag{8–3}$$

This gives the magnitude of the centripetal acceleration a_c. We saw that its direction is *toward* the center of the circular path.

From Newton's law of motion it follows that to give a body of mass m an acceleration a_c requires that a force F_c, given by

$$F_c = ma_c,$$

must act on the body. Therefore, when a body of mass m moves with a speed v in a circular path of radius r, a force F_c whose magnitude is

$$F_c = \frac{mv^2}{r} \tag{8–4}$$

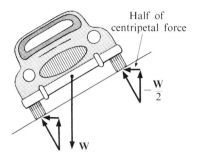

Half of
centripetal force

$-\dfrac{W}{2}$

W

FIG. 8–5. A car on a properly banked track. Normal reaction counterbalances weight and supplies required centripetal force as well.

and whose direction is *toward* the center of curvature of the path must act on the body. This force is called the *centripetal force*.

There are many familiar examples of centripetal force, such as the following. (1) If a stone is whirled on the end of a string (Fig. 8–4), the string exerts a centripetal inward pull on the stone; at its other end the string pulls outwardly on the hand of the person doing the whirling, while the hand pulls inwardly on the string. (2) When a car rounds a curve in the road (Fig. 8–5), the road must exert on the wheels of the car a force which is directed toward the inside of the curve; this force may be supplied by friction or by the normal reaction of a properly banked road. A road is properly banked for a given speed when a normal reaction alone will counterbalance the weight of the vehicle and supply the required centripetal force. Friction is a less dependable source of centripetal force since there is a limit (which varies with road and tire conditions) to how great friction can be. (3) A pilot flying an airplane in a turn banks it so that the air will exert the necessary sidewise centripetal thrust on the plane. (4) An electron circling the nucleus of an atom gets its inward centripetal force through the electrostatic attraction of the oppositely charged nucleus. (5) For a satellite the centripetal force is supplied by gravity, as we shall presently see.

8–4 Centrifugal force

This is the reaction to the centripetal force. Since the latter is directed inward, centrifugal force must be directed outward. However, since action and reaction do not act on the same body, the centrifugal force does not act on the body following the curved path but on the object supplying the centripetal force. This point is often missed. Let us review the examples of the last paragraph.

(1) When a stone is whirled on the end of a string, the stone exerts an outward (centrifugal) pull on the string, which in turn exerts an outward pull on the hand of the operator. (2) When a car rounds a curve, the wheels of the car push down and outwardly against the road. (3) The circling plane pushes outwardly against the air. (4) The atomic electron attracts the nucleus with an outward centrifugal force. (5) The satellite exerts a gravitational pull on the planet around which the satellite is circling.

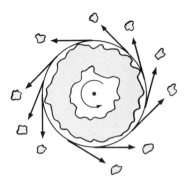

Fig. 8–6.   Mud flung from a rotating wheel seems to fly out in all directions. Actually, each piece of mud flies off tangentially.

While granting all of the above, one may still wonder about the frequently expressed idea that centrifugal force tends to make the circling object fly outward and, indeed, will do so if the centripetal force is reduced. This is a misconception. If the centripetal force is reduced, the object will follow a less sharply curved path than before, but it will not fly *radially* outward. If the centripetal force is made zero, the object will travel out on a path *tangential* to its previously curved track. This follows from Newton's law of motion, for if the force on an object is zero, the acceleration must be zero and the velocity constant in speed and direction.

The impression that mud detached from a spinning wheel flies radially outward is false. However, if particles fly out tangentially from all sides of the wheel (Fig. 8–6), a spectator may get spattered whether he stands on one side or another and the resulting effect on his clothes may be just as disastrous as it would be if the mud were squirted out radially.

In a centrifuge, light and heavy objects in liquid suspension are separated by rotation of the container. As the vessel is rotated faster and faster, the particles tend to move tangentially toward the outer wall, but they do not all get there because of an opposing pressure difference. Since pressure sets inwardly against a surface, the outer side of any suspended particle experiences a force toward the center of the centrifuge and the inner side experiences a force directed outward. The pressure increases outwardly; therefore the net force on the particle is toward the center of the vessel, and hence is a centripetal force. If at a given radius r the centripetal force mv^2/r is just sufficient for a particle of mass m to maintain circular motion, it will not be sufficient for a more massive particle; the heavier particles will spiral outward and particles of mass less than m will spiral inward, and so particles of different mass will become separated.

8–5 Newton's law of gravitation. Fundamental Law III

Newton developed the concept of, and formula for, centripetal force not long after he graduated from Trinity College in Cambridge, England. This led him to conclude that an inward force must act on each planet as it orbits the sun. It had been suspected for some time that the sun might attract the planets, and Newton adopted this view. In his famous book *Principia* he proved mathematically that if a body moves in an elliptical orbit according to Kepler's second law (its radius vector sweeps out equal areas in equal times), then the body must be acted on by a force directed toward one of the foci of the ellipse. He further proved (after inventing the calculus to assist him) that for a body to follow an elliptical orbit, the force acting on it must be inversely proportional to the square of the distance from the attracting focus. Kepler's theory placed the sun at the focus of a planet's orbit, and hence Newton concluded that the sun exerted an inverse square force of attraction on a planet. He then boldly postulated that the attraction of a planet by the sun was just one example of a *universal law of gravitation* which states that:

Between any two objects in the world there exists a mutual force of attraction that is directly proportional to the product of the masses of the objects and inversely proportional to the square of their distance apart, or

$$F_g \propto \frac{m_1 m_2}{s^2}, \tag{8-5}$$

where F_g is the magnitude of the force of gravitational attraction, m_1 and m_2 the respective masses of the attracting objects, and s their separation.

It has been assumed that the objects involved are small in size compared with their distance of separation. Newton proved that when the mass of a body is spherically distributed, the gravitational effect is the same as though all the mass were concentrated at the center of the body.

Let us define the gravitational constant G as the constant of proportionality in (8-5) when F_g, m_1, m_2, and s are measured in terms of previously defined units. We then have

III. $$F_g = G \frac{m_1 m_2}{s^2}. \tag{8-6}$$

as the mathematical formulation of our *Fundamental Law III.*

While Eq. (8-6) defines G, the postulate that G is a universal constant constitutes a fundamental principle or law of nature. We shall discuss its numerical value later.

It was characteristic of Newton's genius that he could make the inductive step of generalizing what he concluded to be the force between a planet and the sun by assuming that this same kind of force accounts for the pull of terrestrial objects toward the center of the earth and for the force that keeps the moon in its orbit around the earth.

8-6 Newton's test of his law of gravitation; the motion of the moon

Let a satellite of mass $m_1 = m$ circle an attracting body of mass $m_2 = M$, the radius of the orbit being R and the period of one revolution T. The speed v of the satellite may be expressed as the ratio of the distance $(2\pi R)$ around the orbit to the time (T) taken to cover this distance, or

$$v = \frac{2\pi R}{T}.$$

As shown in Section 8–3, Newton concluded that the satellite must be acted on by a centripetal force whose magnitude is given by

$$F_c = \frac{mv^2}{R} = \frac{m}{R}\left(\frac{2\pi R}{T}\right)^2 = \frac{4\pi^2 mR}{T^2}.$$

Newton next postulated that this force is the gravitational attraction between m and M, or

$$F_c = F_g = \frac{GmM}{R^2}.$$

He equated the two expressions for F_c and obtained

$$\frac{4\pi^2 mR}{T^2} = \frac{GmM}{R^2}.$$

An m may be cancelled on each side and the equation solved for T^2. The result is

$$T^2 = \frac{4\pi^2}{GM} R^3. \tag{8–7}$$

This is a derivation of Kepler's third law since, for a given planetary system, M is constant and hence T^2 is proportional to R^3. This is a successful *qualitative* accomplishment for Newton's theory.

Newton next considered the case where $M = M_E$, the mass of the earth. As in Section 5–3, he equated the weight (mg) of a terrestrial object to the earth's gravitational attraction on it, i.e., he set

$$mg = \frac{GmM_E}{R_E^2}, \tag{8–8}$$

where R_E is the earth's radius, and m is here the mass of the terrestrial object (it cancels out). This equation states that

$$GM_E = gR_E^2. \tag{8–9}$$

Newton substituted this in Eq. (8–7), where M now equals M_E but R is still the radius of the satellite's orbit, and found

$$T^2 = \frac{4\pi^2}{g} \frac{R^3}{R_E^2}, \qquad T = \frac{2\pi}{R_E} \sqrt{\frac{R^3}{g}}. \tag{8–10}$$

The radius R_E of the earth was known to be about 4000 miles; R for the moon's orbit was estimated to be 60 times R_E, and g was measured as 32 ft/sec^2 or (32/5280) mi/sec^2. Putting these values in Eq. (8–10), Newton found for the period of the moon

$$T_M = \frac{2\pi}{4000 \text{ mi}} \sqrt{\frac{(60 \times 4000)^3 \text{ mi}^3}{(32/5280) \text{ mi/sec}^2}} = 2.37 \times 10^6 \text{ sec.}$$

Since there are $24 \times 60 \times 60 = 8.64 \times 10^4$ seconds in a day, the computed value of T_M is equivalent to

$$T_M = \frac{2.37 \times 10^6 \text{ sec}}{8.64 \times 10^4 \text{ sec/day}} = 27.4 \text{ days.}$$

The measured value of T_M is $27\frac{1}{3}$ days; therefore the above computation furnished a remarkable *quantitative* confirmation of Newton's theory.

8–7 Inertial mass versus gravitational mass

The concept of mass introduced in Chapter 6 associated mass with inertia; therefore the mass m in Newton's law of motion ($\mathbf{F} = m\mathbf{a}$) is more explicitly called the *inertial mass* of the body undergoing acceleration. The masses m_1 and m_2 in Eq. (8–6) are called the *gravitational masses* of the respective objects between which gravitational attraction exists. We have followed Newton's example and assumed that the gravitational mass is the same as the inertial mass of a body. In other words, Newton's law of gravitation postulates a relationship between previously defined quantities (force, mass, and distance). As a result, the weight of a body, which is the gravitational force on it, is proportional to its inertial mass. This in turn explains why Galileo was correct in saying that a light object and a heavy object should fall together with the same acceleration *g* provided that air resistance is negligible. For example, if the heavy object has twice the mass of the light one, then the downward force on the heavy object will also be doubled and the ratio F/m which determines the resulting acceleration, will be the same for both objects.

The equivalence of inertial mass and gravitational mass is not, as far as we now know, logically bound to be true. It was an assumption on Newton's part and it is the cornerstone of Einstein's general theory of relativity. However, this postulate has been subjected to experimental test, and at present it has been verified that inertial mass and gravitational mass are the same to within one part in 10^9. This is really a remarkable result, for it means that the ability of a body to attract another one to it gravitationally increases linearly with the inertia of the body, or, stating it another way, both of these properties are proportional to the quantity of matter in the body. To convince yourself that this is not self-evident, note when we come to electrical forces (Chapter 12) that the ability of a charged body to attract or repel another one is *not* proportional to the mass of the body.

8–8 The determination of *G*

You may have noted that Newton's tests of his theory did not involve knowing the numerical value of *G*. He left this for his successors to determine. Of course, he probably obtained a rough idea of the value of *G* by using Eq. (8–9) and solving

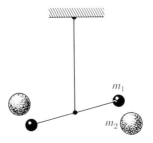

Fɪɢ. 8–7. Schematic diagram of the experiment devised by Cavendish to measure the gravitational constant G.

it for G. The trouble with this method of finding G was that it involved knowing the radius and mass of the earth, and the latter was then far from accurately established. One could only make a guess as to the average density (mass over volume ratio) of the earth and then multiply by the earth's volume $4\pi R_E^3/3$. But how could one make a good guess as to the earth's average density when one could then observe only its thin outermost crust?

It was over 100 years after Newton published his *Principia* that another English-man, Henry Cavendish (1731–1810), determined G accurately by directly measuring the force between *two terrestrial objects*. This experiment is described at the end of this chapter as Experiment 11. As shown in the schematic diagram of Fig. 8–7, the force between a pair of heavy balls (say 1.5 kg each) and a pair of lighter suspended balls is measured by determining the acceleration of each suspended sphere. Since the force is very weak, the restoring torque of the suspension as it twists must be small, and for this reason a fine quartz fibre is frequently used for the suspension. The very small acceleration of the suspended balls is magnified optically. A gravitational force of attraction is found to exist between each large and small ball, and one may verify the mass and distance dependence postulated by Newton. The constant of proportionality G is found to have a magnitude of 6.67×10^{-11} when F_g is expressed in newtons, m_1 and m_2 in kilograms, and s in meters (the mks units); G also has its units, which must be such as to make Gm_1m_2/s^2 equivalent to a force in newtons. This means that the mks units for G are the newton-meter^2/kilogram^2. We therefore write

$$G = 6.67 \times 10^{-11} \text{ n-m}^2/\text{kg}^2. \qquad (8–11)$$

It is because of the smallness of G that gravitational forces are not appreciable unless at least one of the attracting objects is of astronomical size. For two atomic particles the gravitational force is negligible.

It is interesting to speculate on what would be the result of arbitrarily *choosing* the magnitude of G. Suppose, for example, that one wished to define G as equal to unity in a given system of units. This would be a convenient value for G, but having chosen it we would have to give up our choice of some other quantity in mechanics, such as our kilogram unit of mass, and replace it with a new unit (which would be far from convenient) consistent with $G = 1$.

8-9 Velocity and period of satellites

We saw in Section 2–3 that the speed v required for a satellite of mass m to circle in an orbit of radius $(R + h)$ about a parent body of mass M is found by equating the required centripetal force to the gravitational force. Thus we write

$$\frac{mv^2}{(R + h)} = \frac{GmM}{(R + h)^2},$$

which reduces to

$$v = \sqrt{\frac{GM}{R + h}}. \qquad (8\text{-}12)$$

Let us consider $R = R_E$, the earth's radius, and $M = M_E$, the earth's mass. For a satellite to clear the earth's atmosphere (which it must do if it is not to slow down and burn up because of air resistance), the height h must be greater than 100 miles. However, let us first compute v for $h = 0$. Our initial step must be to determine the value of M_E.

Now that we know the value of G, we may use Eq. (8–9) to find the value of M_E. We have

$$M_E = \frac{g}{G} R_E^2.$$

Since the value of G is given in mks units we shall use the mks system throughout. Thus we shall take $g = 9.80 \text{ m/sec}^2$ and $R_E = 6.37 \times 10^6 \text{ m}$. Then

$$M_E = \frac{9.8 \text{ m/sec}^2}{6.67 \times 10^{-11} \text{ n-m}^2/\text{kg}^2} \times (6.37 \times 10^6 \text{ m})^2 = 6.0 \times 10^{24} \text{ kg}.$$

Substitution in Eq. (8–12) shows that, for $h = 0$,

$$v = \sqrt{\frac{(6.67 \times 10^{-11} \text{ n-m}^2/\text{kg}^2) \times (6.0 \times 10^{24} \text{ kg})}{6.37 \times 10^6 \text{ m}}} = 7.9 \times 10^3 \text{ m/sec}.$$

From Table 3–1 we see that $1 \text{ m} = 1/(1.61 \times 10^3)$ of a mile. Also $1 \text{ sec} = 1/3600$ of one hour. Therefore,

$$v = \frac{(7.9 \times 10^3 \text{ m/sec}) \times (3600 \text{ sec/hr})}{1.61 \times 10^3 \text{ m/mi}} = 17,800 \text{ mi/hr}.$$

If $h = 400$ miles, $R + h$ will be 10% larger than when $h = 0$, $\sqrt{R + h}$ will be about 5% greater and v about 5% smaller than the 17,800 mi/hr computed above, which means that v will be about 17,000 mi/hr. This is about the average value of v for man-launched earth satellites.

We may use Kepler's third law, Eq. (8–7), to compare the period T of an artificial earth satellite with T_M, that of the moon, since M is the same for both. Let us take the radii of the orbits to be 4400 miles and 240,000 miles, respectively, and $T_M = 27$ days. We then have, since $T^2 \propto$ (radius of orbit)^3,

$$\frac{T^2}{(27 \text{ days})^2} = \left(\frac{4400}{240,000}\right)^3,$$

$$T = 6.7 \times 10^{-2} \text{ days}.$$

This means that the satellite will complete 15 revolutions per day when circling in an orbit 400 miles outside the earth's surface.

If a satellite is farther above the earth than 400 miles, will it make more or less than 15 revolutions a day? Since the moon makes much less than one revolution per day, must there not be an orbit, whose radius is between 4400 miles and 240,000 miles, for which the period is just one day? A satellite in such an orbit above the earth's equator would seem to hover over the same spot on the earth rotating beneath it; this is the principle of the "space platform" that would be stationary relative to the earth. The computation of the height above the earth of such a platform is left as a problem at the end of the chapter.

8–10 The cause of gravitational forces

Why do two bodies attract one another? Newton wisely refused to answer this question. He pointed out that his theory explained and summarized the known facts in mechanics in terms of the three postulates which we have labeled Fundamental Laws I, II, and III. This was a great simplification. His theory continued to explain new facts and to predict others. "What more," asked Newton, "can be expected of a good theory?"

Of course Newton, and many since Newton, have speculated as to the cause of gravitation. One theory proposed that space was filled with a tenuous, invisible substance called the *ether* and that the action of the sun on the earth was transmitted through the ether, like pressure through the liquid in a hydraulic brake system. This theory was not fruitful; it did not grow gracefully to meet new facts and it has long since been abandoned.

Einstein's general theory of relativity takes a step toward explaining gravity by postulating that the accelerations we attribute to gravitational forces are simply the result of the curvature of space* in the neighborhood of a large mass. This theory predicted the observed bending of light rays that pass near the sun as well as other observed phenomena. Therefore Einstein's theory has not been discarded. However, it is a much more complicated theory than that of Newton, and the effects that relativistic theory alone explains generally do not affect our daily lives. We do not usually bother with the relativity theory when Newton's theory suffices for our purposes.

Einstein's explanation of gravitation may, perhaps, have a certain philosophical appeal. But why is space curved in the presence of mass? The question "Why?"

---

* In curved space a beam of light, or a particle not acted on by a net force, follows a curved path rather than a straight line.

still crops up, and we see that the final explanation is not the task of the scientist. Instead, the scientist should endeavor to follow in Newton's steps and to develop a theory that is clear, useful, and as simple as possible.

PROBLEMS

1. Compute the gravitational attraction in newtons between an electron ($m_1 = 9.1 \times 10^{-31}$ kg) and a proton ($m_2 = 1.6 \times 10^{-27}$ kg) when their separation is that in the normal hydrogen atom, namely 5×10^{-11} m.

2. The Cavendish experiment has recently been repeated using for the attracting masses a glass of water ($m_1 = 0.25$ kg) and a bag of sand ($m_2 = 12$ kg, say). Take the distance s between centers to be 25 cm. Compute (a) the gravitational attraction in newtons and pound-weight, (b) the resulting acceleration of the glass of water (which was suspended on the end of a meter stick supported by a long tape).

3. An airplane has a speed of 300 mi/hr or 440 ft/sec. The pilot wishes to turn as sharply as possible, but he cannot withstand an acceleration greater than $4g$, where g is the acceleration due to gravity. (a) Compute the radius of the smallest circle he can follow and the time it will take him to reverse his direction. (b) Repeat for a pilot flying 500 mi/hr.

4. Derive an expression for the angle of bank θ (with the horizontal) of a road, with a radius of curvature r, that is properly banked for vehicles traveling at a speed v. Does the mass of the vehicle matter?

5. Consider an airplane traveling in a circular and vertical loop-the-loop. (a) Why must the centripetal acceleration at the top of the loop be at least equal to g? (b) If the speed is constant and the centripetal acceleration is $2g$, find the ratio of the *net* force on the pilot to his weight at both the top and bottom of the loop. (c) If the centripetal acceleration is constant and equal to $2g$, find the ratio of the force of the plane against the pilot to the pilot's weight at both the top and bottom of the loop.

6. If a satellite is to serve as a space platform that hovers above a fixed point on the earth's equator, what must be the (a) radius of its orbit, (b) its height above the earth?

7. Show how the mass of the sun may be computed from data relating to the motion of the earth in its orbit.

8. The mass of the sun is about 2×10^{30} kg. Compute the gravitational attraction between the earth and sun.

9. Call the radius of the earth's orbit 1 AU (astronomical unit). The period of Venus is 225 days and that of Mars is 687 days. Find the mean orbital radius for both Venus and Mars.

10. (a) Why is it easier to determine the mass of Jupiter than the mass of the moon? (b) Why is the creation of an artificial lunar satellite an accurate way of determining the moon's mass?

11. If the moon's mass is taken to be $\frac{1}{81}$ that of the earth and its distance from the earth is $60 \times R_E$, where will a space ship experience equal and opposite forces due to the earth and moon?

EXPERIMENT 10

THE NATURE OF CIRCULAR MOTION

Object: To investigate circular motion and to study the relation between force, period, and radius of rotation.

Problem: Motion in a circle is a special kind of motion, although it is very familiar to us. Objects moving in a circle must be given a constant force toward the center of rotation to keep them from flying off along a tangent to the circle. This force which draws the object away from its "natural" path and into circular motion is called centripetal force. It is the "center-seeking force." We shall investigate how this force is related to the radius and the period of rotation. In this experiment we are faced with three quantities which may vary. It will be necessary to hold one constant while varying another to find the dependency of the third. Then we may change the factor earlier held constant and obtain a new family of data.

Procedure:

Step 1. Slide the end of a fishline through a glass tubing with smooth ends and attach the line to a rubber stopper. To the other end fasten a holder to use in attaching objects whose weight will provide the required force. Attach to the cord at this end washers or other objects whose mass will be several times greater than that of the stopper. Now swing the stopper through a horizontal circle above the head noting that the less massive object in this mode of motion can balance the other objects pulled by gravity. While motion is stopped, draw the stopper 80 or 100 cm from the end of the tubing and attach a marker at the other end of the tubing to the cord above the weights. This marker, when it touches the bottom of the tubing in its operating position, will indicate that the stopper is rotating in a circle with a radius of approximately 80 or 100 cm. Now swing the stopper through 100 revolutions at this radius while an associate determines the time required. After these data are recorded, change the radius and repeat the operation until a continuing body of information is obtained from the shortest to the longest practical radius.

Step 2. Repeat the same operation with objects of different mass providing the centripetal force.

Step 3. Plot your data in the form you consider best presents your results.

Step 4. Compare your results with those predicted theoretically.

EXPERIMENT 11

THE CAVENDISH EXPERIMENT
(Newton's Law of Gravitation)

Object: To measure the universal gravitational constant, G.

Problem: Newton's law of gravitation postulates that any two bodies attract one another according to the law

$$F = \frac{GmM}{d^2},$$

where m, M are the respective masses of the bodies, d their separation, and G a universal constant of proportionality. As G is very small, the force is minute unless one (or both) of the masses is large, as for a planetary body. In the Cavendish experiment neither mass is large, and so a very sensitive method of measuring F is called for. This sensitivity is provided by a delicate fiber supporting a pair of equal small balls (each of mass m) on a light cross arm, and by the magnification furnished by an optical level system.*

Two larger balls (each of mass M) are placed one in front of one small ball and one behind the other small ball (Fig. 8–7). The distance between the center of a large ball and the center of the adjacent small one is d. The force F on each small ball causes the cross arm to rotate, but after a certain rotation a position of equilibrium is reached because the effect of F is then balanced by the tendency of the twisted suspension to untwist. This is the situation at the start of the experiment.

The large balls are now shifted so as to *reverse* the F on each small ball. Consider one small ball only. An unbalanced force of $2F$ now acts on it (the difference between F and $-F$) and an acceleration a results, where

$$ma = 2F = \frac{2GmM}{d^2}, \qquad \text{or} \qquad a = \frac{2GM}{d^2}.$$

We shall measure a optically; M may be found by weighing a large ball; and d may be found with the aid of calipers; G may then be computed.

Procedure:

Step 1. Let $t = 0$ when the large balls are shifted. Measure the distance S that the light beam travels along the scale after 10, 20, 30, . . . , 100 seconds. Plot $2S$ against t^2. Then the slope of the best line through your points is $2S/t^2 = A$, the acceleration of the *spot of light on the scale.*

Step 2. To relate A in Step 1 to the a of the small ball, we use the equation

$$a/A = r/2R,$$

where R is the radius (mirror to scale distance) of the rotating light beam and r is the radius

---

* The apparatus may be homemade or purchased from E. Leybold through J. Klinger, 82 160th St., Jamaica 32, N.Y.

of the arc followed by the ball. The latter is half the distance between the small balls. The factor 2 arises because a *reflected* light beam rotates through twice the angle of its reflecting mirror.

Measure R and r and compute a.

Step 3. Find M and d and compute G. Find your actual percent error. What measurement do you think contributed most to your error?

Step 4. Use the value of G to "weigh the earth," taking the radius of the earth as 6400 km and $g = 9.8$ m/sec^2, what is the mass of the earth? Develop the appropriate equation.

CHAPTER 9

The Conservation of Energy Principle

9-1 Work

The concept of work, like the concepts of length, time, and force, originated intuitively. Early civilizations were concerned with transportation and building. Men and animals were said to be "working" when they pushed and pulled objects against the forces of friction and gravity; in so doing they gradually became exhausted and had to be given food and rest. Since rest alone will not enable a laborer to keep going, it must be that the food he eats serves for him as fuel does for an engine.

Suppose that a certain engine does the job of lifting a 50-lb basket of bricks 20 ft. Say that the basket is lifted by a rope passing over a pulley to the engine. The rope must exert a pull, call it F, on the basket. If a second basket with the same load were connected to the same engine by means of another rope and pulley, the engine would exert a force F to lift the second 50 lb. If the two 50-lb loads were lifted by a single rope, the force needed would be $2F$. Should the engine lift the two baskets either separately or together, we would say that it had done "twice the job" of raising one basket alone. To raise the two baskets separately will obviously require of the engine twice the expenditure of fuel needed to raise only one basket. This doubling of the fuel used would also hold true if the engine lifted the two baskets together, assuming that friction is either negligible or proportional to the load. Thus the force needed and the fuel expended to do two equal jobs are here each twice what they are to do one such job.

Should the engine lift a 50-lb basket first 20 ft and then another 20 ft we would say that it again did two equal jobs and must have used twice the fuel needed to do one such job. Hence if the rope exerts a given force F on the basket, the distance through which the force acts and the fuel expended are each proportional to the number of jobs done.

Since we associate work done with the number of unit jobs accomplished and since the number of unit jobs accomplished is proportional to both the applied force F and the distance s its point of application moves (in the direction of the applied force), it is reasonable to define the work W that is done as

$$W = Fs. \tag{9-1}$$

This definition of work makes it not only proportional to the number of unit jobs done, but also proportional to the fuel expended in doing these jobs.

In the mks system force is measured in newtons, distance in meters, and work in newton-meters. For brevity the word *joule* (abbreviated j) has been substituted for newton-meter, that is,

$$1 \text{ joule} = 1 \text{ n-m.}$$

If the force **F** and displacement **s** are in different directions and θ is the angle between them, the work W is defined as

$$W = Fs \cos \theta. \tag{9-2}$$

You will see that Eq. (9-1) is a special case of Eq. (9-2), that is, the case where

$$\theta = 0°.$$

Equation (9-2) may be written as

$$W = (F \cos \theta)s \tag{9-3}$$

and interpreted as stating that work is the product of the force component in the direction of the motion times the distance moved. Thus a person does no work while just holding a suitcase (since $s = 0$), or while moving it horizontally through the air as one's arm hangs vertically (since then $\theta = 90°$, $\cos \theta = 0$). The tiredness developed in one's arm in these examples is evidently not to be attributed to doing work but to some physiological effect on the muscles.

Work always involves an interaction between *two* objects or systems. This follows from Newton's action-reaction law. If an agent applies a force $\mathbf{F}_a$ to an object there is a reaction $-\mathbf{F}_a$ to this force. If the object moves in the direction of $\mathbf{F}_a$ and this force does the work W, then the work $-W$ is done *by* the reaction. We may say that the work W is done *against* the reaction.

If $\mathbf{F}_a$ is the only applied force acting on a body, then the reaction is due to the inertia of the body. The work done by $\mathbf{F}_a$ in this case results in acceleration of the body.

When an applied force is balanced by a second equal and opposite force acting on the body, such as its weight or friction, then no acceleration is possible; however, the body may move at a constant velocity. Suppose that it moves (a) in the direction of $\mathbf{F}_a$, (b) opposite to $\mathbf{F}_a$. In case (a) work, say an amount W, is done by $\mathbf{F}_a$ and work $-W$ is done *by* the opposite outside force, or $+W$ is done *against* this second force. Thus in the case of a freely falling body, $\mathbf{F}_a$ is the weight and the agent the earth, but when a person slowly lifts an object, then he is the agent that does the work *against* gravity, the result being that the object attains a higher position. Should the agent do work against friction, the result is found to be a warming of the surfaces where friction occurs. In case (b) where the object moves opposite to $\mathbf{F}_a$, work is done *by* the opposing force *against* $\mathbf{F}_a$, so that when a body is gently lowered gravity does the work.

When opposing forces acting on a body are not equal in magnitude, a net force acts and acceleration results. Then the work done by (or against) $\mathbf{F}_a$ is not equal to the work done against (or by) the opposing force; the difference is the same as the work that would be done if the net force alone acted.

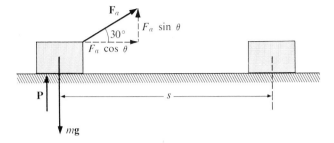

FIG. 9–1. Work done by an applied force.

EXAMPLE 1. To illustrate Eq. (9–3) suppose that a 3-kg box, whose weight mg = 29.4 n, is dragged a distance s = 5 m along a smooth horizontal floor by an applied force $\mathbf{F}_a$ directed at an angle θ = 30° with the horizontal (Fig. 9–1). Let us find the work done by the applied force when its magnitude is 4 n.

Solution. The applied force may be broken up into its horizontal component

$$F_a \cos \theta = 4 \times 0.866 = 3.46 \text{ n},$$

and its vertical component

$$F_a \sin \theta = 4 \times 0.500 = 2.00 \text{ n}.$$

Since the displacement is horizontal, only the horizontal component of $\mathbf{F}_a$ does work. This work amounts to

$$W = F_a \cos \theta \times s$$
$$= 3.46 \text{ n} \times 5 \text{ m} = 17.3 \text{ j}.$$

The vertical component of $\mathbf{F}_a$ does no work, but serves to reduce by 2 n the force of the box against the floor, and hence the upward push $\mathbf{P}$ of the floor against the box. Since there is no vertical acceleration, the sum of the vertical forces acting on the box must equal zero. The weight mg acts down, hence choosing up as positive,

$$P - mg + F_a \sin \theta = 0,$$
$$P = mg - F_a \sin \theta$$
$$= 29.4 - 2.0 = 27.4 \text{ n}.$$

EXAMPLE 2. An upward force of magnitude F_a = 30 n is applied to an object of mass m = 3 kg. Find the work done by F_a and by gravity if the box moves (a) 5 m upward, (b) 5 m downward.

Solution. (a) Since F_a exceeds the weight (mg = 3 × 9.8 = 29.4 n) the net force and acceleration are up. For accelerated motion upward

Work done *by* F_a = 30 n × 5 m = 150 j.
Work done *against* gravity = 29.4 n × 5 m = 147 j.
Work done *by* gravity = −147 j.

(b) If the box moves downward while the acceleration is upward, it must have a decreasing downward velocity. Then

$$\text{Work done } \textit{against } F_a = 150 \text{ j},$$
$$\text{Work done } \textit{by } \text{gravity} = 147 \text{ j}.$$

We shall discuss presently the significance of the fact that these two amounts of work are not numerically equal.

EXAMPLE 3. An object is pulled 5 m along a horizontal floor by a horizontal force $F_a = 30$ n. Frictional resistance $f = 10$ n. Find the work done by F_a and f.

Solution. Work done *by* $F_a = 30$ n $\times$ 5 m $= 150$ j.

Work done *against* $f = 10$ n $\times$ 5 m $= 50$ j.

Again the two amounts of work are not numerically equal. In this case there is a net force $F = 20$ n acting on the object and accelerating it. The work done by this *net* force is 20 n $\times$ 5 m $= 100$ j, which is the same as the difference between the work done by F_a and that done against f. What does this mean?

9–2 Energy

We have chosen our definition of work so that it is a measure of the number of unit jobs done. In the example of the engine lifting bricks, we saw that work done by a system is also proportional to the fuel used up by the system. Let us say that when a system does the work W, it takes an amount of *energy* equal to W from some source such as fuel. According to this definition, energy represents the *capacity for doing work*. This agrees with our intuitive concept of energy, for when we are rested we say we "feel full of energy," or "have more energy" than after we have done a lot of work and become tired.

Of course, work is not always done by using the energy of some fuel. What about the case of a freely falling body? Gravity does work, but what is the source of energy for this work? Or, what is the source of energy for the work done against friction as a sliding object comes to rest? We shall see that we can answer these questions better after we consider the following question: What becomes of the energy used to do work?

In the three examples of the last section we saw that work enables one to (1) increase the speed of an object, (2) raise an object to a greater height, and (3) move an object against friction. Suppose that we try saying (and this is of course, a postulate) that when a system does the work W and so (according to our definition) gives up the energy W, then this same amount of energy is transferred somewhere else, namely to that other system (or part of the surroundings) against which the first system exerts the force that does the work. The idea is that *energy is transferred through work*, but not created or destroyed, and this is the fundamental postulate of this chapter. The test of this hypothesis is whether its predictions are consistent with experimental facts. We shall see that to ensure this consistency, we must invent different forms of energy, but we shall find that each such form becomes a very useful concept that leads us on into new discoveries.

Let us call ΔE the energy transferred from one form and place to another through performance of the work W. Then we say that

$$\Delta E = W. \tag{9-4}$$

Next we shall consider the various forms of energy one at a time. Besides fuel (chemical) energy, which we have already mentioned, we shall say that when work results in an increase in speed, then energy is transferred from its initial form into energy of motion (kinetic energy); when work results in an increase in height of an object, then energy is transferred into energy of position (potential energy); and when work is done against friction, then surfaces are warmed and gain internal energy. Other forms of energy will also be discussed.

9-3 Kinetic energy

This is defined as *energy of motion*, and its magnitude is determined by computing how much work is required to change the state of an object from one of rest to the given state of motion.

If a net force $\mathbf{F}$ acts on a body of mass m the acceleration will be

$$\mathbf{a} = \frac{\mathbf{F}}{m}.$$

In a time t the speed v that is gained and the distance s traveled from rest will be, respectively,

$$v = at, \qquad s = \tfrac{1}{2}at^2.$$

When the time is eliminated between these last two equations we get

$$s = \frac{1}{2} a \left(\frac{v}{a}\right)^2 = \frac{1}{2}\frac{v^2}{a},$$

or, since $a = F/m$,

$$s = \frac{1}{2}\frac{mv^2}{F}. \tag{9-5}$$

The work done by $\mathbf{F}$ in the distance s is

$$W = Fs = \tfrac{1}{2}mv^2.$$

As in Eq. (9-4), we call this the gain in kinetic energy (abbreviated K.E.). Since a body's K.E. in motion equals its gain in K.E. over what it had at rest (the K.E. at rest is zero),

$$\text{K.E.} = \tfrac{1}{2}mv^2. \tag{9-6}$$

To stop a moving object, one must apply a force $\mathbf{F}$ opposite to the motion. The acceleration $\mathbf{a} = \mathbf{F}/m$ will be opposite to the velocity. The work $W = \tfrac{1}{2}mv^2$ will be done against the braking force $\mathbf{F}$. The body will lose K.E. (because *it* does the work) and the system supplying the braking force will have an equal amount of work done on it; as we shall see, the braking system will gain in one form or another the energy $\frac{1}{2}mv^2$. In this case Eq. (9–5) gives the distance s in which a braking force of magnitude F will slow a moving object down from a speed v to rest. Note that since s is proportional to the *square* of v, a car going 60 mi/hr will require a distance in which to stop that is four times greater than that required when the car is going 30 mi/hr. To stop a car going 60 mi/hr, one must take from it four times as much K.E. as when the car is going only 30 mi/hr.

EXAMPLE 1.   Refer to Example 2 of Section 9–1.   An object whose weight is 29.4 n is lifted, say from rest, by a force of 30 n. The net force is 0.6 n up, and in a distance $s = 5$ m the work done by the net force is $0.6 \times 5 = 3$ j. This is the difference between the work done by the applied force and that done against gravity; it equals the gain in K.E. For proof compute a, v^2, and $\frac{1}{2}mv^2$.

EXAMPLE 2.   Refer to Example 3 of Section 9–1.   Here the net force is 20 n, and in a distance $s = 5$ m the K.E. gained is $20 \times 5 = 100$ j, which is the difference between the work done by the applied force and that done against friction. Proof: the net force $F = 20$ n, $a = F/m = (20/m)$ m/sec^2, (change in v^2) $= 2as = (200/m)$ m^2/sec^2, (change in $\frac{1}{2}mv^2$) $= 100$ j.

EXAMPLE 3.   A ball of 0.4-kg mass moving at 2 m/sec collides head-on with another 0.4-kg ball that is at rest. The second ball is observed to gain a speed of 1.5 m/sec. How much K.E. does the first ball lose and how much does the second gain as a result of the collision?

Solution.   Let v_1 represent the speed of the first ball just after the collision. From the conservation of momentum principle, which applies to any collision or explosion (see Chapter 6), we have

$$(0.4 \text{ kg}) \times (2 \text{ m/sec}) = (0.4 \text{ kg}) \times v_1 + (0.4 \text{ kg}) \times (1.5 \text{ m/sec}),$$

$$v_1 = 0.5 \text{ m/sec}.$$

Before the collision only the first ball possessed K.E. and it was

$$(\text{K.E. before}) = \frac{1}{2} \times 0.4 \text{ kg} \times (2 \text{ m/sec})^2 = 0.8 \text{ j}.$$

After the collision the K.E. of the first ball will be $\frac{1}{2} \times 0.4 \times 0.5^2 = 0.05$ j and that of the second will be $\frac{1}{2} \times 0.4 \times 1.5^2 = 0.45$ j. Thus the first ball loses 0.75 j and the second ball gains 0.45 j of K.E. The total K.E. after the collision will be

$$(\text{K.E. after}) = 0.05 \text{ j} + 0.45 \text{ j} = 0.5 \text{ j}.$$

Therefore 0.3 j of K.E. is lost.   What happens to this energy?   Is it just destroyed? Not according to our previous postulate!

9–4 Potential energy

This may be regarded as *energy due to position*. When an object is moved from a position C to a position D and the work W that must be done by the agent depends only on the positions C and D, we say that the object has gained *potential energy* (abbreviated P.E.) in the amount W. If V represents P.E. and ΔV the gain in P.E., then

$$\Delta V = W, \qquad (9\text{--}7)$$

when the work W is associated only with the change in position of the object.

If the work done is independent of the path and more than one path is possible, then for two paths, say 1 and 2, between C and D, $W_1 = W_2$. If path 2 is traversed in the reverse direction, the work done along it becomes $-W_2 = -W_1$. Therefore the energy transferred while taking the object from C to D is recoverable. By "recoverable" we mean that if on the outward trip $(C \rightarrow D)$ the energy W is transferred from system A to system B, then on the return trip $(D \rightarrow C)$ the energy W is transferred back from system B to system A.

It is assumed in Eq. (9–7) that W does not include work that may be done to speed up the object, which results in a gain in K.E., nor work done against friction, which results in heating. Work done against friction varies with the length of the path taken between A and B, it does not reverse when the motion is reversed, and it may also depend on the speed of the particle, so it does not depend on just change in position.

When *is* work done against an opposing force independent of the path (and speed) and reversible with respect to the displacement? The answer is "in most situations where the opposing force is only a function of the position of the object that is moved." Such forces are called *conservative*, since work done against them transfers energy into a form such that, by reversing the displacement, the energy is recoverable. The most common example of such a force is *gravity*. Another familiar example is the reaction of a stretched or compressed elastic coil spring.

Near the earth the magnitude of the force of gravity on an object of mass m is $F = mg$, where g is practically constant. When the object is lifted through a height h, the work done against gravity is independent of the horizontal motion, since no work is done against gravity except during the vertical displacement. Therefore in Eq. (9–3) we let $F \cos \theta = mg$ and $s = h$ and obtain

$$W = mgh$$

for the work done against gravity. If we substitute this in Eq. (9–7), we see that

$$\Delta V = mgh. \qquad (9\text{--}8)$$

We have defined only *change* in P.E. One may, if he wishes, arbitrarily choose some level such as sea level, the ground, floor, or table top, as the level of zero P.E., then when the object is at a height h above this reference level its P.E. will be given by

$$\text{P.E.} = mgh. \qquad (9\text{--}9)$$

When dealing with rockets and earth satellites one must consider the variation in the force of gravity as given by Newton's law of gravitation. The magnitude

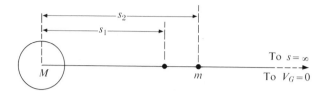

FIG. 9–2.   Gravitational potential energy at large distances.

of the force of gravity on a body of mass m at a distance s_1 from the earth's center is

$$F = \frac{GmM}{s_1^2},$$

where M is the mass of the earth (see Fig. 9–2). If the distance is increased to s_2, F will decrease to

$$F' = \frac{GmM}{s_2^2}.$$

Let $s_2 - s_1$ be small compared with s_1; then the mean force $\overline{F}$ acting during this increase in s will differ percentagewise very little from the geometric mean, or

$$\overline{F} = \frac{GmM}{s_1 s_2}.$$

The corresponding work ΔW_1 done against gravity will be

$$\Delta W_1 = \overline{F}(s_2 - s_1) = GmM\left(\frac{1}{s_1} - \frac{1}{s_2}\right).$$

Similarly, the work ΔW_2 done when the distance increases from s_2 to s_3 will be

$$\Delta W_2 = GmM\left(\frac{1}{s_2} - \frac{1}{s_3}\right),$$

and so on, for further increases in distance. Let us increase s up to infinity. Then the total work W needed to remove the object completely from the earth's gravitational attraction is given by

$$W = \Delta W_1 + \Delta W_2 + \Delta W_3 + \cdots$$
$$= GmM\left(\frac{1}{s_1} - \frac{1}{s_2} + \frac{1}{s_2} - \frac{1}{s_3} + \cdots \frac{1}{\infty}\right).$$

Since $1/\infty = 0$ and all intermediate terms cancel in pairs, we have

$$W = \frac{GmM}{s_1}$$

for the work to take a mass m from a distance s_1 to infinite distance from the earth's center. In this case it is convenient to take the P.E. to be zero at infinite distance; then at a finite distance the P.E. will be *negative*, since gravitational P.E. decreases with height.   At a distance $s_1 = r$ from the earth's center the gravitational P.E. then becomes

$$V_G = -\frac{GmM}{r}.$$ (9–10)

EXAMPLE.   A 2-kg mass is situated 1 m above a table that is 1.5 m high, the floor being 5 m above ground level and the ground 42.5 m above sea level.   Find its gravitational potential energy relative to (a) the table top, (b) the floor, (c) the ground, (d) sea level, (e) infinity.

Solution.   Near the earth's surface Eq. (9–9) applies, with $g = 9.8$ m/sec^2.   Therefore (a) relative to the table top

$$\text{P.E.} = (2 \text{ kg}) \times \left(9.8 \frac{\text{m}}{\text{sec}^2}\right) \times (1 \text{ m}) = 19.6 \frac{\text{kg-m}^2}{\text{sec}^2} = 19.6 \text{ j.}$$

(b) Relative to the floor

$$\text{P.E.} = 2 \times 9.8 \times 2.5 = 49 \text{ j.}$$

(c) Relative to the ground

$$\text{P.E.} = 2 \times 9.8 \times 7.5 = 147 \text{ j.}$$

(d) Relative to sea level

$$\text{P.E.} = 2 \times 9.8 \times 50 = 980 \text{ j.}$$

(e) When comparing the P.E. near the earth's surface with that at infinite distance we must use Eq. (9–10), with $G = 6.67 \times 10^{-11}$ n-m^2/kg^2, $M = 6 \times 10^{24}$ kg, $r = R = 6.4 \times 10^6$ m (the earth's radius), so that

$$\text{P.E.} = -\frac{6.67 \times 10^{-11} \times 2 \times 6 \times 10^{24}}{6.4 \times 10^6} \text{ n-m} = -1.25 \times 10^8 \text{ j.}$$

These different values for the P.E. represent the work to move the mass from different starting points to its final position 1 m above the table.   In practice one should choose one reference point and maintain it throughout a given problem.   In any event the *difference in the potential energy* of the mass when first at a point A and then at a point B will come out the same.   For example, at the table top (6.5 m above ground) the P.E. will be $2 \times 9.8 \times 6.5 = 127.4$ j greater than at ground level.   Note that $147 \text{ j} - 19.6 \text{ j} = 127.4 \text{ j.}$

9–5 The conservation of mechanical energy

Suppose that an object of mass m is allowed to fall freely from rest starting from a height h_0 above the floor.   Its P.E. will be computed relative to floor level.   At the start we have that the object's

$$\text{K.E.} = 0, \qquad \text{P.E.} = mgh_0.$$

After a time t the object will have fallen a distance $s = \frac{1}{2}gt^2$ and acquired a speed $v = gt$. Elimination of t between these two equations shows that

$$v^2 = 2gs.$$

The height above the floor will be

$$h = h_0 - s,$$

so that now we have

$$\text{K.E.} = \tfrac{1}{2}mv^2 = mgs,$$

$$\text{P.E.} = mgh = mgh_0 - mgs.$$

This shows that

$$\text{(K.E.} + \text{P.E.) at time } t = mgh_0$$
$$= \text{(K.E.} + \text{P.E.) at the start.}$$

Thus after *any* time t the sum of the K.E. and P.E. will have the value it had at the start, i.e., the

$$\text{K.E.} + \text{P.E.} = \text{a constant.} \tag{9-11}$$

The theorem expressed by Eq. (9–11) may be extended to cover any situation where an object moves under the influence of a conservative field of force. This theorem expresses the *conservation of mechanical energy;* when only conservative forces are concerned.

$$\text{Gain in K.E.} = \text{Loss in P.E.,}$$

and vice versa.

What this means is that if an object and the environment with which it interacts constitute a closed system, unaffected by the rest of the universe, and if the only forces within this system are conservative ones, then only two forms of energy need be considered, K.E. and P.E., and within the system energy may be exchanged back and forth between these two forms without altering the total amount of energy. Thus for such restricted cases our postulate, that work transfers energy without creating or destroying it, is in accord with the facts, and this in turn is due to the way in which we defined K.E. and P.E.

ILLUSTRATION 1.   *The pendulum.* Figure 9–3 shows a simple pendulum. At the highest point of the swing the K.E. is zero and the energy is all potential. Let us compute the P.E. relative to the lowest point (the midpoint) of the swing. If the maximum angle that the string makes with the vertical is θ_0, then at the top of the swing the height h of the bob above its lowest point is $h = l - l \cos \theta_0$, where l is the length of the string. Therefore the P.E. $= mgl (1 - \cos \theta_0)$, and Eq. (9–11) tells us that

$$0 + mgl (1 - \cos \theta_0) = C, \qquad \text{a constant.}$$

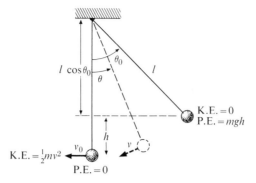

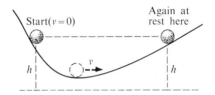

FIG. 9-3. Oscillating pendulum. The sum of the potential energy and kinetic energy is constant.

FIG. 9-4.   Ball in a frictionless trough.

When the angle between string and vertical is less than θ_0, say θ, the speed v may be found from Eq. (9-11) as follows:

$$\tfrac{1}{2}mv^2 + mgl\,(1 - \cos\theta) = C = mgl\,(1 - \cos\theta_0),$$

$$v = \sqrt{2gl(\cos\theta - \cos\theta_0)}. \qquad (9\text{-}12)$$

As the bob swings back and forth, P.E. is converted into K.E. at the middle of the swing and then back into the original P.E. at the far end of the swing, the process then being repeated.

In a similar manner, a ball that rolls down one side of an incline and up another (Fig. 9-4) will reach on the second incline the elevation it had when it started from rest, *provided* that frictional forces (which are not conservative) are negligible. The normal force exerted by the plane does no work, since this force is at right angles to the motion.

ILLUSTRATION 2.   *Escape velocity for a rocket.* Suppose that above the earth's atmosphere and at a height h above the earth a rocket is given an outward speed v_e that allows it just to escape from the influence of the earth's gravitational attraction. What is the value of v_e?

We see from Eq. (9-10) that the rocket must gain P.E. in the amount

$$\text{Gain in P.E.} = \frac{GmM}{r},$$

where m is the mass of the rocket, M that of the earth, and $r = R + h$, R being the radius of the earth. To gain this P.E. the rocket just uses up all of its K.E. Therefore, the

$$\text{Loss in K.E.} = \tfrac{1}{2}mv_e^2.$$

Since the gain P.E. equals the loss in P.E., the two expressions may be equated. We get

$$\tfrac{1}{2}mv_e^2 = \frac{GmM}{R + h} \cdot$$

The factor m cancels out. Solving for v_e, we find that

$$v_e = \sqrt{\frac{2GM}{R + h}} \cdot \tag{9-13}$$

Comparison with Eq. (8-12) will show that this is just $\sqrt{2}$ times the orbital speed required for an orbit of radius $= (R + h)$. If the orbital speed is 17,000 mi/hr, then v_e must $= \sqrt{2} \times 17{,}000 = 24{,}000$ mi/hr. To raise the speed of an object from v to $\sqrt{2}v$, one must double its K.E. Thus, if air resistance is not considered, an orbiting satellite has only *half* the energy needed to escape from the earth's attraction.

It is not difficult to picture K.E. intuitively. But what about P.E.? When a pendulum swings up and gains P.E., it is said to have acquired *stored energy*. Where is the energy stored? The answer to this question is not important, although one may, if he wishes, invent some sort of a model, such as a field (Section 12-3), to explain how the energy is stored. However, the important point is that the concept of P.E. is useful and enables us to arrive at formulas such as Eq. (9-12) and Eq. (9-13), which are found to be experimentally correct. Furthermore, this sort of theorizing may be greatly extended and serve many useful purposes. When such concepts as internal energy, etc., are defined, each is introduced so as to enable us to account for what happens when, through work, energy is transferred from a familiar form to a less familiar form, or vice versa. This is a deliberate effort on the part of scientists to avoid saying that energy is ever destroyed or created out of nothing. It is the postulate that this method of reasoning will simplify our description of nature and bring us useful results which forms the core of this whole chapter. We shall lead up to it through further steps.

9-6 Internal thermal energy

When an unbalanced force does work against the inertial reaction of a body, K.E. is gained by the body. When work is done against a conservative force such as gravity, P.E. is gained. Now let us consider what happens when work is done against frictional forces.

A body under the action of an applied horizontal force $\mathbf{F}_a$ and an opposing force $\mathbf{f}$ due to friction, can move at a constant horizontal velocity if $\mathbf{F}_a = -\mathbf{f}$ (see Fig. 9-5). There will be no acceleration and no gain in height, hence no change

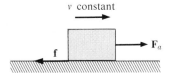

FIG. 9–5.   Work done against friction alone.

in K.E. or P.E. Yet work is done by the applied force. What is the result? Careful observations by such men as Davy, Rumford, and Joule revealed that in a system whose parts rub frictionally against one another, a rise in temperature occurs, or parts of the system "heat up."

Let us postulate that a substance can store energy within itself as *internal energy U*, and that a rise in the temperature, or the melting, boiling, or evaporation of a substance, indicates an increase in this internal energy. (For the definition of temperature see Chapter 3.) Internal energy may be regarded as energy associated with the motion and relative positions of the molecules of a body. We define the change ΔU in the internal energy of a system, such as the block and table of Fig. 9–5, as equal to the work done against friction, so that if the block moves a distance s,

$$\Delta U = fs. \tag{9-14}$$

This gain in internal energy is initially shared by the block and table, though it may later be passed on to their surroundings and dissipated. Nonconservative forces such as friction are also called dissipative forces.

EXAMPLE. A force $\mathbf{F}_a = 20$ n is applied to an object of mass $m = 2$ kg that is initially at rest on an inclined plane; the angle between the plane and the horizontal is 30° (see Fig. 9–6). The force of friction is 3 n. If $\mathbf{F}_a$ acts up the plane and pushes the object a distance $s = 0.8$ m, (a) what is the work done by $\mathbf{F}_a$, and (b) how is this work accounted for?

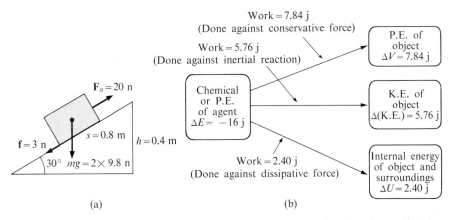

FIG. 9–6.   Acceleration up a rough inclined plane. Work done by the applied force equals that done against friction and gravity plus the gain in K.E.

Solution. (a) The work done by the applied force is

$$W = 20 \text{ n} \times 0.8 \text{ m} = 16 \text{ j}.$$

(b) The work done against friction is fs. Therefore

$$\Delta U = 3\text{n} \times 0.8 \text{ m} = 2.4 \text{ j}.$$

The increase in potential energy is $\Delta V = mgh$, where h is the vertical height gained as the object is pushed 0.8 m up the plane. Since $h = s \sin 30° = 0.8 \times 0.5$ m, we have

$$\Delta V = 2 \text{ kg} \times (9.8 \text{ m/sec}^2) \times 0.4 \text{ m} = 7.84 \text{ j}.$$

The gain in kinetic energy equals the unbalanced force up the plane multiplied by s. The weight $mg = 19.6$ n has a component $mg \sin 30° = 0.5 \ mg$ down the plane. Friction also acts down the plane. Therefore the unbalanced force $\mathbf{F}$ up the plane must have the magnitude

$$F = F_a - mg \sin \theta - f = 20 \text{ n} - 9.8 \text{ n} - 3 \text{ n} = 7.2 \text{ n}.$$

Hence the gain in K.E. is

$$\Delta(\text{K.E.}) = 7.2 \text{ n} \times 0.8 \text{ m} = 5.76 \text{ j}.$$

Note that

$$\Delta U + \Delta V + \Delta(\text{K.E.}) = 16.0 \text{ j},$$

so that all of the work done by $\mathbf{F}_a$ has been accounted for.

The introduction of the concept of internal energy thus further extends the scope of the conservation of energy principle.

9–7 Chemical energy

Up to now we have avoided saying anything about the original form of the energy transferred to a body when it is accelerated or lifted by an applied force. If work is a method of transferring energy, from where does the energy come? In the case where work is done by man or beast, we say that the energy comes from *chemical energy* stored in the living organism; in the case of work done by a gas engine, the energy is supplied by chemical energy stored in the fuel that is used.

Chemical energy is a form of potential energy attributed to the relative positions of individual atoms and their electrons in a molecule. For example, separate carbon and oxygen atoms possess more potential energy than they do when they are combined to form a carbon monoxide molecule. The explanation is that the two atoms attract each other at short distances, just as (for a different reason) the earth attracts a stone, and when objects move the way such forces urge them to move, they lose potential energy. Note that associated with every form of energy there must be some kind of force. The atomic forces involved in chemical energy are electromagnetic in nature and will be discussed in later chapters.

The amount of chemical energy released in the consumption of a given amount of fuel is defined in terms of the work that is done when this energy is transferred into other forms. This definition extends our conservation of energy principle to include chemical energy.

Chemical energy may, of course, be expressed in joules. However, it has become a custom to use in this connection a larger unit called the *calorie*, defined as 1 calorie = 4180 joules.* It has been determined experimentally that complete burning in oxygen yields the following calories per kilogram for common fuels: about 8000 for coal, 10,000 for fuel oil, 11,500 for gasoline.

The chemical energy supplied by a person's daily food intake varies greatly with the person's age, weight, occupation, and standard of living. Perhaps 2800 calories per day is a fair average for western countries. The calorie content of various foods is well known, so that one may compute and regulate one's own personal intake. For example, the calorie content of an average serving of some common food items is as follows: bread (1 slice) 100 calories, butter ($\frac{1}{2}$ oz) 100 calories, cake 250 calories, egg 80 calories, meat (3 oz) 300 calories, potato (medium size) 100 calories, baked beans (3 oz) 300 calories.

EXAMPLE. It is found that a force of 700 n is required to keep a certain car going at 15 m/sec (about 35 mi/hr) and that at this speed the car consumes one gallon of gasoline in 18 miles. What is the useful energy (for driving the car) obtained from the car's motor per gallon of gasoline?

Solution. The work done against frictional forces in 18 miles is $W = Fs$, where $F = 700$ n, $s = 18$ mi $\times$ 1.61 $\times 10^3$ m/mi = 2.9 $\times 10^4$ m. Therefore

$$W = 700 \text{ n} \times 2.9 \times 10^4 \text{ m} = 2.03 \times 10^7 \text{ j} = \frac{2.03 \times 10^7 \text{ j}}{4180 \text{ j/cal}} = 4850 \text{ calories.}$$

To measure the total energy released per gallon, the gasoline must be burned in a special combustion chamber from which no energy can escape. The value obtained is about 30,000 calories/gallon, more energy than in 10 days' food supply for one man! when spent in a car only about one sixth goes toward propulsion, the rest being wasted.

9–8 Heat

Just as energy may be transferred through work, it is found that energy transfer also occurs in nature due to temperature differences. *Energy transferred because of a temperature difference is called heat.* The amount of heat Q that is transferred is determined by measuring that amount of work which alone will accomplish the same change as does Q in the internal energy (as indicated by the temperature or state) of a system. For example, if a system of paddle wheels is used to stir

---

* Many physics texts define a calorie as 4.18j and call our unit the *kilocalorie*. Our unit is used by dieticians and is the proper unit in the mks system.

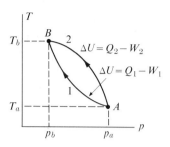

Fig. 9–7. The first law of thermodynamics. The change in the internal energy does not depend on the path taken between state A and state B.

a quantity of water, the temperature of the water rises because of the work done against internal friction (or viscous forces). The force driving the paddles may be regulated and measured, as well as the distance the paddles move in a given time, so that the work done may be computed. It is found that if 1 kg of water is "heated" 1°C (or 1°K), the heat which must be supplied is equivalent to about 4180 j (1 calorie) of work.

The heat Q required to raise a mass m of a substance by ΔT degrees is usually found to be nearly proportional to m and ΔT, so that we may write

$$Q = cm \, \Delta T, \qquad (9\text{–}15)$$

where c is approximately constant for a given substance. Equation (9–15) defines c, which is called the *specific heat capacity* of the substance. The statement that c is constant for a given material constitutes one of the many *restricted* laws of physics. Values of c for water, copper, iron, etc., are listed in tables. Numerous other restricted laws have been discovered in connection with heat, each with its constant, a constant that is characteristic of a given material, such as the latent heat, the coefficient of thermal conductivity, the coefficient of linear expansion, etc. For more information of this specialized nature, the reader is referred to other texts.

Of more fundamental importance is the relation between work, heat, and internal energy. This brings us to a branch of physics called *thermodynamics*.

Let us consider a gas that is initially in a state A defined by its temperature T_a and pressure p_a (Fig. 9–7). The gas will have an internal energy U_a. Suppose that the gas is taken to the state B, for which $T = T_b$, $p = p_b$, and $U = U_b$, by letting the gas take in the heat Q and causing the *gas* to do the work W. The postulate that

$$U_b - U_a = Q - W \qquad (9\text{–}16)$$

is called the *first law of thermodynamics*. This postulate contains the definition of Q ($Q = W$ when $\Delta U = U_b - U_a = 0$), but it goes much further. It extends the conservation of energy principle to include energy transfer by heat as well as by work. It states that if the gas is taken from state A to state B by two *different* processes (or paths 1 and 2 in Fig. 9-7), then $Q - W$ must be the same for each, or

$$Q_1 - W_1 = Q_2 - W_2$$

for two different processes leading from state A to state B. This is analogous to saying that the monthly change in one's bank balance depends only on the net difference between deposits and withdrawals and not on whether they are large or small.

EXAMPLE. A gas is taken from state A to state B in such a way that $Q = 200\,\mathrm{j}$ and $W = 150\,\mathrm{j}$. For the same initial and final states, find (a) Q when $100\,\mathrm{j}$ of work are done *by* the gas, (b) Q when $100\,\mathrm{j}$ of work are done *on* the gas, (c) W when $Q = 50\,\mathrm{j}$.

Solution. Since for the first process by which the gas is taken from state A to state B we have

$$Q - W = 200 - 150 = 50\,\mathrm{j},$$

we know that $U_b = U_a = 50\,\mathrm{j}$.
   (a) When $W = 100$, $Q = 50 + W = 150\,\mathrm{j}$.
   (b) When $W = -100$, $Q = -100 + 50 = -50\,\mathrm{j}$, or $50\,\mathrm{j}$ of heat must be transferred *from* the gas.
   (c) When $Q = 50$, $W = 0$.
   Work is done by a gas when it expands and work is done on it when it is compressed (see Example of Section 3-3).

9-9 The conservation of energy principle. Fundamental Law IV

We have seen that in those new instances in which energy seems to appear or disappear in an unaccountable way, it has proven useful to introduce and define a new form of energy, and in this way to maintain the conservation of energy principle. This procedure furthers our aim of explaining in terms of general laws how the world behaves. We therefore postulate the following.

Energy may be transformed from one form to another, but it cannot be created or destroyed. In other words, *the total energy content of a closed system is constant.* This is our *Fundamental Law IV.*

One consequence of this principle is that a so-called *perpetual motion* machine is impossible. Such a machine is pictured as a device which will run without fuel and yet do work against friction, gravity, and other external forces. The fact that no such machine has ever been devised is experimental proof that up to now no exceptions to the conservation of energy principle have been found.

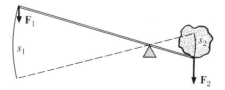

FIG. 9-8. The lever. A simple machine for transforming a small force into a larger one.

Actual machines, such as the lever (Fig. 9–8), the screw, pulley systems, inclined plane, etc., are devices whereby one may exert a small force $\mathbf{F}_1$ over a large distance s_1 and thereby counterbalance a large force $\mathbf{F}_2$ that acts over a correspondingly small distance s_2, or vice versa. Since the work input is $W_1 = F_1 s_1$ and no energy is supplied by other means, the useful work output $W_2 = F_2 s_2$ plus the work W_f done against friction must equal work input, according to the conservation of energy principle. Therefore

$$F_1 s_1 = F_2 s_2 + W_f. \tag{9-17}$$

Although W_f can be made relatively small by using good bearings and lubrication, $F_2 s_2$ can never exceed or even quite equal $F_1 s_1$. However, when F_2 represents the weight of a heavy load that is to be lifted and F_1 the required effort, it is a decided advantage when the ratio F_2/F_1 is considerably greater than unity.

There is, as suggested earlier, an instructive analogy between energy and money; in fact money buys energy, but the exchange rate (joules per penny) is not fixed, varying with one's geographical location, the time, and the kind of fuel purchased. However, when energy in one form is exchanged for energy in another form, one always gets a joule for a joule. This is the conservation of energy principle. Money in one form (say dollars) can be exchanged for money in another form (such as French francs, Italian lira, gold bullion, etc.). The "commission" one must pay corresponds to the work done against friction that is dissipated into thermal energy. When exchange rates are firm and fixed, one cannot make money, even if commissions are negligible, by trading dollars for francs, francs for lira, and lira back into dollars. One will end up losing the commissions. There was a time around 1950 when one could buy on the "black market" 500 francs for a dollar, while a bank would give one back his dollar for 350 francs. Thus $7 could be turned into 3500 francs via the "black market" and changed back into $10 via normal channels. This is termed *arbitrage* in financial circles. Evidently the conservation of energy principle states that there is no arbitrage when it comes to energy; nor is inflation possible either, for although printing presses can create new money, no process has been found for creating energy.

ILLUSTRATION. *The neutrino.* It has been found in connection with radioactive beta decay that a nucleus A may decay into nucleus B and an electron [Fig. 9–9(a)], with the energy E released in the decay appearing as K.E. of the electron. On the other hand [Fig. 9–9(b)], a nucleus identical with A may decay into one just like B and an electron, the electron receiving a K.E. of $E/2$. In a third case, the K.E. of the electron may be only $E/4$. Where does the missing energy go?

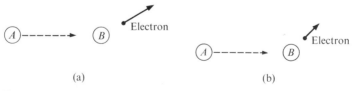

(a)   (b)

FIG. 9–9. Beta decay. The emitted election has a range of energies.

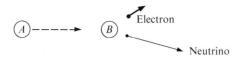

FIG. 9–10.   Neutrino emission in beta decay.

Physicists could have said (and some did) that here energy was just destroyed and that this was a case in which the conservation of energy principle failed. However, Fermi proposed that the missing energy was *not* lost, but was carried away by an elusive particle first suggested by Pauli and called the *neutrino* (see Fig. 9–10). A neutrino is supposed to have no mass or charge, so that it can slip away unobserved. While at first thought this proposal may seem amusing, be assured that it is taken very seriously by most physicists. This is because (1) the neutrino concept has simplified our understanding of many nuclear phenomena; (2) it has even led to several successful predictions, and finally (3) more than 20 years after the neutrino's existence was postulated the first direct experimental detection of neutrinos was obtained by observing the rare capture of neutrinos by matter.

9–10 Summary of important forms of energy

Important forms of energy are the following:

(a) Mechanical energy $\begin{cases} \text{Kinetic.} \\ \text{Gravitational potential.} \\ \text{Elastic potential.} \end{cases}$

(b) Internal thermal energy.

(c) Chemical energy—fuel energy.

(d) Sound energy: K.E. and P.E. of vibrating particles.

(e) Electromagnetic energy $\begin{cases} \text{Electric, due to charges at rest.} \\ \text{Magnetic, due to charges in motion.} \\ \text{Light, due to time-varying fields.} \end{cases}$

(f) Nuclear energy, due to nuclear forces.

(g) Neutrino energy, carried by neutrinos.

The term *light* includes all electromagnetic radiation: radio waves, infrared, visible, ultraviolet, x-rays, and gamma rays.

Solar energy is believed to be radiated by the sun at the expense of the sun's nuclear energy.

Mass should not be regarded as another form of energy, but rather as an attribute of energy. Einstein's equation

$$\Delta E = c^2 \Delta m \tag{9–18}$$

states that when the energy of a system changes by ΔE, then the mass of the system changes by $\Delta m = \Delta E/c^2$. This will be discussed further in Chapter 16.

In everyday happenings Δm is too small to be observed, but in atomic physics there is abundant experimental evidence that (1) the mass and K.E. energy of a particle increase together, and (2) the mass and internal energy of a system are proportional; in both cases the factor of proportionality is $\Delta m/\Delta E = 1/c^2$.

PROBLEMS

1. Compute the work done against gravity when a 75-kg man (a) climbs stairs rising 4 m, (b) climbs a mountain whose summit is 400 m above its base.

2. The man in problem 1 could easily climb the stairs in 8 sec, while 70 min should be allowed for the mountain climb. Find the rate at which the man does work (this is his power output) in each case. Express your answers in j/sec (or watts) and convert to horsepower. (1 H.P. is about 750 j/sec.)

3. How much work is needed to push an object of 10-kg mass at constant speed up a frictionless inclined plane that is 1 m long and 0.5 m high? Does it matter whether the applied force is up the plane or horizontal?

4. How much work is needed to push the 10-kg mass at constant speed up an inclined plane 1 m long and 0.5 m high if there is a frictional force of 10 n? Account for what becomes of the energy transferred by this work.

5. A horizontal force of 50 n is applied to an object whose mass is 5 kg. The force of friction is 10 n. What is the gain in K.E. if the object (a) moves horizontally 10 m, (b) moves horizontally for 10 sec? (c) Compute the work done against friction in (a).

6. Assume that the brakes of a car exert a constant retarding force. (a) Find the ratio of the distance needed to stop a car going 75 mi/hr to the distance needed to stop the car when it is going 30 mi/hr. (b) Find the ratio of the corresponding times in (a). (c) For a given braking force, how does the distance depend on the weight of the car?

7. A 2-kg stone is dropped from a bridge 10 m above a river. Take its P.E. $= 0$ at the river's surface. Account for what becomes of the original P.E. when the stone is (a) 5 m above the river, (b) 1 m above the river. (c) If the stone comes to rest 1 m beneath the river's surface, how much internal thermal energy does the system (river plus stone) gain?

8. Suppose that it takes a force of magnitude $F = kx$ to stretch a spring by an amount x. If k is constant, what will be the elastic potential energy when the stretch is A?

9. Write an expression for the gravitational P.E. of a moon rocket of mass m when it is at the point where the attractions of the earth and moon balance. Call the mass of the earth M_e, that of the moon $M_e/81$, and the earth-moon distance D. Take $V = 0$ far from any object.

10. A gun of mass M fires a bullet of mass m; Q units of chemical energy are transformed into K.E. What fraction of Q does the bullet receive? [*Hint:* Remember the conservation of momentum theorem!]

11. An elastic collision is one in which no K.E. is lost. When freight cars couple together, is the collision elastic? Prove your answer.

12. If a ball of 0.5-kg mass is moving at 4 m/sec and collides head-on with a 1-kg ball at rest, what will the final velocities be if the collision is elastic?

13. Suppose that a system could be taken from state A to state B by two processes such that for the first $Q_1 = 40$ j, $W_1 = 35$ j, while for the second $Q_2 = 40$ j, $W_2 = 20$ j. Show if the system is taken in a *cycle* from A to B by process 1 and from B to A by the reverse process 2, work will be done for nothing, or perpetual motion will result.

14. Devices that change energy from one form to another are called *transducers*. Name a common transducer that will change (a) sound energy into electrical energy, (b) electrical energy into sound, (c) light energy into electrical energy, (d) chemical energy into electrical energy, (e) electrical energy into mechanical energy, (f) internal thermal energy into mechanical energy?

EXPERIMENT 12

INCLINED PLANE
(The Conservation of Energy)

Object: To verify the principle of conservation of energy for a body being pulled up an inclined plane.

Problem: Consider a block of mass m on an inclined plane; a string attached to the block runs over a pulley at the top of the plane and supports a hanging weight. If the plane were perfectly smooth or frictionless, the block would be in equilibrium if the string exerted a pull up the plane equal and opposite to the force exerted down the plane by the weight of the block. Call this force F_0.

Next consider the actual, somewhat rough plane. To pull the block at constant velocity up the plane will require a force.

$$F_u = F_0 + f, \tag{1}$$

where f is the frictional force. To let the block slide down the plane at constant velocity will require a force up the plane equal to

$$F_d = F_0 - f, \tag{2}$$

since f always acts opposite to the motion and so acts up the plane when the block slides down it. Then,

$$F_u - F_d = 2f, \tag{3}$$

so that by measuring F_u and F_d one may compute f.

Now suppose that the force F_u is used to pull the block the whole length L up the plane. The work done is,

$$W = F_u L. \tag{4}$$

Part of this is expended in increasing the potential energy of the block, while the rest is done against friction. The work done against friction is $W_f = fL$, and we assume that this work is completely converted into thermal energy. The potential energy of the block is increased by,

$$\text{P.E.} = mgh, \tag{5}$$

where h is the vertical rise or height. Thus if energy is conserved, we have

$$W = \text{P.E.} + W_f, \tag{6}$$

or

$$F_u L = mgh + fL. \tag{7}$$

Our problem is to test Eq. (7) experimentally.

Procedure:

Step 1. Determine F_u and F_d experimentally. Remember that the motion of the block must *not* be accelerated or there will also be a gain or loss of kinetic energy. *Express all forces in newtons.* You may now compute the force of friction from Eq. (3).

Step 2. Measure L and h: also weigh the block and so find its mass m. Now you may check Eq. (7). Find your actual error in joules and also your percent error.

Step 3. Try to justify your error in joules by considering the possible error in each term in Eq. (7). What quantities are mainly responsible for error: F_u, L, m, h, or F_d?

CHAPTER 10

The Degradation of Energy Principle

10–1 The statistical approach

The position, velocity, and acceleration of a rigid body, or of Newton's mass particle, are definite quantities that may in principle be observed and measured. It was for such objects that Newton's laws could be clearly formulated and tested.

There are, however, in nature many materials whose atoms or molecules are not rigidly connected. Since a small volume of even such a low-density substance as air contains billions of molecules, how can we possibly follow and describe the motion of each? Our problem is made simpler if we know either that the particles are elastically connected, or that they are flowing along together with a definite velocity at any point. When neither of these restrictions holds true, there is no course left except to adopt a *statistical* approach to the problem. The fundamental postulate of this chapter is essentially the assumption that one may apply statistics to such physical problems. This hypothesis may not seem so self-evident when we realize that it amounts to saying that God lets our physical world run according to the laws of chance. However, let us make the assumption and test some of its predictions.

10–2 The hypotheses of the kinetic theory of gases

In a gas the molecules are much farther apart than in solids and liquids; as a consequence, intermolecular forces should be much less important in gases. Let us then start with a statistical theory of gases. Such a theory must commence with a set of *restricted* hypotheses, or educated guesses, about the structure of a gas. These hypotheses are the following.

(1) Gas molecules are very small; their diameters are much less than their distances apart.

(2) Gas molecules are very numerous.

(3) Gas molecues are in continuous *random* motion.

(4) Gas molecules collide with one another and with the container walls, as would hard elastic spheres.

It is in hypothesis (3) that the statistical approach is assumed, and it is because of hypothesis (2) that this seems reasonable. Statistics apply best to groups containing large numbers of individuals. Measurements of atomic masses indicate the large number of atoms in, say, a gram of any substance.

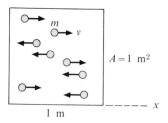

FIG. 10–1. Pressure is due to molecular impacts against the walls of the container.

10–3 The concept of pressure in kinetic theory

Pressure (p) has been defined as force per unit area and force as time rate of change of momentum. Let us combine these definitions with the hypotheses about the nature of a gas.

How, according to kinetic theory, do gas molecules exert pressure against the walls of their container? We answer this question by saying that the molecules must make frequent impacts with the walls and that at each impact the momentum of a molecule *toward* the wall changes to momentum *away from* the wall; this continuing change in momentum is equivalent to a force against the wall.

For simplicity let us consider a gas that is contained in a cubic box of unit volume. Let

$$m = \text{mass of each molecule,}$$

$$n = \text{number of molecules in unit volume,}$$

$$v = \text{speed of a molecule.}$$

First consider all molecules to have the same speed v. Assume a cubical container 1 m on an edge. Since the molecules are assumed to be in random motion, we may treat them as though one-third were moving perpendicular to each pair of opposite walls of the container. (If one wishes to consider oblique incidence, the calculus must be used, but the result is the same.) Consider the right-hand wall perpendicular to the x-axis (Fig. 10–1). On the average, $n/3$ molecules will be moving toward or away from this wall. A molecule that strikes the wall at the time $t = 0$ will have to go to the opposite wall and back, a distance of 2 m, before making its next impact on the same wall. The time to travel the 2 m at a speed v will be $2/v$ sec. The number of such impacts per second will be $v/2$ per molecule, or $(n/3)(v/2)$ altogether:

$$\text{Number of impacts/sec/m}^2 = nv/6.$$

At each impact the momentum of a molecule changes from mv to the right to mv to the left. Therefore the change in momentum per impact is

$$\Delta\mu = 2mv.$$

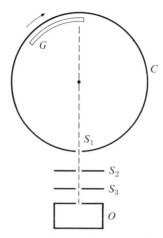

FIG. 10–2. Measurement of molecular speeds (by Zartman and Ko).

Since force equals change in momentum per second, the force on the wall will be

$$F = (2mv)(nv/6) = nmv^2/3.$$

This is the force on a wall of unit area, so this must be the pressure p. Hence

$$p = \tfrac{1}{3}nmv^2.$$

We may now remove the restriction that the molecules all have the same speed v. We see that if v varies from one molecule to the next, the average or mean pressure (which is all we measure anyway) will be proportional to the average value of v^2, or

$$p = \tfrac{1}{3}nm\overline{v^2}, \tag{10–1}$$

where $\overline{v^2}$ is called the *mean square speed* of the molecules.

Since nm is the mass per unit volume, or density ρ, of the gas, we may write Eq. (10–1) as

$$p = \tfrac{1}{3}\rho\overline{v^2}. \tag{10–2}$$

This last equation is subject to experimental test. For instance, Zartman and Ko used the apparatus diagrammed in Fig. 10–2 in which O is an oven where a metal is heated until vaporized, S_1, S_2, and S_3 are slits, and C is a rotating cylinder, all placed in an evacuated region. A beam of metal molecules from O is collimated by the slits. As the slit S_3 passes in front of the beam, a pulse of molecules is admitted into the cylinder, traveling across its diameter and striking the glass plate G, which is attached to the inner wall. The beam condenses on G, leaving a deposit. The time taken for the molecules to travel the known distance across C is found by measuring how much the deposit is displaced when C is first at rest and then rotating at a known rate. Although the deposit is not sharply defined, because the molecules have varying speeds, $\overline{v^2}$ may easily be determined. The results obtained confirm Eq. (10–2) and thus support our theory.

EXAMPLE 1. If five molecules have respective speeds of 100, 200, 200, 400, and 600 m/sec, find their mean square speed and show that it is not the same as the square of the mean speed.

Solution. The mean square speed is

$$\overline{v^2} = \frac{100^2 + 200^2 + 200^2 + 400^2 + 600^2}{5} = 122{,}000 \left(\frac{m}{sec}\right)^2.$$

The mean speed $\overline{v}$ is

$$\overline{v} = \frac{100 + 200 + 200 + 400 + 600}{5} = 300 \frac{m}{sec},$$

so that the square of the mean speed is

$$(\overline{v})^2 = 90{,}000 \left(\frac{m}{sec}\right)^2,$$

which is less than $\overline{v^2}$.

EXAMPLE 2. Calculate the mean square speed of an air molecule at standard temperature and pressure, given that the density of air is 1.29 kg/m³ under these conditions.

Solution. Standard temperature means 273°K (or 0°C), the freezing point of water. Standard pressure means average sea level pressure, which is about 10^5 n/m² (or 14.7 lb-wt/in²). Substitution in Eq. (10–2) gives

$$10^5 \frac{n}{m^2} = \frac{1}{3} \times 1.29 \frac{kg}{m^3} \times \overline{v^2},$$

$$\overline{v^2} = 2.32 \times 10^5 \frac{n\text{-}m}{kg} = 2.32 \times 10^5 \frac{m^2}{sec^2}.$$

(Note that 1 n = 1 kg-m/sec²). The *root mean square* (rms) speed is defined as the square root of $\overline{v^2}$. In this example

$$\text{rms speed} = \sqrt{\overline{v^2}} = 480 \text{ m/sec.}$$

Some molecules will be going faster and some slower than this.

At 0°C the speed of sound in air is 331 m/sec, which is less than, but of the same order of magnitude as, the rms speed just calculated. Is there any connection between these two speeds? Could the thermal speed of air molecules limit the speed of sound in air?

10–4 The concept of temperature in kinetic theory

We have assumed gas molecules to be separated by many diameters. This suggests the further postulate that intermolecular forces are negligible. The only form of energy that such molecules can possess is kinetic. While complex molecules can rotate and vibrate and monatomic molecules cannot, all must possess K.E. of translation as they move about in three-dimensional space. This K.E. will be, on the average,

$$\text{Average K.E. of translation per molecule} = \tfrac{1}{2}m\overline{v^2}. \qquad (10\text{–}3)$$

It was assumed in the last chapter that the internal energy of a substance in a given state varies directly as its temperature. This assumption is supported by the fact that when $Q_1 - W_1 = Q_2 - W_2$, or the change in internal energy is constant, the resulting change in temperature is the same. Let us now go a step further and postulate that the internal energy of an "ideal gas," such as we are considering, is all kinetic and that *the translational K.E. is proportional to the Kelvin absolute temperature T*, defined in Chapter 3, or

$$\tfrac{1}{2}m\overline{v^2} \propto T. \tag{10-4}$$

We shall take the constant of proportionality to be $\tfrac{3}{2}k$, thus defining k; k is a universal constant called *Boltzmann's constant*. Then for gas molecules

$$\tfrac{1}{2}m\overline{v^2} = \tfrac{3}{2}kT, \tag{10-5}$$

where k is a universal constant. The factor $\tfrac{3}{2}$ is introduced so that our subsequent equations will have no numerical factor. This, of course, is hindsight but perfectly logical. If one prefers, one may replace our $\tfrac{3}{2}k$ with another constant K, but this K would not be the conventional Boltzmann's constant.

The kinetic theory concept of temperature is that absolute temperature is a measure of, and proportional to, the kinetic energy of gas molecules at that temperature.

We must now test this assumption. To do this let us eliminate $m\overline{v^2}$ between Eqs. (10–1) and (10–5); the result is

$$\frac{p}{n} = kT. \tag{10-6}$$

A mole was defined as the mass of a substance in kilograms equal to its molecular weight and Avogadro's number N_0 was defined as the number of molecules in a kg-mole. Let V be the volume per kg-mole of a gas at a given T and p. Then

$$n = N_0/V.$$

If we substitute this in Eq. (10–6), we get

$$pV = N_0kT. \tag{10-7}$$

Let us define $R = N_0k$. Then we have

$$pV = RT. \tag{10-8}$$

The remarkable thing about Eq. (10–8) is that it is identical with an empirical equation based on extensive measurements of the behavior of gases at low densities. Equation (10–8) is called the *equation of state* of an ideal gas, or the *gas-law equation*, and our R is termed the *gas constant per kg-mole*. Equation (10–8) formed the basis of our definition of absolute temperature in Chapter 3.

EXAMPLE 1. Compare the rms speed v_0 of an oxygen (molecular weight = 32) molecule at 300°K (27°C) with (a) the rms speed v_1 of a hydrogen (mol. wt. = 2) molecule at 300°K, and (b) the rms speed v_2 of an oxygen molecule at 1200°K (927°C).

Solution. (a) At the same temperature $\overline{mv^2}$ is the same for all molecules [see Eq. (10–5)]. Therefore since m is proportional to the molecular weight,

$$32v_0^2 = 2v_1^2, \qquad v_0/v_1 = \tfrac{1}{4}.$$

On the average the hydrogen molecules move four times as fast as do the oxygen ones. (The speed of sound is four times greater in hydrogen, too.)

(b) For the same gas at two different temperatures m is constant and $\overline{v^2} \propto T$. Hence,

$$v_0^2/v_2^2 = \tfrac{300}{1200}, \qquad v_0/v_2 = \tfrac{1}{2}.$$

To double the rms speed one must quadruple the absolute temperature. (The speed of sound also increases with the square root of the absolute temperature.)

EXAMPLE 2. Compute R and k, given that $V = 22.4 \text{ m}^3/\text{kg-mole}$ at standard temperature (273°K) and pressure ($1.01 \times 10^5 \text{ n/m}^2$).

Solution. From Eq. (10–7)

$$R = \frac{pV}{T} = \frac{(1.01 \times 10^5 \text{ n/m}^2) \times (22.4 \text{ m}^3/\text{kg-mole})}{273°K}$$

$$= 8310 \text{ n-m/kg-mole-°K} = 8310 \text{ j/kg-mole-°K}.$$

Thence we have

$$k = \frac{R}{N_0} = \frac{8310 \text{ n-m/kg-mole-°K}}{6.03 \times 10^{26} \text{ molecules/kg-mole}}$$

$$= 1.38 \times 10^{-23} \text{ j/molecule-°K}.$$

EXAMPLE 3. Find the energy that must be transferred to a kg-mole of helium (4 kg) in order to raise its temperature 1°K.

Solution. Helium molecules are monatomic so that the internal energy of helium gas is entirely K.E. of translation. There are N_0 molecules/kg-mole. Hence

$$U = \tfrac{1}{2}\overline{mv^2}N_0 = \tfrac{3}{2}kTN_0 = \tfrac{3}{2}RT.$$

To raise T by 1° we must increase U by $\tfrac{3}{2}R$ j/mole, so that

$$\Delta U = 1.5 \times 8310 \text{ j/kg-mole} = 1.25 \times 10^4 \text{ j/kg-mole}.$$

This is the amount of energy that must be transferred to raise the temperature of 4 kg of helium by 1°.

10–5 Heat engines

A heat engine is a device in which fuel energy is transferred as heat to a system (usually a gas), and the system is thereby made to do mechanical work. An engine

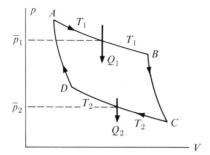

FIG. 10–3.   The Carnot cycle.

operates in a *cycle*, which means that after a series of operations it returns to its starting state and then repeats the same operations over and over again.

Let Q_1 represent the energy taken from the fuel per cycle and given to the engine's system as heat. Let W be the work done per cycle. We shall see that W must be less than Q_1. The ratio W/Q_1 is called the *efficiency* of the cycle.

In Fig. 10–3 a cycle is represented by plotting the successive values of the pressure and volume of the gas contained in the cylinder of the engine. The French engineer Carnot (1796–1832) proved that, for an engine working between a highest temperature T_1 and a lowest temperature T_2, the greatest efficiency will be obtained if all of the heat Q_1 is taken in at the highest temperature and any heat that must be given up is emitted by the engine at its lowest temperature. That some heat must be emitted in the exhaust (e.g., that of a car), or given to a condenser, is a well-known fact. Let Fig. 10–3 represent a *Carnot cycle* in which (1) the heat Q_1 is taken in as the gas expands along AB at the constant temperature T_1; (2) the gas expands along BC without gaining heat and so cools down to the temperature T_2; (3) the gas is compressed along CD at the temperature T_2, and since the gas does not warm up it must give up an amount of heat Q_2; (4) the gas, now insulated, is compressed and warms up as it returns along DA to its initial state. Here Q_2 is taken as positive even though it represents heat given up.

Along AB the expanding gas does work as it pushes the cylinder piston out; since the temperature does not change, we know that $\Delta U = 0$, and so Q_1 must equal the work done. This work is equal to the product of the average pressure $\bar{p}_1$ and the increase in volume (see Example of Section 3–3). Similarly, along CD, Q_2 must equal in magnitude the work done on the gas, work that equals the average pressure $\bar{p}_2$ times the change in volume. While the two volume changes are nearly the same, $\bar{p}_2$ is definitely less than $\bar{p}_1$, and hence Q_2 is smaller than Q_1.

From the conservation of energy as expressed in the first law of thermodynamics, we have

$$W = Q_1 - Q_2, \tag{10–9}$$

since for a complete cycle $\Delta U = 0$ and $Q_1 - Q_2$ is the net heat taken in.

From the gas-law equation, $pV = RT$, one may, with the aid of calculus, compute the work done along AB and along CD, put these amounts of work equal to

Q_1 and Q_2, respectively, and find the ratio Q_1/Q_2. The result is

$$\frac{Q_1}{Q_2} = \frac{T_1}{T_2}. \tag{10-10}$$

Kelvin actually started with this equation as his definition of absolute temperature and then proceeded to derive the gas-law equation and show that a gas thermometer measures the Kelvin temperature. We have argued in reverse sequence; taking the gas-law definition of absolute temperature and the postulates of kinetic theory as our starting point, we finally arrived at Eq. (10–10).

With the aid of Eqs. (10–9) and (10–10) we find, for the efficiency of a Carnot cycle,

$$\text{Efficiency} = \frac{W}{Q_1} = \frac{Q_1 - Q_2}{Q_1} = \frac{T_1 - T_2}{T_1}. \tag{10-11}$$

This is the so-called thermodynamic efficiency in which W includes useful work plus work done against friction. The ratio of useful work to Q_1 would be less.

EXAMPLE. An engine operates between the temperatures $T_1 = 500°K$ (227°C) and $T_2 = 300°K$ (27°C). (a) Find its efficiency if it operates in a Carnot cycle. (b) Find the efficiency if the heat given up at 300°K is the same, but the heat taken in at 500°K is half as much as in (a) and the rest of the heat that is taken in is received at 400°K (see Fig. 10–4). (c) Find the efficiency if the heat taken in is the same as in (a) but only half as much heat is exhausted at 300°K and the rest is emitted at 400°K (Fig. 10–5).

Solution. (a) For the Carnot cycle we have

$$\text{Efficiency} = \frac{T_1 - T_2}{T_1} = \frac{200°}{500°} = 0.40, \text{ or } 40\%.$$

Suppose that $Q_1 = 500$ j, then Q_2 would have to be equal to 300 j and $W = 200$ j. (b) If $Q_2 = 300$ j, then the heat taken in at 500°K would in this case be $\frac{1}{2}(500) = 250$ j. The heat received at 400°K would be $\frac{1}{2}(400) = 200$ j. Therefore, $Q_1 = 250 + 200 = $

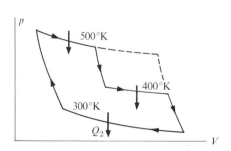

FIG. 10–4. A cycle in which not all of the heat taken in is received at the highest temperature.

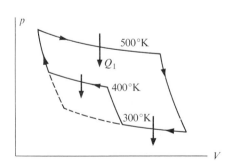

FIG. 10–5. A cycle in which the heat exhausted is not all released at the lowest temperature.

450 j, and $W = Q_1 - Q_2 = 150$ j. Thus the

$$\text{Efficiency} = \tfrac{150}{450} = 0.33, \text{ or } 33.3\%.$$

(c) If we take $Q_1 = 500$ j, then $Q_2 = \tfrac{1}{2}(300) + \tfrac{1}{2}(400) = 350$ j and $W = Q_1 - Q_2 = 150$ j. Hence the

$$\text{Efficiency} = \tfrac{150}{500} = 0.30, \text{ or } 30\%.$$

These results show the greater efficiency of the Carnot cycle. Unfortunately the Carnot cycle is not one that can be easily duplicated in practice, and so actual engines do not attain the efficiency given by Eq. (10–11) but fall short of this mark, just as do those illustrated in (b) and (c) above.

10–6 The second law of thermodynamics. Fundamental Law V

We have seen that a machine can be built to do work by taking in heat at a higher temperature and giving up a lesser amount of heat at a lower temperature. If another kind of machine could be built that also did work, but took in heat from a *colder* body and gave up what was not spent as work to a *hotter* body, then the second machine could be used to replenish the heat reservoir of the first and the first machine could consequently be run indefinitely at no expense. (The heat supplied to the second machine could be taken from the ocean.) This two-machine combination has been termed a *perpetual motion machine of the second kind* since, unlike the kind mentioned in Section 9–10, its operation does not involve a violation of the conservation of energy principle. Since no one has ever succeeded in building such a device, it seems reasonable to postulate the following two statements:

A. *A perpetual motion machine of the second kind is impossible.*

B. *It is impossible to construct a device which, operating in a cycle, has the sole result of transferring heat from a cooler to a hotter body.*

Statement B was first made by Clausius. Both statements are forms of what is termed the *second law of thermodynamics*, our *Fundamental Law V*.

When a gas engine is run backwards it constitutes a refrigerator. A Carnot engine running in reverse (Fig. 10–6) would take in the heat Q_2 at the lower temperature T_2 and give up still more heat Q_1 at the higher temperature T_1; it thus transfers heat from a cooler to a hotter body. Why does a refrigerator not violate statement B above? The answer is that in a refrigerating cycle the work $W = Q_1 - Q_2$ is not done *by* the engine, but must be done *on* its gas from outside. It takes electrical energy to run your refrigerator and this affects the electric power company serving you and costs you money. Hence the transfer of heat from a cold box to a warm kitchen is not the *sole* result of the device. A refrigerator is not *self-operating*.

Further consideration of the theory of heat engines shows that while the heat Q_1 that is taken in represents the energy supplied by the fuel used, not all of this

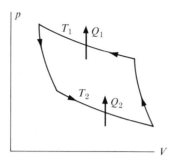

Fig. 10-6.   A Carnot refrigerator cycle.

heat can be turned into work. The heat Q_2 rejected at the cooler temperature is usually emitted in the exhaust and thrown to the winds, never to be used again, and the work done is only $Q_1 - Q_2$. From Eq. (10–10) we see that Q_2 can be made equal to zero only by making T_2 zero, which, of course, is a practical impossibility. This leads us to a third statement of the second law of thermodynamics, known as the Kelvin-Planck law.

C. *It is impossible to construct a device which, operating in a cycle, has the sole effect of extracting heat from a reservoir and performing an equivalent amount of work.*

10-7 The unavailability of energy; entropy

We have seen that stored energy can be put to work by means of a device such as a heat engine, but that some (Q_2) of the original energy is not put to work and becomes unavailable, though not destroyed. The work done may be used to lift weights, stretch springs, etc., and thus partly replenish our supply of stored energy. Work done against friction, however, is usually converted into internal thermal energy and dissipated. Since we cannot make $Q_2 = 0$ or avoid friction, it is inevitable that our supply of available energy must be continually decreasing. Kelvin first recognized this *principle of the degradation of energy*. It leads us to a fourth statement of the second law of thermodynamics.

D. *As a result of natural processes, the energy in our world available for work is continually decreasing.*

A scientist likes to be able to measure things. Hence thought has been given to devising a way of measuring how the state of a system, as determined by its temperature, pressure, and volume, is related to the unavailability of its energy for useful purposes. The concept involved, called *entropy*, is a difficult one to define in simple terms, but its definition is stated in such a manner that whenever energy is dissipated the entropy of our world increases. Thus statement D of the second law of thermodynamics plus the definition of entropy leads us to the following fifth form of the law.

E. *As a result of natural processes, the entropy of our world is continually increasing.*

10–8 The direction of natural processes

There is a natural direction in which thermal processes proceed. Heat will flow spontaneously from a warmer to a cooler body if some means, namely, conduction, convection, or radiation, are provided, but the reverse process does not occur. Potential and kinetic energy, concentrated in one body, may, through the action of frictional forces, be entirely dissipated as the random kinetic energy of the molecules of the bodies in contact; but internal thermal energy can never be completely converted into available energy by a self-acting machine. The energy of an electric current may be entirely converted into thermal energy; by means of a thermocouple the process may be partly, but not completely, reversed because a thermocouple takes in heat at its warm junction, converts *some* of the heat into electric energy, and gives up the remainder at its cold junction. Finally, air will rush out of an inflated tire, but a tire will never inflate itself.

It is evident that we need a law or principle to summarize all of these facts, and that is just what the second law of thermodynamics does.

In a sense our world is "running down." We are using up available chemical energy in our fossil fuels and available nuclear energy in our uranium and hydrogen. We shall never get this available energy back. On the other hand, the sun continually furnishes us with more available energy in the form of direct sunlight, the energy of wind and rain, and the chemical energy in growing plants. This is possible because the sun's temperature is much higher than that of the earth. Eventually the sun will burn itself out and cool down. Even if the sun gave up all its available energy and thereby warmed our world throughout to a comfortable 70° Fahrenheit, life could not exist, since there would be no *difference* in temperature anywhere and hence no possibility of doing useful work.

The British astronomer Hoyle and others have suggested that there may be distant regions of the universe in which the second law of thermodynamics does not hold true; in such regions available energy could be built up, as may once have been the case for our world.

The way in which our earth, solar system, and galaxy of stars (the Milky Way) were "born" and evolved into their present state is the subject of much speculation. Here theoretical physicists have found a fine opportunity to use their wits. A popular theory postulates that the universe is and has been expanding, that nearly ten billion years ago all matter and energy were concentrated in a very small region at a tremendously high temperature; this theory has passed a number of experimental tests, but perhaps not enough to give it the stature of the kinetic theory, or of Newton's planetary theory.

10–9 The statistical interpretation of the degradation of energy

As suggested at the beginning of this chapter, its fundamental postulate, the second law of thermodynamics, or the degradation of energy principle, may be given a statistical interpretation. This means that if this principle holds true (and it seems to), then the laws of statistics apply to the physical world.

Consider, as an example of natural processes involving the degradation of energy, the situation in which a warm and a cold body come in contact. The molecules of the warm body are, on the average, moving faster than those of the cold body. Upon contact the faster molecules and slower molecules make impacts on one another and, as the theory of elastic collisions will show, on the average the fast molecules slow down and the slow ones speed up until the rms speeds of the molecules in each body are the same. Thus the two bodies come to a common final temperature, which will represent a state of equilibrium.

As another example, take the case of air rushing out of a tire. Since the pressure and density outside the opened valve are less than inside, fewer molecules will happen to be heading into the tire than are heading out. When equilibrium is reached, the numbers heading in and out will be the same because the pressure and density of the air on each side of the open valve will be the same.

In the above examples it is easy to explain statistically why the processes tend to proceed in only one direction. In a closed room the molecules of air do have different speeds, but the molecules moving faster than average are not likely to be found in one part of the room and the slower molecules in another part. Why? Because such a distribution is *improbable*, which means that according to the laws of chance, there are far fewer random distributions that are equivalent to a sorting out of fast and slow molecules than there are random distributions that are equivalent to a nearly complete mixing of fast and slow molecules. For the same reason the density of molecules in a room is not likely to fluctuate much from the mean density, so that the local pressure (if we could measure it) is not likely to vary much from the observed overall mean pressure. Thus a tire is unlikely to inflate itself.

When dealing with a large number of individual objects, arrangements that involve little order can be obtained in many more ways than ordered arrangements. Hence if molecular motions are subject to the laws of chance, then disordered arrangements are much more likely to occur than ones in which the fast molecules are sorted out from the slow ones, etc. This leads to the following statement of the second law of thermodynamics.

F. *As a result of natural processes, the order in our physical world is continually decreasing.*

Can an intelligent being violate the second law of thermodynamics? Most assuredly! We do so when we arrange cards in a deck, put bricks together to form houses, set up corporations, etc. The British physicist Maxwell imagined a "demon" who, placed at the open valve of a tire, would shut the valve when a molecule approached him from within the tire, but would open the valve to molecules entering from outside and thereby inflate the tire without pumping. The second law rules out the existence of such demons in the physical world. A Supreme Being could certainly violate the second law, but would He have to, or want to, in order to run the world wisely? He would not, it may be contended, because when a sufficiently large number of individual particles and events are involved, then the laws of chance become most reliable laws. When fluctuations about the most probable situation are percentagewise negligible, one may take the occurrence of this most probable situation as a practical certainty. This being the case for thermal processes in our physical world, what difference does it make whether they are governed by fixed laws or by the laws of chance? In many instances reliance on the laws of chance proves to be the most practical procedure. As Alexander Pope put it:

> "Remember, man, the Universal Cause
> Acts not by partial, but by gen'ral laws;
> And makes what happiness we justly call,
> Subsist, not in the good of one, but all."

> From *An Essay On Man*

ILLUSTRATION 1. A government passes a law that applies to all of its citizens. The law may be unfair to a few individuals, but prove to be beneficial to the vast majority. Substitution of a set of laws, one for each individual citizen, would impose a costly burden of administration and be quite impractical.

ILLUSTRATION 2. In a new deck of playing cards the cards are all sorted by suit and number. In the course of shuffling, the original order is *very* unlikely to return again. However, any arrangement obtained is no more likely than the original one! What, then, does shuffling accomplish?

If a shuffled deck is dealt to four hands in a game of bridge, there are certain *classes* of hands that can occur in many more ways than others. Thus you are much more likely to obtain a hand headed by a 5-card suit than one headed by a 9-card suit. There are enough cards in a bridge deck so that the laws of statistics apply well if the shuffling is thorough; the result is a definite type of game, one that has proven immensely popular for many years.

PROBLEMS

1. Suppose that a machine gun fires forty 10-gm bullets per second at a target whose area is 0.5 m^2 and that the initial speed of a bullet is 500 m/sec. (a) Express all quantities in mks units and find the pressure exerted on the target if the bullets all become imbedded in the target. (b) Find the pressure if each bullet rebounds from the target with half of its initial speed.

2. Find the mean and root mean square speeds of four molecules whose individual speeds are 100, 300, 700, and 900 m/sec, respectively.

3. Prove that the rms speed of a gas molecule is independent of the pressure if the temperature is kept constant. Does the speed of sound in air depend on the barometric pressure?

4. At a depth of 34 ft the pressure in a lake is one atmosphere greater than at the surface. Suppose that an air bubble whose initial volume is 0.28 cm^3 rises from a depth of 17 ft to the surface, its temperature increasing from 7°C to 17°C. Find the volume of the bubble just beneath the surface.

5. Find the number of molecules in 1 cm^3 of gas at (a) standard temperature and pressure, (b) 0°C and a pressure of 10^{-15} atmospheres (the pressure of the best vacuum obtained by man).

6. Find the mean K.E. of translation of a gas molecule at 27°C in (a) joules, (b) electron-volts. (1 electron-volt = 1.6×10^{-19} joule.)

7. Explain why you would not invest in the development of an engine for which the inventor claimed either of the following sets of data: (a) $T_1 = 400°K$, $T_2 = 300°K$, $Q_1 = 20,000$ j, $Q_2 = 15,000$ j, $W = 10,000$ j, or (b) $T_1 = 400°K$, $T_2 = 300°K$, $Q_1 = 20,000$ j, $Q_2 = 10,000$ j, $W = 10,000$ j.

8. A Carnot engine operates between 1500°K and 300°K and performs 1000 j of work per cycle. How much heat must it take in and how much must it give up per cycle?

9. In a nuclear explosion temperatures of millions of degrees are attained. Why is it then not possible to reach efficiencies of nearly 100% in a nuclear power plant?

10. A Carnot refrigerator is operated between 280°K and 300°K and requires 200 j of work per cycle. Find the heat absorbed at 280°K and the heat ejected at 300°K.

11. A *heat pump* is a device designed on the principle of a refrigerator cycle. Suppose that in problem 10, 300°K is the temperature within a house and 280°K that outside. (a) What fraction of the energy given to the house would one have to pay for? (b) If the outdoor temperature dropped to 260°K and the house needed to receive twice as much heat per hour (because of greater heat loss through its walls), how many times greater would the fuel bill per hour be than when the outdoor temperature was 280°K?

12. A swinging pendulum gradually comes to rest. Is there a resulting entropy gain by the world? Explain.

13. (a) A coin is tossed four times; find the ratio of the chance of getting 50% "heads" to that of getting 75% "heads." (b) Repeat for the case where the coin is tossed eight times. (c) What conclusion can you draw from your calculations?

EXPERIMENT 13

THE GAS THERMOMETER
(Absolute Zero)

Object: To calibrate a gas thermometer and determine absolute zero.

Problem: The ideal temperature scale should not depend on the thermal properties of any particular substance. Such a temperature scale is called "absolute." The change in pressure of a fixed volume of a dry gas, such as air, furnishes an easy practical means of measuring temperature on a scale that closely approximates the ideal absolute scale.

In defining a temperature scale one must make two further arbitrary choices: (1) fix the size of the interval which is to be called one degree, and (2) choose the zero point of the scale. For the Fahrenheit scale we choose (1) one degree equals 1/180 of the interval between the freezing and boiling points of water, (2) zero is 32 degrees below the freezing point of water. For the Centigrade or Celsius scale we choose (1) one degree equals 1/100 of the interval between freezing and boiling, (2) zero is the freezing point of water. For the Kelvin scale we choose (1) one degree equals 1/100 the interval between freezing and boiling, (2) zero is the temperature at which molecules would cease to move and so exert no pressure. Since the last represents a sort of ultimate in coldness, it is called *absolute zero*.

We shall calibrate a constant volume gas thermometer and use it to measure room temperature and to compute absolute zero in degrees C and F.

Procedure:

Step 1. Your gas thermometer bulb has stood in the room since the previous day. The manometer attached will thus be ready to give readings corresponding to room temperature, so note both mercury levels before you touch the bulb in any way.

Step 2. Surround the bulb with finely crushed ice and flood with ice water. When the mercury levels are stationary, bring the mercury in the closed tube to where it was in Step 1 and read the level in the open tube.

Step 3. Surround the bulb with hot water and heat to boiling. With the mercury in the closed tube at the same level as before, read the level in the open tube.

Step 4. Read the barometer. Compute in centimeters of mercury the absolute pressure of the gas in each previous step. Consider carefully in each instance whether to add or subtract the manometer difference to the barometer reading.

Step 5. Construct a graph of pressure vertically against temperature horizontally. Start with the boiling point pressure at the extreme right, then plot the ice point pressure ten lines to the left. Connect these two points with a straight line and extend the line to where it crosses the *p* equals zero axis.

Step 6. Label the ice point and steam point according to the definitions of both the Fahrenheit and Centigrade scales and then compute absolute zero on each of these scales. Now compute the Kelvin temperatures for melting ice and boiling water.

Step 7. Use your graph and the computed pressure at room temperature to find the room temperature in degrees F and C.

CHAPTER 11

Huygens' Principle of Wave Propagation

11–1 Definition of a wave

A change in the state or condition of a medium may be called a *disturbance* of the medium. Then we may say that *a wave is a disturbance that is propagated through space.* Since there are many ways of disturbing a medium, there are many kinds of waves, and a description of the physical world would not be complete without summarizing the properties of waves in general. Waves are important in the theories of sound, light, electricity, and magnetism, and even atomic physics.

After classifying waves to some extent, we shall turn to the study of wave propagation, about which many experimental facts are known. Our problem will be to show how all of these facts may be summarized as theorems derived from a single basic principle or postulate.

The disturbance in a wave may be an actual displacement of a material medium, as in the case of water waves, sound waves, and waves in vibrating strings, or the disturbance may be simply a change in a field (electric, magnetic, or possibly gravitational) in empty space, as in the case of light and radio waves. However, in all waves, something is passed on; there is a connection between the disturbance at one point in space and the disturbance at a neighboring point. This connection may be due to intermolecular forces and so be related to the elastic properties of a material medium or, as in the case of waves in empty space, it may be a property of the field that is being propagated. For wave propagation a changing displacement or varying field at a point *A* must result in a similar sort of disturbance at the neighboring point *B*.

Waves are never static. A diagram of a wave shows only what the disturbance is at various points in space at one given instant of time. A picture of a wave is like one frame in a moving-picture reel; the next frame will show a little different picture, and so on. Figure 11–1 is such a picture; it shows a pulse of transverse displacement in a rope as viewed at a particular instant. This is called a *waveform* diagram; in it the disturbance at a given instant is plotted as a function of position in space.

FIG. 11–1.   Waveform diagram of a transverse pulse in a rope.

178

FIG. 11–2. Vibration diagram showing disturbance at point P in Fig. 11–1. (The pulse shown in Fig. 11–1 must be approaching P. Why?)

To describe a wave more completely one may show waveform diagrams for different times, i.e., show a moving picture of the wave, or one may draw a *vibration diagram* showing the disturbance at a given position plotted as a function of time. Figure 11–2 shows the displacement, as a function of time, of the point P in the rope of Fig. 11–1; the displacement is plotted for a time interval covering the passage of the pulse past P.

It is often possible to describe a wave most concisely in terms of mathematics, particularly if the wave is periodic, or repeats itself. Such a description is given by a *wave function*, which expresses the functional relationship between the disturbance, which we shall call Ψ, the position in space (such as the distance x measured along a rope), and the time t. For a wave moving in the positive x-direction with the speed v, the wave function must be some function of $x - vt$, that is,

$$\Psi = f(x - vt), \tag{11–1}$$

where $f(x - vt)$ means "function of $(x - vt)$," *not* f times $(x - vt)$. To see that this is so, note that at a later time $t + \Delta t$ the disturbance Ψ will have the same value at the position $x + \Delta x$ as it had at x at the time t if

$$x + \Delta x - v(t + \Delta t) = x - vt,$$

or $\Delta x = v\,\Delta t$. This means that the disturbance has traveled the distance $v\,\Delta t$ in the time Δt, or that its speed of propagation in the x-direction is v. Similarly, $\Psi = f(x + vt)$ represents a wave moving in the negative x-direction with a speed v.

The description of waves that move in three-dimensional space is more complicated and will be discussed later.

11–2 Types of waves

There are many ways of classifying waves; the following are offered in order to point out in what ways waves may differ.

(a) *Mechanical versus field waves. Mechanical waves* include all kinds in which material particles are displaced. Sound waves, earthquake waves, water waves, and waves in strings all involve the motion of the particles of the medium through which they pass.

Field waves include those in which electric and magnetic fields are propagated through space. Our most familiar examples are the various kinds of electromagnetic waves (radio, infrared, visible light, ultraviolet, x-rays, and gamma rays). Such waves may pass through material media, but they do not depend on the presence of matter for their propagation and are transmitted best through a vacuum. Such waves all have the same speed $c = 3 \times 10^8$ m/sec (or 186,000 mi/sec) in vacuo.

(b) *Transverse versus longitudinal waves.* A *transverse* wave is one in which the disturbance is directed at right angles to the direction in which the wave is being propagated. A taut rope may be shaken in any plane that passes through the rope. In a vertical rope the disturbance may be east and west, north and south, or a combination of these. If the vibration occurs only in one plane, as it would have to if a rope were passed through a picket fence and shaken, the wave is said to be *polarized* in that plane. Waves in strings and ripple waves on the surface of a liquid are familiar examples of transverse waves. The polarization of light indicates that light is propagated as a transverse wave.

In a *longitudinal wave* the disturbance occurs parallel to the direction in which the wave is proceeding. Such waves cannot be polarized. Sound waves are our most familiar example of longitudinal waves.

There are also types of waves in which the disturbance is neither transverse nor longitudinal. In deep-sea water waves the particles move approximately in circles; such motion may be viewed as a combination of longitudinal and transverse motion.

(c) *Pulses versus sustained waves.* Figure 11–1 shows a *pulse*, or disturbance of short duration. Pulses include shock waves, such as those set up in air by jet aircraft flying at speeds greater than that of sound. Shock waves are also produced in air by explosions, in water by speedboats, in rocks by earthquakes and blasting. A line of falling dominoes carries another kind of pulse. In the nonphysical world, the spread of information is somewhat analogous to a pulse. The disturbance due to a pulse does not last long at any one spot, but the pulse travels on, carrying energy with it.

Sustained waves are emitted by vibrating bodies. When such waves pass through space or some material medium, the disturbance cannot continue in one direction only but must alternate. The reversal in the direction of the disturbance is a built-in property of electromagnetic waves, while in the case of elastic waves (including sound) reversal occurs because of the tendency of a deformed elastic body to spring back to its original state. Gravity supplies the restoring force for deep-sea water waves.

(d) *Nonperiodic versus periodic waves.* In a *nonperiodic wave* the disturbance at a given point does not repeat itself in a regular manner and the waveform diagram does not show any repetitive pattern. Examples of such waves are noise and radio static.

In a *periodic wave* the disturbance is repeated at a regular interval called the *period T*. The number of vibrations passing a given point in unit time is called the *frequency f*. The distance at any instant between a point on the wave and the next successive point at which the whole wave pattern starts to be repeated is termed the *wavelength* λ (see Fig. 11–3). During the time T a wave crest moves forward to the position occupied by the preceding crest at the start of this time interval. The distance from crest to crest is the wavelength λ. Therefore the speed v with

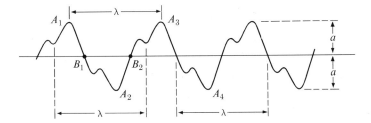

FIG. 11–3. Periodic wave. Definition of wavelength.

which a periodic wave is propagated forward is

$$v = \frac{s}{t} = \frac{\lambda}{T}.$$

(11–2)

Since $1/T = f$, we have

$$v = \lambda f.$$

(11–3)

This relationship, which follows solely from definitions, holds for all kinds of periodic waves. Since for many types of waves the speed v is well known, Eq. (11–2) makes it possible to compute λ when f is known, of f when λ is known.

EXAMPLE 1. The speed of sound in air at 0°C is 331 m/sec. Find the wavelength of a periodic sound wave in air at 0°C if the frequency of the wave is 500 cycles* per second.

Solution. From Eq. (11–2) we have

$$\lambda = \frac{v}{f} = \frac{331 \text{ m/sec}}{500 \text{ cycles/sec}} = 0.662 \text{ m/cycle},$$

which is about 2 ft.

EXAMPLE 2. A radio station emits radio waves whose wavelength is 250 m/cycle. What is the frequency?

Solution. As stated above, $v = 3 \times 10^8$ m/sec for all radio waves. Therefore

$$f = \frac{v}{\lambda} = \frac{3 \times 10^8 \text{ m/sec}}{250 \text{ m/cycle}} = 1.2 \times 10^6 \text{ cycles/sec}.$$

This frequency may be expressed as 1.2 megacycles/sec (1 megacycle/sec $= 10^6$ cycles/sec), or as 1200 kilocycles/sec, which is a frequency in the AM (amplitude modulated) broadcast range.

---

* The word "cycles" refers to what is being *counted*; it is not part of the mks system of units. One may also speak of "vibrations per second," or "waves per second," but the words "cycles," "vibrations," etc., may be omitted if it is understood what is being counted.

TABLE 11-1

THE ELECTROMAGNETIC SPECTRUM

Type of radiation	Source	Approximate frequency range, cycles/sec	Approximate wavelength range
Micro pulses	Celestial	0.01–1	3×10^{10} m–3×10^8 m
Radio			
Long waves		10^4–5×10^5	3×10^4 m–600 m
AM broadcast	Electric	5×10^5–1.6×10^6	600 m–188 m
FM broadcast	circuits	88×10^6–108×10^6	3.4 m–2.8 m
TV broadcast		55×10^6–900×10^6	5.5 m–0.33 m
Radar		10^9–10^{11}	30 cm–0.3 mm
Atomic			
Infrared	Excited	10^{11}–3.8×10^{14}	0.3 mm–8000 A*
Visible	molecules	3.8×10^{14}–7.5×10^{14}	8000 A–4000 A
Ultraviolet	or atoms	7.5×10^{14}–10^{17}	4000 A–30 A
x-rays		10^{17}–10^{21}	30 A–0.003 A
Nuclear	Radioactive		
Gamma rays	nuclei	To above 3×10^{22}	To below 10^{-4} A

* 1 A = 1 angstrom = 10^{-10} m.

For your information, the complete electromagnetic spectrum is outlined in Table 11-1. (Some of the ranges are being extended further.)

Two other important concepts related to *periodic* waves are amplitude and phase. By *amplitude* we mean the maximum magnitude of the disturbance produced by the wave. For the wave shown in Fig. 11-3 the disturbance is greatest at A_1, A_2, A_3, A_4, etc.; if the horizontal line represents the state of no disturbance, the amplitude of the wave is a, that is, the disturbance varies from a in the positive sense to a in the negative sense.

The term *phase* is used with the same connotation as when we speak of the phases of the moon, or of the phase our economy has reached in a business cycle. Points on a wave that are a wavelength apart (measured in the direction the wave is moving) are, from the definition of wavelength, points of equal disturbance, or points whose respective disturbances are "in phase." Points 2, 3, 4 ... wavelengths apart are also points of equal phase. The symmetric waves that have the shape represented by $\Psi = a \sin x$, as shown in Fig. 11-4, are ones of common occurrence; they are called *harmonic waves*. For such waves two points on the wave whose x-coordinates differ by half a wavelength, such as A_1 and A_2, B_1 and B_2, C_1 and C_2, are pairs of points for which the disturbances are half a cycle out of phase or, as we say, "completely out of phase." However, B_1 and C_1 represent

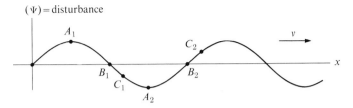

FIG. 11-4.   Periodic harmonic wave.

a pair of points whose disturbances are only a little out of phase, A_1 and B_1 points whose disturbances are a quarter of a cycle out of phase, and so on.

As time passes these relative phases do not change. Thus when the next crest reaches B_1 the next trough will reach B_2, and a crest and trough are completely out of phase.

In the case of waves in elastic media the force F required to produce the disturbance x is proportional to x, so that $F = kx$. The average force needed to increase x from 0 to a is $\frac{1}{2}ka$, so that for $s = a$ the work done and energy transferred are given by $Fs = \frac{1}{2}ka^2$. Thus the *square of the amplitude* of such waves *is a measure of the energy* being transferred through the medium by the wave. This relationship holds for most periodic waves.

11-3 Objective versus subjective approaches to sound and light

It is instructive when trying to understand the difference between the scientific and the nonscientific point of view, to compare the way in which a physicist describes a sound or a colored light with the description an artist would give of the same sound or light. The scientist is first of all objective, while the artist is subjective. Furthermore, the artist is concerned with human emotions, and these in turn are related to the physiological and psychological makeup of man. What we hear depends both on the sound striking our ears and on the structure of our ears; light will produce a different sensation when seen by a colorblind person than when seen by one with normal eyes.

In the case of a sound produced, say, by a musical instrument, the description given by the physicist would consist of stating the intensity and the harmonic analysis of the wave. By *intensity* is meant the energy per second reaching a unit area placed at right angles to the direction of propagation of the wave. We saw that for a sinusoidal wave the intensity is proportional to the square of the amplitude. *Harmonic analysis* means a description of the component frequencies present and of the amplitude of each. Thus in Fig. 11-5 the wave W is the result of the superposition of two harmonic waves, one with twice the wavelength, half the frequency, and nearly three times the amplitude of the other.

For a musician, the important ingredients of a musical sound are its loudness, its pitch, and its tonal quality, or timbre. *Loudness* is not the same as intensity because loudness refers to the relative response of the ear. If the intensity is increased from a value I to $10I$, then to $100I$, and finally to $1000I$, the ear interprets

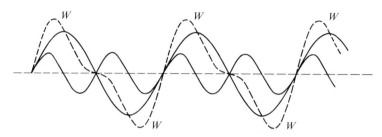

FIG. 11–5.   A wave W that is not sinusoidal may be represented as the sum of sinusoidal waves.

these three unequal increases in intensity as equal increases in loudness; in other words, the response of the human ear is logarithmic and the decibel scale of loudness is based on this fact: Each of the intensity increases mentioned above corresponds to an increase in loudness of 10 decibels.

Pitch is the frequency the ear identifies with a musical sound.   It is usually, though not always, the frequency of the lowest harmonic component.

Tonal quality depends on what harmonic components are present and the intensity of each.   However, doubling the intensity of all the components may change the tonal quality, because the ear's response may reach a saturation point when the intensity of one frequency is doubled but not when the intensity of another frequency is doubled.   It is, of course, in tonal quality that the sound of the note A from a violin differs from the sound of the note A from a piano.   The value of a fine violin rests on the timbre of the sounds it emits.

Light is described by the scientist in terms of intensity, wavelength, and (if more than one wavelength is present) spectral distribution.   We shall see presently how light waves of different wavelengths are separated out in different directions, or *dispersed*, by a prism or a ruled grating and the wavelengths present measured. In this way one may compare the output of an incandescent light bulb with that of a fluorescent lamp and show that the former emits a larger percentage of its energy in the wavelength range around 7000 A (red light) than does the latter.

A nonscientist does not ask what wavelengths are present in the light from some source, but he is interested in its brightness and color.   That *brightness* is not the same as intensity is obvious when one realizes that ultraviolet light, even when intense, is "dark light" to the eye.   The normal eye is sensitive to a very narrow band of the electromagnetic spectrum, a band extending from about 4000 A to 8000 A, for which the ratio of the respective frequencies is only 2 to 1; this corresponds to but one octave of the musical scale.

By *color* we mean that quality of visible phenomena which we associate with red, green, blue, etc.   Light of a single frequency will have a spectrum color, that is, a color found in the rainbow, or the spectrum of white light.   Average daylight, often referred to as "white light," contains all of the visible spectrum colors in definite proportions.   All possible colors may be made by mixing two or more colors in various proportions.   The eye, however, does not analyze color this way, but it has the remarkable ability of combining colors to form new sensations;

nevertheless, although one person can match two colors, it is doubtful if two people looking at the same color receive the same sensation. The ear, in contrast, is more analytical and can recognize two or more different frequencies at the same time, thus making possible the enjoyment of harmony and the complexities of contra-puntal music.

11–4 Wave propagation in three dimensions

Let us consider some of the properties of waves as they move through space, encounter obstacles, and enter different media.

Suppose that a wave travels out from a source and reaches all points on a certain surface at the same time t. Then this surface is one of constant phase for a given wavelength, and it is called a *wavefront*. Lines normal to wavefronts, or *rays*, represent the direction in which a wave is proceeding at any point.

Three-dimensional waves, regardless of type, all show the following properties: spreading out, reflection, refraction, diffraction, and interference. These will now be described.

In a homogeneous medium a curved wavefront spreads out as it advances, but retains the same shape.

When a wave encounters a new medium, *reflection* occurs to a greater or less extent depending on various circumstances. It is found experimentally that the angle i between the incident ray and the normal to the interface equals the angle i' between the reflected ray and the normal (see Fig. 11–6); also, the two rays and the normal lie in the same plane. These statements constitute the *law of reflection*.

When a wave encounters another transparent medium, then, in addition to the reflected wave, a wave enters the second medium, but in the new medium the waves proceed in a different direction (Fig. 11–7). This bending of the rays and waves upon entering a new medium is called *refraction*. Let r be the angle between the refracted ray and the normal to the interface. It is found experimentally that at a given interface an increase in the angle i results in an increase in the angle r; however, the ratio i/r is not constant, as one might at first suppose. Further investigation shows that the ratio of the *sines* of the two angles is constant, or sin i

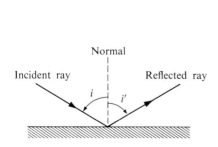

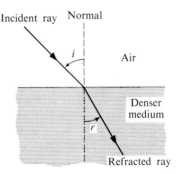

FIG. 11–6. Law of reflection. $\angle i = \angle i'$.   FIG. 11–7. Refraction.

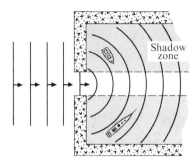

FIG. 11–8. Diffraction of water waves passing into a harbor.

∝ sin *r*. Let us define the *index of refraction n* of the second medium relative to the first as

$$n = \frac{\sin i}{\sin r}.$$ (11–4)

The statement that *n* is a constant for various angles of incidence constitutes *Snell's law of refraction*. This is one of the many restricted laws in physics; Snell's law is limited in its applicability and *n* is constant only for two given media. Values of *n* for various media relative to air may be found listed in tables.

When a wave encounters an obstacle, so that part of the wave surface is cut off, effects result that are referred to as *diffraction*. One such effect is the apparent bending of the waves into the shadow zone behind the obstacle. A familiar example is furnished by sound; one can hear a person talking in the next room, or behind a screen, because the sound waves bend as they pass through a doorway or past the edge of a screen. Similarly, ocean waves bend around a breakwater into a harbor and cause boats moored behind the breakwater to bob up and down (Fig. 11–8).

Finally, when waves from a source *S* (or from two synchronous sources) reach a point *P* via two different paths, *SAP* and *SBP* (Fig. 11–9), then the two sets of waves reinforce one another and produce a greater disturbance at *P* (than would either wave alone) if the two path lengths differ by a whole number of wavelengths, or

$$|\overline{SAP} - \overline{SBP}| = m\lambda, \qquad m = 0, 1, 2, 3 \ldots.$$ (11–5)

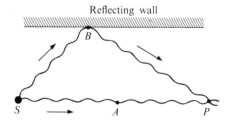

FIG. 11–9. Interference.

This is called *constructive interference*. On the other hand, *destructive interference*, or a lessening of intensity at *P*, results when the two paths differ in length by λ/2, 3λ/2, 5λ/2, etc.

11–5 Huygens' principle of wave propagation. Fundamental Law VI

The properties of waves discussed in the last section are independent bits of experimental knowledge. Nevertheless, scientists are always on the lookout for a unifying postulate, or principle, that will tie together many facts. (It is the aim of this book to set forth these fundamental postulates of physics in a clear and prominent fashion.) It should not seem unreasonable to look for a single principle that will explain all general wave propagation phenomena. Such a principle was first proposed by the Dutch physicist Huygens (1629–1695). His postulate may be stated as follows.

Every point on a wavefront may be regarded as a source of a secondary disturbance, which spreads out with the speed v of the wave at that point; after a time Δt these secondary wavelets will have radii v Δt and the envelope of these wavelets will be the new wavefront at the end of the time interval Δt.

This is essentially our *Fundamental Law VI.*

Since a wavefront is by definition a surface of constant phase, the phases of the secondary wavelets will all be the same. The envelope of these wavelets is the surface whose every point lies on one such wavelet, and hence it will also be a surface of constant phase, or a wavefront. As shown in Fig. 11–10, Huygens' principle immediately accounts for the spreading of a wave and the retention of its earlier shape in a homogeneous medium.

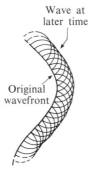

Wave at
later time

Original
wavefront

FIG. 11–10. A spreading wave retains its general shape, according to Huygens' principle.

Since Huygens' principle also made some erroneous predictions, it was subsequently modified and extended by Fresnel and others. Fresnel pointed out that when a set of waves of a single frequency falls on a slit, then every point on the slit may be regarded as a source sending out waves into the region beyond the slit; the disturbance at some point *P* behind the slit may be computed by adding the contributions of the wavelets reaching *P* at a given instant; but in making this

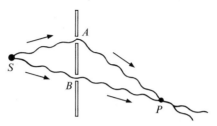

FIG. 11–11.   Interference between waves diffracted at two slits.

addition, one must consider the relative phases of the contributing wavelets. Should the slit not be on a wavefront, then one must make allowance for the difference in phase of the original waves reaching the various points in the slit at the same time.   Thus the *phase* of a wave is most important.   This explains the phenomenon of interference and Eq. (11–5).   If A and B in Fig. 11–11 are two narrow slits and the path lengths $\overline{SAP}$ and $\overline{SBP}$ differ by a whole number of wavelengths, the phase of the waves reaching P via the two slits must be the same.   A crest of one wave will meet a crest of the other, and the disturbance will be a maximum. If, on the other hand, $\overline{SAP}$ and $\overline{SBP}$ differ by an odd number of half wavelengths, then the two sets of waves reaching P will differ in phase by half a cycle, and a crest of one will meet a trough of the other, producing minimum disturbance. Most of us are familiar with the "dead" spots found in some lecture or concert halls; these are places where sound waves from the stage or podium reach the listener by a direct path and also to a considerable extent by a path that involves reflection off a wall (Fig. 11–9).   For a single wavelength the condition for destructive interference may not be met, but when listening to music or speech one is receiving sound waves of many frequencies or wavelengths and, for a given path difference Δs, there are bound to be wavelengths present for which Δs equals $\frac{1}{2}, \frac{3}{2}, \frac{5}{2}$, etc. times that wavelength.   Thus the existence of both a direct path and a reflected path must result in inferior reception.

11–6 Reflection of waves

The law of reflection may be derived from the modified Huygens' principle.

Consider a plane wavefront ABC which is just reaching a reflecting surface MM' at the time t, as in Fig. 11–12.   Suppose that at the time $t + \Delta t$ a wavelet from C reaches the point C', CC' being perpendicular to ABC.   If the speed of the wave is v, then $\overline{CC'}$ must equal $v\,\Delta t$.   Now consider a wavelet spreading out from the midpoint B of the original wavefront.   It will reach the reflecting surface at P at the time $t + \Delta t/2$; if a wavelet starts to spread out from P at this moment, it will attain a radius of $v\,\Delta t/2$ by the time the wavelet from C reaches C'.   A similar analysis may be applied to wavelets originating at other points on ABC and producing secondary wavelets at various points on MM'.   Finally, since the original wavefront has reached the mirror at A at the time t, the wavelet spreading out from A will have a radius of $v\,\Delta t$ at the time $t + \Delta t$.   The secondary wavelets

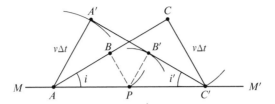

FIG. 11–12.   The law of reflection derived from Huygens' principle.

referred to here are all in phase; hence their envelope $A'B'C'$ will be the new wavefront at the later time $t + \Delta t$.

In the right triangles ACC' and $AA'C'$, the side AC' is common and the sides CC' and AA' are each equal in length to $v \Delta t$. Therefore these triangles have equal third sides (from the Pythagorean theorem) and are equal triangles. Therefore the reflected wavefront $A'C'$ makes the same angle with the mirror as does the incident wavefront AC. Since rays are perpendicular to wavefronts and the normal is perpendicular to a surface, the angle $CAC' = i$ and the angle $A'C'A = i'$. Hence $i = i'$, or the angle of incidence equals the angle of reflection.

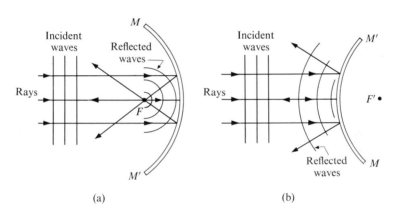

(a)   (b)

FIG. 11–13.   (a) Reflection from a concave mirror.   (b) Reflection from a convex mirror.

Application of Huygens' principle to curved surfaces will show that when a plane wave is reflected from a *concave* mirror, as in Fig. 11–13(a), the reflected wave will *converge* toward a point F called the *focus* of the mirror. On the other hand, if a plane wave strikes a *convex* mirror, as in Fig. 11–13(b), the reflected wave will *diverge* away from the point F'. In general, reflection from a concave mirror makes converging waves converge more and diverging waves diverge less, or perhaps converge, while convex mirrors produce the opposite effect. A continuation of this line of reasoning leads one to the theory of image formation by mirrors.

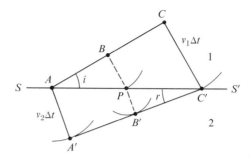

FIG. 11–14. The law of refraction derived from Huygens' principle.

11–7 Refraction of waves

Let us refer to Fig. 11–14 and derive Snell's law of refraction from the modified Huygens' principle.

The surface SS' separates medium 1, in which the speed of the waves is v_1, from medium 2, in which the speed is v_2. Here we make no assumption as to whether v_2 is or is not equal to v_1. The original wavefront at the time t is ABC. Let a wavelet from C reach the surface SS' at C' in the time Δt, so that $\overline{CC'} = v_1 \Delta t$. A wavelet from the midpoint B of AC will reach the surface at P in the time $\Delta t/2$, and so from P a secondary wavelet will spread out during the remainder $\Delta t/2$ of the time interval Δt. In medium 2 the wavelet from P will attain a radius of $v_2 \Delta t/2$ by the time the wavelet from C reaches C'. From A, a wavelet of radius $v_2 \Delta t$ will spread out into medium 2 in the time Δt. The new wavefront is thus $A'B'C'$.

In the right triangle ACC', the angle CAC' is i, the angle of incidence, and

$$\sin i = v_1 \Delta t/\overline{AC'}.$$

In the triangle $AA'C'$, the angle $AC'A'$ is r, the angle of refraction, and

$$\sin r = v_2 \Delta t/\overline{AC'}.$$

If we divide one equation by the other, we obtain

$$\frac{\sin i}{\sin r} = \frac{v_1}{v_2}. \tag{11–6}$$

Since the speed of a wave in a noncrystalline medium is independent of its direction of motion, the ratio v_1/v_2 is independent of i and r for two given media. This is Snell's law.

Note that Eq. (11–6) tells us something new, namely that when $r < i$, or $\sin r < \sin i$, then $v_2 < v_1$. Thus if rays are bent toward the normal upon entering a new medium, then the speed of the waves must be less in the second medium. In general, if rays bend on entering a new medium, the speed v must change. The converse statement is also true. This relationship between speed and direction has been verified experimentally.

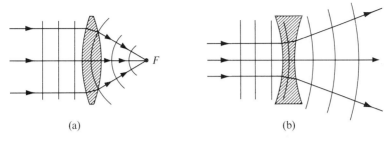

FIG. 11-15. (a) Converging lens. (b) Diverging lens.

The fact that light travels more slowly in glass than in air accounts for the converging and diverging properties of various kinds of lenses. If a lens is *thicker in
the middle*, rays passing through the middle will be slowed down more than those
passing through the edges of the lens and the lens will increase the convergence or
decrease the divergence of the waves striking it [Fig. 11-15(a)]. A lens that is
thinner in the middle will have the converse effect and so is called a diverging lens
[Fig. 11-15(b)]. Let us consider other illustrations of refraction.

ILLUSTRATION 1.   Figure 11-16 shows a ray of light striking a slab of *plate glass*
with parallel sides. Upon entering the glass the light is bent toward the normal,
or in a clockwise sense as viewed in the diagram. When passing back into the air,
the ray is bent away from the normal, or counterclockwise in the figure. Since
the angle r is the angle between the ray in the glass and the normal to *either* surface,
the final direction of the ray is the same as its original direction, although the ray
is slightly displaced sidewise.

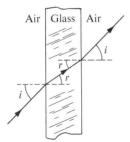

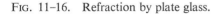

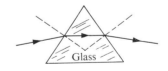

FIG. 11-16.   Refraction by plate glass.   FIG. 11-17.   Refraction by a prism.

ILLUSTRATION 2.   Figure 11-17 shows the bending of a ray of light by a *glass
prism*. Again the light enters the glass and the ray is bent toward the normal; then
the light leaves the glass and the ray is bent away from the normal. Why is the
bending in the figure clockwise *each* time?

The deviation (change in direction) produced by a prism is found to be greater
for blue than for red light, and the two colors are dispersed in different directions.
(Which must go faster in glass?) Because the deviation is different for every wavelength, a prism may be used to separate out the colors present in white light, or
light from any source, into the spectrum of that light.

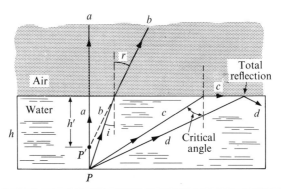

FIG. 11–18.   Refraction of rays passing from water to air.

ILLUSTRATION 3.   Figure 11–18 shows a pool of water of depth h. From the point P on the bottom of the pool, rays travel upward and strike the water-air surface at various angles of incidence i. For the ray labeled a, $i = 0°$, and the ray emerges unbent into the air. Ray b has a small angle of incidence i in the water, and this ray is bent away from the normal as it passes into the air because the speed of light in air is greater than in water. To a person in the air above the point P, the rays a and b will seem to diverge from the point P', the apparent position, or *image*, of P. The apparent depth h' will thus be less than the true depth of the water.

For rays going from water to air we may take the experimental value of v_1/v_2 to be $\frac{3}{4}$. Equation (11–6) then tells us that

$$\sin r = \tfrac{4}{3} \sin i. \tag{11–6'}$$

Suppose that $\sin i = \frac{3}{4}$ (or i is just under 49°), as for ray c, then $\sin r = 1, r = 90°$. This ray emerges parallel to the surface and is called the *critical ray;* the angle of incidence i_c of the critical ray is called the *critical angle*. For rays whose angles of incidence in the water exceed the critical angle, $\sin r$ would, according to Eq. (11–6'), be greater than unity; as no angle can have a sine greater than unity, Eq. (11–6') must fail to hold for these rays. Experiments show that such rays are *totally reflected* at the water-air surface.

11–8 Diffraction and interference of waves

According to Huygens' principle, when waves pass through an opening, every point in the opening may be regarded as the source of new wavelets. These wavelets will spread out in all directions in the region beyond the slit. This then explains why sound waves seem to bend as they pass through doorways and why water waves will bend around a breakwater. This bending, which is an example of *diffraction*, is not due to a change in the speed of the waves, but is an inherent property of waves in general.

Francesco Grimaldi (1618–1663), a professor of mathematics at the University of Bologna, Italy, made the first observations of the diffraction of light. In a narrow

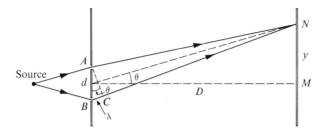

FIG. 11–19. Young's experiment. Diffraction and interference with two slits.

beam of sunlight he placed an opaque screen with a very small hole through which the light passed to a distant wall. Later he substituted for the screen a tiny obstacle. He observed that with the screen plus hole the spot of light on the wall was *larger* than expected, while with the tiny obstacle the shadow on the wall was *smaller* than the obstacle. In both cases the effects are equivalent to a slight bending of the light around whatever obstacle it passes. Grimaldi also noticed narrow color fringes near the edge of the light pattern on the wall. This was also partly a diffraction effect, and its explanation is related to the one we shall presently give of Young's color fringes produced by a double slit.

Thomas Young (1773–1829) made the discovery that light exhibits the property of interference. This was around the year 1800. Why was this discovery made so late when Newton and others had observed some time earlier the interference of two sets of water waves? The answer now given to this question is as follows. The wavelength of light in the visible region of the spectrum is *much less* than that of sound and water waves. When waves bend around an obstacle they pass into the geometric shadow zone determined by the line drawn from the source of the waves to the edge of the diffracting object (see Fig. 11–8). Both experiment and a more detailed theory show that the intensity of the diffracted waves falls off rapidly as a function of distance into the shadow zone if this distance is expressed in terms of number of wavelengths; for a sharp obstacle the intensity is appreciable for distances into the shadow zone of only a few wavelengths. Thus sound can be heard, but light cannot be seen, when the source is hidden by a tree.

When observing diffraction and interference effects with slits, it is necessary to make the slit width the order of a wavelength of the waves to be diffracted and, if more than one slit is used, the slit separation should be only some 100 times greater. Young made two very narrow slits *A* and *B* (see Fig. 11–19) close together on a screen. These slits were placed equidistant from a source *S*, such as a sodium lamp, that emitted a single wavelength λ of light. The light waves in such an experiment reach each slit in phase. The slits themselves may be regarded as synchronous sources of two new sets of waves of wavelength λ. It is important when one wishes to obtain interference effects with light that the two sets of overlapping waves come from a common source. This is because the wave trains from a light source are not of infinite length and abrupt changes in phase occur from one wave train to the next. For the interference of sound waves and the ripple waves in a pond or tank, one may use synchronous vibrators to produce the two sets of waves.

Returning to Young's experiment, the two sets of waves, spreading into the region behind the slits, overlap one another. At a point P on a second screen, placed at a distance D behind the first, the condition for constructive interference is given by Eq. (11–5), namely

$$\left|\overline{SAP} - \overline{SBP}\right| = m\lambda, \qquad m = 0, 1, 2, 3 \ldots.$$

The point M that is on the second screen and on the perpendicular bisector to AB is the point equidistant from the two slits, or the point for which $m = 0$. Hence, M will be a point of maximum brightness.

Let N be the point, above or below M, for which $m = 1$. This will be the next point on either side of M where maximum brightness will be obtained. Let y be the distance from M to N; then in Fig. 11–19, $y/\sqrt{D^2 + y^2} = \sin\theta$, where θ is the angle of diffraction. Since $m = 1$ for the point N, the distance $\overline{BN}$ must be one wavelength λ longer than the distance $\overline{AN}$. The difference in these two distances is essentially the distance $\overline{BC}$ in the figure, where AC is perpendicular to BN. (We assume here that the second screen is many wavelengths behind the first.) The angle BAC is essentially the same as θ. Let d be the distance between the slits. Then, since $\overline{BC} = \lambda$, we have $\lambda/d = \sin\theta$. When θ is a small angle, so that $y \ll D$, we may neglect y^2 compared with D^2 and write

$$\sin\theta = \frac{\lambda}{d} = \frac{y}{D},$$

$$\lambda = \frac{yd}{D}. \qquad (11\text{–}7)$$

If the slits are long and narrow, one will obtain a bright fringe through M, a parallel one through N, and others, about equally spaced, on beyond. This is called an *interference pattern*.

EXAMPLE. Suppose that $d = 0.2$ mm, $D = 1$ m, and $y = 2.5$ mm when $m = 1$. What is the value of λ?

Solution. Express d and y in meters. Then $d = 2 \times 10^{-4}$ m and $y = 2.5 \times 10^{-3}$ m, so that

$$\lambda = \frac{2.5 \times 10^{-3} \text{ m} \times 2 \times 10^{-4} \text{ m}}{1 \text{ m}} = 5 \times 10^{-7} \text{ m}.$$

This is about the wavelength of green light. It is remarkable that a quantity as small as the wavelength of visible light may be measured by this rather simple experiment.

Since the intensity of diffracted light is low, the use of a large number of equally spaced slits is an improvement over Young's two-slit experiment. A ruled *grating* may contain some 15,000 lines per inch, which is equivalent to the same number of slits, each of which contributes to the diffracted light. The condition for constructive interference is the same as for the two slits, namely that the additional path length of each successive ray must be equal to a whole number of wavelengths, i.e.,

$$d \sin \theta = m\lambda, \tag{11–8}$$

where d is the line separation, θ the angle between the diffracted rays and the normal to the grating, and m is an integer. Note that when $m = 0$, $\theta = 0$ for *all* wavelengths, while when $m = 1$ the value of θ increases with the wavelength. Longer waves of red light are diffracted more than shorter waves of blue light; again we have a separation of different colors, or dispersion.

11–9 Theories of light

The attempts of physicists to explain the properties of light illustrate well the nature of physical theory.

In the time of Newton (1642–1727) it was known that light seemed to travel in straight lines, and that light rays obeyed the laws of reflection and refraction. The diffraction and interference properties of light had not yet been discovered. In view of this state of the knowledge about light, Newton proposed a *corpuscular theory* of light which adequately explained the known facts. He postulated that a beam of light consists of a stream of fast-moving tiny particles, somewhat like the stream of bullets from a machine gun. This immediately explained the apparent sharp shadows cast by obstacles to a beam of light. Reflection could be explained as due to elastic collisions between the light particles and the reflecting surface. To explain refraction, Newton had to postulate that the light particles are attracted by glass and water, so that when a light particle approaches, say, a glass surface from air, the normal component of the velocity increases and the other components do not change. Thus Newton drew a new conclusion from his theory, namely that light must go *faster* in glass than in air. The inability of 17th and 18th century physicists to measure the speed of light in glass or water left a situation in which Newton's theory was completely adequate and even superior to the wave theory, in that Newton's theory extended the well-known laws of mechanics to light.

With the discovery of diffraction and interference, Newton's theory of light became inadequate. It did not "grow gracefully" and furnish an explanation of these new effects, whereas the wave theory did. The wave theory predicted that the speed of light would be found to be *less* in glass than in air, which is the opposite of Newton's prediction. Finally, in 1850, Foucault succeeded in showing experimentally that the wave theory's prediction was the correct one.

In the 20th century further facts about light have been discovered. These facts concern the emission and absorption of light. Since the wave theory attempts to explain only the propagation properties of light, these new facts do not invalidate the wave theory; rather they call for an additional theory that explains how light is emitted and absorbed. This additional theory is the quantum theory, which we shall discuss later. In summary we may say that Newton's theory was adequate for his day, but it did not prove fruitful and new facts could not be explained by it.

PROBLEMS

1. Show that $\Psi = (x + vt)^{1/2}$ represents a wave moving in the negative x-direction with the speed v.

2. Suppose that at $t = 0$, $\Psi = 0$, except between $x = 1$ m and $x = 1.5$ m where $\Psi = 5$ units, and that this pulse is moving in the x-direction with a speed $v = 0.5$ m/sec. Plot Ψ against x at $t = 0$, 1, and 2 sec, respectively.

3. Find the frequency of (a) a radar wave of 10-cm wavelength, (b) green light of 5000 A wavelength.

4. Given that, at the time t, $\Psi = 10 \sin(ax - bt)$, where $a = 3\pi/$m and $b = 6\pi/$sec. (a) Plot Ψ against x at $t = 0$ and $t = \frac{1}{6}$ sec. (b) What are the amplitude, wavelength, frequency, and speed of the wave?

5. The Greek scientist Pythagoras discovered that a note of frequency f_1 and a note of frequency f_2 sounded together will make a chord that is pleasing to the ear if the ratio $f_2/f_1 = m/n$, where m and n are different integers between 1 and 6. In the diatonic musical scale, the frequencies of the eight notes relative to do are: do 1, re $\frac{9}{8}$, mi $\frac{5}{4}$, fa $\frac{4}{3}$, sol $\frac{3}{2}$, la $\frac{5}{3}$, ti $\frac{15}{8}$, do 2. Find all the pleasant two-note chords obtainable from these eight notes.

6. Make up a six-note scale such that the highest note has twice the frequency of the lowest and for which there exist a maximum number of pleasant two-note and three-note chords.

7. Look up and describe the *chromaticity diagram* for colors. What are *complementary* colors?

8. Show that in reflection from a plane mirror the image is as far behind as the object is in front of the mirror.

9. (a) How long must a mirror be for a 6-ft man to see his full length in it? (b) In what respect do you see yourself in a mirror differently than your friends see you face-to-face?

10. Show that when a mirror is turned through θ degrees, light reflected from the mirror is rotated through 2θ degrees.

11. Show that the ratio of actual depth to apparent depth of a pool of water is the ratio of the speed of light in air to the speed in water, namely $\frac{4}{3}$.

12. A glass prism whose angles are 45°, 45°, 90°, has an index of refraction $n = 1.5$. (a) What is the critical angle for the glass? (b) How could this prism be used to reflect light and change its direction by 90°? (c) by 180°?

13. Suppose that Young's experiment is done with water waves (ripples) of 1-cm wavelength and $d = 6$ cm. Find the distance between points of reinforcement at a distance $D = 120$ cm.

14. Suppose that a grating has 5000 lines per centimeter. (a) From Eq. (11-8) find θ for $m = 1$, 2, and 3 and $\lambda = 4.4 \times 10^{-7}$ m (blue light). (b) Find θ for $m = 1$, 2, and 3 and $\lambda = 6.6 \times 10^{-7}$ m (red light). (c) Show on a diagram the relative directions of the three diffracted blue waves in (a) and the three diffracted red waves in (b).

15. A plane glass plate is separated from a similar plate at one end by a hair (Fig. 11-20). The hair creates an air wedge, and light reflected from the top of the bottom plate must travel down and back across this air wedge, while light reflected from the bottom of the top plate does not travel across the air wedge at all. Interference between these two beams results. As the air wedge gets thicker, bright and dark fringes alternate. Suppose that for light of 6×10^{-7} m wavelength, successive bright fringes are 2 mm apart. The plates are 10 cm long. How thick is the hair?

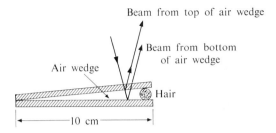

Beam from top of air wedge

Beam from bottom
of air wedge

Air wedge

Hair

10 cm

FIG. 11-20.   Interference of light produced by a thin air wedge.

16. The colors of thin films are due to interference effects. In explaining these effects one must include the following facts. (1) Light waves undergo a phase change of half a cycle when reflected from the near surface of the film back into air, but not when reflected from the far surface back into the film. (2) Due to the change in speed, a distance d traveled by the light in the film is equivalent to a distance nd in air. If white light falls normally on a film whose $n = 1.5$, what color will the film have by reflected light if its thickness is (a) 1.1×10^{-7} m, (b) 7.5×10^{-8} m, (c) zero? (For relations between wavelengths and colors see problem 14.)

EXPERIMENT 14

THE GRATING
(Diffraction and Interference of Light)

Object: To measure the wavelength of sodium light and to observe the diffraction of white light using a diffraction grating.

Apparatus: Plane diffraction grating with about 200 lines per centimeter, if possible, slit, optical bench, sodium burner, micrometer microscope.

Procedure:

Step 1. Place the sodium burner behind a V-shaped slit in a scale and observe through a grating in front of the scale the many orders of the spectrum. Keeping the eye close to the grating so that the distance from the slit to the eye is essentially the distance to the grating, slide a piece of paper over the scale until it coincides with the first image. Record its position and repeat for at least the first ten orders on either side of the central image. Record the distance from the grating to the plane of the images.

Step 2. Put an incandescent lamp in place of the sodium burner and record carefully the various characteristics of the resulting spectra. Draw labeled diagrams.

Step 3. Remove the grating and measure the grating space with a micrometer microscope. It is better to measure the distance between ten or more lines and find the average value of *d*. Why? Check your value by taking another reading.

Step 4. Calculate the average value of the wavelength of sodium light from your data. Compare your results with the correct value of 5893 A.

Step 5. Discuss the white light spectra.

EXPERIMENT 15

THE SPEED OF LIGHT

Object: To measure directly the speed of light.

Problem: The speed of light in empty space is one of our important constants. It is the fundamental constant in electromagnetic theory and the postulate that it is a universal constant forms part of the basis of relativity theory. Light has been found to have practically the same speed in air as in empty space. The difficulty in measuring this speed arises because it is so high.

When speed is constant we may define it as distance traveled (s) divided by the time taken (t). Calling the speed of light c, we have

$$c = s/t.$$

In the laboratory, where distances of about 100 ft are usually the best available, the time t is found to be around one ten-millionth of a second. Our problem is to measure this short time interval. This is done by using a rapidly rotating mirror.*

Light is reflected from a rotating mirror and then sent down a corridor to a fixed mirror and back to the rotating mirror. While the light travels the distance down the corridor and back, the rotating mirror turns through a small angle θ. This angle is measured by observing the resulting deflection d of the reflected light on a scale placed at a distance r from the rotating mirror. Then in radians

$$\theta = d/2r.$$

Why the factor 2?

If the mirror is making N revolutions/sec, it will turn through $2\pi N$ radians/sec. What will be the time to turn through θ radians?

N may be measured by matching the hum of the mirror either with the pitch of a calibrated turning fork, or with the output of a calibrated signal generator.

Procedure:

Step 1. Note the zero position p_1 of the beam of light on the scale with the rotating mirror at rest. Start the mirror rotating (be sure the key is taken out) and run it up to the speed for which there are no beats between its output and that of the turning fork or signal generator. Notice the new position p_2 of the light beam on the scale. Then

$$d = p_2 - p_1.$$

Step 2. Measure r and s and compute c. Compare your value with the accepted value. Can you justify your percent error?

Step 3. Sketch a diagram showing the optical path of the light beam from source to scale and indicate on your diagram $s/2$ and r.

---

* Such a mirror is made by E. Leybold and may be purchased from J. Klinger, 82 160th St., Jamaica, N.Y.

CHAPTER 12

Coulomb's Law of Electrostatic Force

12-1 Electric charge

Experiments on static electricity were performed by the Greeks. For example, they found that when amber was rubbed, it possessed the ability to attract small objects, such as a piece of thread. They offered no scientific theory to explain this phenomenon, but just stated that a "sympathy" existed between the amber and the attracted objects. Electrical effects related to the atmosphere (lightning, St. Elmo's fire, etc.) were, of course, known to ancient man, but no explanation of them was offered until modern times. The application of the experimental method to electrification phenomena and the development of a quantitative theory culminated in the work of the French scientist Coulomb (1736–1806).

For a time electricity was postulated to be a fluid that could be added to or taken from a body. There was some discussion as to whether there were two kinds of fluid or only one. The present view, based on the electron theory of matter, has proved to be the most fruitful and we shall adopt it.

As mentioned earlier, matter is considered to be composed of atoms and each atom to consist of a positive nucleus surrounded by a cloud of orbiting negative electrons. Normally an atom is *neutral*, that is, the sum of the negative charges on the electrons is just equal and opposite to the positive charge on the nucleus. When two objects (say glass and silk) are rubbed together and one has a greater affinity for electrons than the other, some electrons will rub off of one object onto the other. This will result in an excess of electrons, or a net *negative* charge, on the object with the greater electron affinity and a deficit of electrons, or a net *positive* charge, on the other object. We see that according to this theory, there are two kinds of charge and a charge of one sign may be separated from a charge of the opposite sign, but charge cannot be created or destroyed. This conservation of charge principle is one that so far has met every experimental test; it must, therefore, either be taken as a fundamental law or it must be contained within our other fundamental laws. We shall follow the latter alternative.

Just what is charge? All we can say at present is that it is an additional property that some bodies possess and uncharged bodies do not. Every material body possesses the property of mass and as a result (1) is subject to gravitational force and (2) shows reluctance to change its state of motion. Charged bodies are also subject to electric and magnetic forces, the nature of which will be discussed in this and the next chapter.

Benjamin Franklin arbitrarily chose to take the charge left on glass rubbed with silk as positive. When the electron was discovered just before 1900, it was found, according to Franklin's terminology, to have a negative charge, and this convention has been argeed upon.

12–2 Coulomb's law of electrostatic force. Fundamental Law VII

Before the time of Coulomb, it had been found that a charged body retains its charge when the body is suspended by a silk thread, but not when suspended by a metallic wire. Silk was termed an *insulator* and metals were called *conductors*. We now know that electrical conductivity implies the presence of charges free to move, and that there are all degrees of conductivity, running from the high conductivity of metals and electrolytes down through that of the so-called *semiconductors* to that of such good insulators as amber, porcelain, and certain plastics.

Suppose that a small conducting ball is suspended by a silk thread and charged positively by touching it to a glass rod rubbed with silk, then if the negatively charged silk is brought close to the ball, the ball will be attracted to the silk. If, on the other hand, an uncharged ball is touched to a charged one, or two uncharged balls are touched to the same charged rod, then the similarly charged balls will repel one another. Thus unlike charges attract and like charges repel each other. These facts indicate the existence in nature of another fundamental type of force besides gravitational attraction. This second kind of force may be attractive or repulsive and it only exists between charged bodies. Since this force exists between charged bodies at rest, it is called the *electrostatic*, or *electric*, *force*.

Coulomb knew of the experiments just described. Being a first-rate experimental physicist, he next asked himself this question: On what factors does the electric force depend and how does it depend on each? He sought for the law relating the electric force to other physical quantities.

By means of a delicate torsion balance capable of measuring a force of less than 10^{-7} n, Coulomb found that the force between two charged balls varied inversely as the square of the distance between their centers. This relationship had been proposed by others, but Coulomb's work gave it a firm experimental foundation.

Realizing that the electric force between two charged bodies must also depend on their respective charges, q_1 and q_2, Coulomb devised a way of determining the *relative* charges on bodies. He suspended a ball with a charge which we shall call q; he then touched this ball to an uncharged ball of the same size as the first so that the charge q became equally shared. Each ball then had a charge of $q/2$. By letting one of these balls share its charge with a third similar ball, charges of magnitude $q/4$ could be obtained, and so on. This gave him a set of charges of various magnitudes and made it possible for him to measure how the electric force depends on the charges on the interacting bodies. His results may be summarized as follows.

Bodies with like charges repel and with unlike charges attract one another; for point charges (or small charged spheres) the force of interaction is proportional to the product of the charges and inversely proportional to the square of their distance apart.

Expressed mathematically, Coulomb's law states that the electric force $\mathbf{F}_e$ on a point charge q' due to the presence of another point charge q is

VII. $$\mathbf{F}_e = k_e \frac{qq'}{r^2} \mathbf{r}_1, \tag{12-1}$$

where k_e is the constant of proportionality, r the distance of separation, and $\mathbf{r}_1$ a unit vector directed from q toward q'. Unit vectors are introduced to give the proper direction to a vector quantity; since the magnitude of $\mathbf{r}_1$ is unity in any system of units, it is dimensionless. Thus the magnitude of $\mathbf{F}_e$ is

VII. $$F_e = k_e \frac{qq'}{r^2}. \tag{12-2}$$

This is our *Fundamental Law VII.*

You will note the close resemblance between this law and Newton's law of gravitation. Coulomb and his immediate predecessors were undoubtedly guided by this analogy. The inverse-square-of-the-distance factor in both laws may be attributed to the geometric properties of Euclidean space in which anything that spreads out with spherical symmetry across successive spherical surfaces of area $4\pi r^2$ must become diluted in inverse proportion to such an area. But it is not obvious that gravitational and electric forces must be central and spherically symmetrical; it is just a fact that they are.

In Newton's law of gravitation,

$$F_g = G \frac{m_1 m_2}{s^2},$$

we took the units of force, mass, and distance to have been defined, so that this equation defined the new quantity G; the value of G which makes the equation balance had to be determined experimentally, because it depends not only on our choice of units but also on the *strength* of gravitational forces. The strengths of the various forces in our world are inherent properties of our world.

Coulomb's postulate implies the existence of the electric force as another fundamental force in addition to the gravitational force. We shall see that the electric force is relatively much stronger. As with Newton's law, we shall take the units of force, charge, and distance to have been chosen and let Eq. (12-2) define k_e, the value of which must be found experimentally. Our unit of charge, the coulomb, was defined in Chapter 3 under "fundamental quantities"; it will be defined again in the next chapter, and we will see that its definition is based on another fundamental law (Ampere's) and another type of force (magnetic). With F_e measured in newtons, q and q' in coulombs, and r in meters, the experimental value found in air or vacuum for k_e is almost, but not exactly,

$$k_e = 9 \times 10^9 \text{ n-m/coul}^2. \tag{12-3}$$

Unfortunately (because of the resulting confusion) other valid but less convenient systems of electric and magnetic units have been introduced in the past.

Two of these systems, the electrostatic system and the electromagnetic system, employ cgs units for mechanical quantities and different units for charge. Since the electrostatic system may be encountered in other texts, we will simply state here that the electrostatic unit of charge, the *statcoulomb*, is chosen so as to make $k_e = 1$ when F_e is expressed in dynes and r in centimeters. At first it may seem more advantageous to have $k_e = 1$, but when one passes on to current electricity, this advantage is lost because a statcoulomb/sec is not the familiar unit of current we call the ampere. For the relation between the coulomb and the statcoulomb, see the following Example 2.

EXAMPLE 1. Compare the electric force between an electron and a proton with the gravitational force between these particles for the same separation.

Solution. From experimental information we have $q = 1.6 \times 10^{-19}$ coul and $m_1 = 9.1 \times 10^{-31}$ kg for the electron, and $q' = 1.6 \times 10^{-19}$ coul, $m_2 = 1.6 \times 10^{-27}$ kg for the proton; $G = 1.67 \times 10^{-11}$ n-m^2/kg^2. Both forces are attractive and

$$\frac{F_e}{F_g} = \frac{k_e}{G} \frac{qq'}{m_1 m_1}$$

$$= \frac{9 \times 10^9 \times 1.6 \times 10^{-19} \times 1.6 \times 10^{-19}}{6.67 \times 10^{-11} \times 9.1 \times 10^{-31} \times 1.6 \times 10^{-27}}$$

$$= 2.4 \times 10^{39},$$

which is one of the largest numbers in our physical world. The value of the ratio F_e/F_g varies with the masses of the elementary particles chosen; the ratio is about 10^{36} for two protons, 10^{38} for two mesons, and 4×10^{42} for two electrons. On the average it is about 10^{38}.

EXAMPLE 2. Suppose that for a certain pair of charges, each of magnitude q, with a separation of 1 cm ($= 10^{-2}$ m), the electric force of repulsion is 9×10^{-3} n. Find q in coulombs and in statcoulombs.

Solution. From Eq. (12–2) we have

$$9 \times 10^{-3} \, n = 9 \times 10^9 \, \frac{n\text{-}m^2}{coul^2} \times \frac{q^2}{10^{-4} \, m^2},$$

$$q^2 = 10^{-16} \, coul^2,$$

$$q = 10^{-8} \, coul.$$

Since $1 \, n = 10^5$ dynes, the force between these two equal charges 1 cm apart is 900 dynes. In the electrostatic system $k_e = 1$ and the force between two charges, each *one* statcoulomb, 1 cm apart would be $F_e = 1 \times 1 \times 1/1^2 = 1$ dyne. If each charge were 30 statcoulombs the force would be $30^2 = 900$ dynes, as in our problem. Hence

$$q = 30 \, statcoul.$$

From the above we see that 10^{-8} coul $= 30$ statcoul, 1 coul $= 3 \times 10^9$ statcoul.

12–3 The electric field

Since an electric force exists between charged particles located in even the best vacuum, such a force furnishes an example of what has been called "action at a distance," and it cannot be given a mechanistic explanation. This point was one that the followers of Newton found hard to accept, and the reader may find it bothersome if he has not become accustomed to it. There is, however, another way to look at the situation, a way that has proved fruitful; it is to introduce the concept of a *field*. This was first suggested by the English physicist Michael Faraday (1791–1867).

Faraday proposed the following alternative statement of Coulomb's law, a statement that summarizes the same experimental facts.

(1) Around every charged body there exists an *electric field* **E**, which is a vector quantity.

(2) The *direction* of the electric field is away from a positive charge and toward a negative charge.

(3) The *strength* of the electric field at a distance r from a charge q, due to q, is

$$E = \frac{k_e q}{r^2}.$$
(12–4)

(4) The *force* of an electric field **E** on a charge q' placed in the field (but not contributing to it) is

$$\mathbf{F}_e = q'\mathbf{E},$$
(12–5)

where **E** represents the field at that point.

We see that (2), (3), and (4) together are equivalent to Coulomb's law. These statements are illustrated by Fig. 12–1.

Faraday made the further postulate that if q' is in the neighborhood of more than one charge, then **E** in Eq. (12–5) must be regarded as the vector sum of the electric fields due to each of the charges (other than q'). In other words, the electric field of one charge exists independently of that of any other charge. It is thus possible to compute the field due to any given charge distribution.

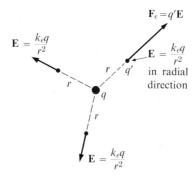

FIG. 12–1.   Field around a point charge q exerts a force on a test charge q' placed in this field.

From Eq. (12–5), $E = F_e/q'$, so that the mks-coulomb unit for E must be the newton per coulomb (n/coul).

EXAMPLE.   A charge $q_1 = -4 \times 10^{-9}$ coul is located at the point $x = -0.15$ m, $y = 0$, and a charge $q_2 = +4 \times 10^{-9}$ coul is located at $x = 0.15$ m, $y = 0$ (see Fig. 12–2).   Find the electric intensity E at (a) the origin O, (b) the point P for which $x = 0.45$ m, $y = 0$.   (c) Find the direction of E at a point R on the Y-axis.

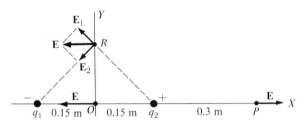

FIG. 12–2.   Field due to two equal and opposite charges.

Solution.   Let E_1 be the field due to the negative charge and E_2 that due to the positive one.

(a) At O, where $r_1 = 0.15$ m, the magnitude of E_1 is

$$E_1 = \frac{k_e q_1}{r_1^2} = \frac{9 \times 10^9 \times 4 \times 10^{-9} \text{ n}}{0.15 \times 0.15 \text{ coul}} = 1600 \frac{\text{n}}{\text{coul}}.$$

E_2 has the same magnitude as E_1, since $r_2 = r_1$ and q_2 has the same magnitude as q_1, so that

$$E_2 = 1600 \text{ n/coul.}$$

Since q_1 is negative, E_1 must be toward q_1 at all points so that, at O, E_1 is to the *left*. Since q_2 is positive, E_2 must be away from q_2 at all points so that, at O, E_2 is also to the *left*.   Hence E_1 and E_2 must be added numerically, or

$$E = E_1 + E_2 = 3200 \text{ n/coul to the } left.$$

(b) At P we have $r_1 = 0.6$ m and $r_2 = 0.3$ m,

$$E_1 = \frac{9 \times 10^9 \times 4 \times 10^{-9} \text{ n}}{0.6 \times 0.6 \text{ coul}} = 100 \text{ n/coul,}$$

$$E_2 = \frac{9 \times 10^9 \times 4 \times 10^{-9} \text{ n}}{0.3 \times 0.3 \text{ coul}} = 400 \text{ n/coul.}$$

At P, E_1 is again to the *left*, but E_2 is to the *right*.   Hence we must subtract E_1 from E_2, and $E = E_1 + E_2 = 300$ n/coul to the *right*.
    (c) At R, on the Y-axis, E_1 and E_2 have equal magnitudes and are directed as shown. Vector addition (placing vectors end to end) shows that $E = E_1 + E_2$ is horizontal and to the *left*.

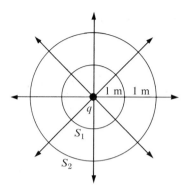

Fɪɢ. 12–3.   Same total number of lines of force cross any closed surface surrounding a charge.

12–4 Lines of force

Lines of force are drawn to help us visualize the field at all points; they show us quickly the whole pattern of the field. A line of force is, by definition, a line or curve such that at any point on it the tangent to the curve is parallel to $\mathbf{E}$ at that point. Thus lines of force show us the *direction of the field* at many points. At points between lines of force we can usually guess the direction of the field by interpolation.

How many lines of force should we draw? We must choose a *scale* determined by how many lines we wish to draw altogether. Perhaps the most logical scale, and the one easiest to remember, is that according to which we draw E lines per unit surface perpendicular to $\mathbf{E}$. Thus if $E = 20{,}000$ n/coul in a certain region, one would then show 20,000 lines crossing an area of 1 m^2, or 2 lines/cm^2. For weaker fields this scale might result in too few lines to represent the field adequately, and then we might prefer to choose another scale, say $100E$ lines/m^2. The important thing is to maintain the same scale throughout a lines-of-force diagram, because then the lines will not only portray the direction of the field, but also its relative *strength*. Where the lines are close together the field is strong, while where they are far apart the field is weak.

Suppose that we have an isolated plus charge q around which there is a symmetric field $\mathbf{E}$. This field may be represented by lines of force radiating symmetrically outward from q (Fig. 12–3). Consider the spherical surface S_1 whose radius is 1 m and whose center is at q. From Eq. (12–4), $E = k_e q$ on S_1, so let us draw $k_e q$ lines/m^2 across the surface. The area of S_1 is 4π m^2, and hence we must draw $4\pi k_e q$ lines altogether. At the surface S_2, whose radius is 2 m, $E = k_e q/4$ and we must draw $k_e q/4$ lines/m^2 across a total area of 16π m^2, or $4\pi k_e q$ lines in all. Thus across every surface surrounding q we must draw $4\pi k_e q$ lines. This makes the whole lines-of-force idea practical, for evidently we can draw $4\pi k_e q$ lines emanating from q and continue the same lines out across larger and larger surfaces. Conversely, if we count the total number of lines of force crossing a closed surface in the outward direction, then we can compute the net charge

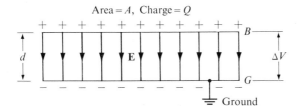

Fig. 12–4.   Electric field between charged parallel plates.

within the surface. This is possible only because Coulomb's law is an inverse square law and $\mathbf{F}_e$ is a central force.

We may summarize the last paragraph as follows. Suppose that one chooses to space lines of force so that there are nE lines per unit area, where n is kept constant. Let N represent the total number of such lines crossing a closed surface in the outward direction and $\sum q$ the net sum of all the charges inside this surface. Then

$$N = 4\pi n k_e \sum q. \tag{12–6}$$

This theorem, derived from Coulomb's law, is known as *Gauss' law.*

ILLUSTRATION 1.   *Electric field between parallel plates.* The use of parallel conducting plates makes it possible to produce a uniform electric field whose magnitude may be computed from measurable quantities.

Figure 12–4 shows a metal plate B separated by a distance d from a similar parallel plate G. Suppose that B is insulated and given a charge $+Q$, while G is connected to the earth ("grounded"). The earth is a tremendous conducting sphere, and the positive charge on B will attract electrons up from the earth onto G, which is as near as these electrons can get to B. If the plates are close together compared with their diameters, the charges on the two plates will be on the surfaces facing one another. There can be no field inside conductor B, for, if there were, it would cause electrons in B to move until all fields were cancelled, and we would then have the static situation that has been assumed. Therefore every line of force leaving B will end on G. Lines leaving a charge $+Q$ end on a charge $-Q$. Thus the so-called *induced charge* on G is equal and opposite to the inducing charge Q.

At a point between the plates and not too near their edges, the field will, from symmetry, be directed down from B to G in Fig. 12–4. Since we are neglecting edge effects, we have no reason to assume the field to be different at one place than at another and so the field must be uniform.

Let us choose to draw nE lines of force per unit area. Then we must draw $4\pi n k_e Q$ lines from plate B to plate G, according to Eq. (12–6). Let A be the area of either plate, so that the

$$\text{lines per unit area} = nE = 4\pi n k_e Q/A.$$

Thus

$$E = 4\pi k_e Q/A. \tag{12–7}$$

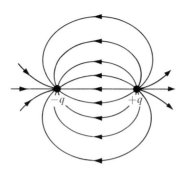

FIG. 12–5.   Electric field due to a dipole.

The ratio Q/A is called the *charge density* on the plate B, and E evidently depends only on this quantity (provided edge effects are neglected). We shall see in the next section how E, and hence Q, may be determined.

ILLUSTRATION 2.   *Electric field due to a dipole.* An electric dipole is defined as two equal and opposite charges that are situated a relatively small distance apart. In the Example of Section 12–3 the two charges constitute a dipole for an observer several meters or more away. Whereas in that example we computed **E** at only two points and its direction at a third, Fig. 12–5 shows, with the aid of lines of force, the whole overall pattern of the field of a dipole.

12–5 Electric potential

We have seen that when a body is moved against the force of gravity, it is useful to say that the resulting work W done *on* the body by some agent has gone to increase the potential energy of the body by an amount $\Delta V = W$. The concept of potential energy is only possible when the work done by the agent against the natural forces present is independent of the path by which the body is moved from a given point A to a given point B; this is equivalent to saying that the field must be *conservative*.

We know that an electric field **E** exerts a force $\mathbf{F}_e = q'\mathbf{E}$ on a charge q' placed in the field. To move this charge against this force requires that the agent do work. It should be possible to equate this work to a gain in P.E. of the charge if this work is also independent of the path followed between two given points, i.e., if the electric force is conservative. Let us investigate this point.

We have seen that the electric field due to static charges possesses the following properties.

(1) Electric lines of force diverge from a positive charge and converge on a negative charge.

(2) Electric lines of force never form closed paths, i.e., they never circle back through the same point again.

(3) The electric intensity is a function of position only.

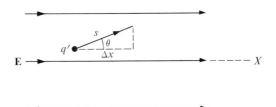

FIG. 12–6.   Work done on a charge q' as it moves in a uniform field **E** is $W' = q'E\Delta x$.

Because of these properties, an electrostatic force and field are conservative, just as are a gravitational force and field.   Therefore we may introduce the concepts of electric potential energy and the electric potential.

Suppose that we have a uniform field **E** and choose our x-axis so that it is in the direction of **E**, as in Fig. 12–6.   Then the components of **E** are $E_x = E$, $E_y = E_z = 0$.   Let us put a positive test charge (one that does not contribute to the field under discussion), of magnitude q', into the field **E**.   The force of the field on q' will be

$$\mathbf{F}_e = q'E_x \text{ in the } x\text{-direction.}$$

If q' is allowed to move a distance Δx in the x-direction, the force $\mathbf{F}_e$ will do work in the amount

$$W' = q'E_x \,\Delta x \qquad (12\text{–}8)$$

on the charge.   Motion in the direction of the field involves a *loss* of potential energy, just as when a body falls under the pull of gravity.   Therefore the change in the electric potential must be negative.   Since W' is proportional to q', we take the ratio $-W'/q'$, which is independent of q', and call it the *change in the electric potential*, designated as ΔV, so that

$$\Delta V = -\frac{W'}{q'}. \qquad (12\text{–}9)$$

If q' is to be moved against the field, an agent must perform an amount of work W and, since ΔV must now be positive, $\Delta V = W/q'$, where W is now the work done by the *agent* and not, as in Eq. (12–9), by the *field*.

Should the charge q' move a distance s in a direction making an angle θ with the field **E** (Fig. 12–6), the work done by the field would be

$$W' = F_e s \cos\theta = q'E_x s \cos\theta.$$

Since $s \cos\theta = \Delta x$, the distance moved parallel to the field, we again have

$$W' = q'E_x \,\Delta x.$$

If we substitute this value for W', which applies to a uniform field, in Eq. (12–9), which is the definition of ΔV and applies to *any* field, we get for a uniform field,

$$\Delta V = -E_x \,\Delta x. \qquad (12\text{–}10)$$

Since any small region of a field may be treated as though it were a uniform field, we have

$$E_x = - \frac{\Delta V}{\Delta x} \qquad (12\text{--}11)$$

for any field when Δx is small. This tells us that we may compute the components of the field $\mathbf{E}$, and hence $\mathbf{E}$ itself, if we know the value of the electric potential V at all points. The component of $\mathbf{E}$ in any direction is just the negative of the space rate of change of the electric potential in that direction. Change in electric potential is also called *potential difference* (abbreviated p.d.).

From Eq. (12–9) we see that in the mks-coulomb system the unit of p.d. is the joule per coulomb; this unit is also called the *volt*, so that

$$1 \text{ volt} = 1 \text{ joule/coulomb.} \qquad (12\text{--}12)$$

From Eq. (12–11) it follows that an electric field may be expressed in *volts per meter*. (See problem 12 at end of chapter.)

While we have only defined change in potential, it is often convenient to choose some reference point and arbitrarily call its potential zero. Such a reference point is usually taken to be the earth, since most terrestrial systems are at some point electrically connected to the ground. However, when dealing with a point charge or an isolated conductor, it is convenient to take $V = 0$ at a great distance away.

The total p.d. between two points A and B is the sum or, as it is called in the calculus, the *integral*, of all the small ΔV's computed along a path taken from A to B. Thus

$$V_B - V_A = \sum_{A \to B} \Delta V = \int_A^B dV, \qquad (12\text{--}13)$$

where the last expression is the mathematician's way of defining and writing the integral. Since, in a conservative field, the work does not depend on the path taken, and since an electrostatic field *is* conservative, $V_B - V_A$ has a definite value between two given points.

If $\Delta V = 0$ for a certain small path, then $\mathbf{E}$ cannot have a component along this path, and so $\mathbf{E}$ must be perpendicular to the direction of such a path. Surfaces over which $\Delta V = 0$ and V is constant are called *equipotential surfaces;* $\mathbf{E}$ must be perpendicular to such surfaces at all points. Thus equipotential surfaces and lines of force are mutually perpendicular.

The reader is probably more familiar with the following examples of mutually perpendicular sets of surfaces and lines, or (in two dimensions) two mutually perpendicular sets of lines.

(a) *Topographic map.* On such a map contour lines are drawn connecting points of equal altitude, or gravitational P.E. Contour lines are the equipotentials. The corresponding lines of force are the *"fall lines"* which, at any point, represent the direction "straight down," or the direction of fastest descent for a skier.

(b) *Weather map.* Here the *isobars*, or lines through points of equal barometric pressure (reduced to sea level), are the equipotentials. The analogous lines of force, drawn from high- to low-pressure areas, represent at any point the direction of the greatest pressure change per unit distance; they would also represent the flow of the winds if the earth did not rotate.

(c) *Heat flow diagram.* To compute the direction of heat flow through a conducting medium one may plot surfaces of constant temperature, called *isothermals*, and then the curves perpendicular to these isothermals will represent the paths along which the temperature changes most rapidly with distance, or the paths along which the heat will be conducted.

Let us now return to our discussion of the electric potential and consider two important illustrations.

ILLUSTRATION 1.   *Uniform field between parallel plates.* Here we may use Eq. (12–10), putting $\Delta x = d$, the separation of the plates. Then the change in potential as one goes *against* the field from the negative plate G to the positive plate B (see Fig. 12–4) is

$$\Delta V = Ed,$$

or

$$E = \frac{\Delta V}{d}. \tag{12–14}$$

The ΔV may be measured with a voltmeter, an instrument which may be calibrated absolutely in terms of the definitions of the joule and the volt (see next chapter). Hence we may use Eq. (12–14) to determine E.

The charge Q on the plus plate may now be computed from Eq. (12–7). We see that

$$Q = \frac{AE}{4\pi k_e} = \frac{A \Delta V}{4\pi k_e d}. \tag{12–15}$$

What is the electric force on the plus plate? The field given by Eq. (12–14) is the combined field, due half to the charge $+Q$ on the upper plate and half to the charge $-Q$ on the lower, grounded plate. Thus the field E_s at the surface of the plus plate *due to charges other than its own charge* is

$$E_s = \frac{E}{2} = \frac{\Delta V}{2d}.$$

This is the field that acts on Q. (A charge does not act on itself.) From Eq. (12–5) we have $F_e = QE_s$, since here $q' = Q$, or

$$F_e = Q\left(\frac{\Delta V}{2d}\right). \tag{12–16}$$

If we use Eq. (12–15) to eliminate Q, we get

$$F_e = \frac{A(\Delta V)^2}{8\pi k_e d^2}. \tag{12–17}$$

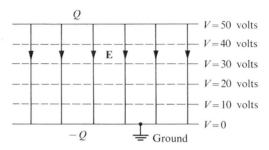

FIG. 12–7.   Equipotential surfaces.

A simple method of determining k_e is to measure the force F_e, the p.d. ΔV, the area A, and the plate separation d (see Experiment 17 at end of chapter), and then to compute k_e from Eq. (12–17).

In a uniform field the equipotential surfaces, which must be perpendicular to the field, are parallel to the plates. Since in a uniform field, p.d. is proportional to distance, equipotentials corresponding to $V = 10, 20, 30, 40, \ldots$ volts are spaced equally (Fig. 12–7).

ILLUSTRATION 2.   *Electric potential due to a charged sphere.* Let a charge Q be placed on a conducting sphere of radius R (Fig. 12–8). Since the charge must be symmetrically distributed over an isolated spherical conductor, and since the same total number of lines of force must leave such a distributed charge Q as leave a point charge Q, we may conclude that *outside* the sphere the field is the same as though the sphere were replaced by a charge Q at its center. Therefore, at a distance $r > R$ from the center of the sphere a test charge q' would experience the force

$$F_e = \frac{k_e Qq'}{r^2}.$$

Let us assume that Q and q' are both positive so that q' is repelled by Q. If q' moves away from Q, so that r increases to $r + \Delta r$, the work done by the field will

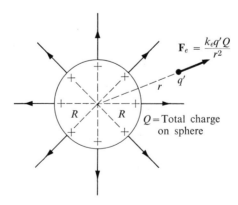

FIG. 12–8.   Electric field due to a charged sphere.

be equal to the average value of F_e times Δr. We may apply the same line of reasoning as in Section 9–4 leading to Eq. (9–10), where we also computed work done under an inverse square type of force. The two cases differ in that (1) k_e now replaces G, (2) Qq' replaces mM, and (3) the force is repulsive rather than attractive, so that the field and not the agent does a positive amount of work in taking the charge from $r = r$ to $r = \infty$. This work is

$$W' = \frac{k_e Qq'}{r},$$

so that

$$\Delta V = -\frac{W'}{q'} = -\frac{k_e Q}{r}.$$

The potential at $r = \infty$ is lower than that at $r = r$ by the amount $k_e Q/r$, so if we let $V = 0$ at $r = \infty$, then

$$V = \frac{k_e Q}{r} \tag{12–18}$$

is the potential relative to infinity either at a distance r from a point charge Q, or outside and at a distance r from the center of a sphere bearing a charge Q. This formula applies up to the surface of the conducting sphere, so that if we take $V = 0$ at $r = \infty$, then $V = k_e Q/R$ at the sphere itself.

In this illustration the field is radially outward and therefore the equipotential surfaces must be spheres outside and concentric with the charged sphere. Will equipotentials corresponding to $V = 10, 20, 30, 40, \ldots$ volts be equally spaced in this case? (See problem 7 at the end of the chapter.)

ILLUSTRATION 3. *The Van de Graaff generator.* This is a device in which a hollow conducting sphere is mounted on an insulating hollow cylinder containing a moving belt (Fig. 12–9). Charge is sprayed onto the belt at the bottom and taken off at the top. It is no problem to transfer the charge on the belt to the hollow sphere because there is no electric field within a hollow conductor due to its own charge. (Can the reader prove this from the properties of electric fields?) The charge transferred accumulates on the outside of the sphere and raises its potential to the point where charge leaks off (into the air and down the insulating stand) as fast as more charge is brought up by the belt.

Let the radius of the sphere be R and its charge Q. From Eq. (12–18) its potential above ground will be

$$V = \frac{k_e Q}{R}. \tag{12–19}$$

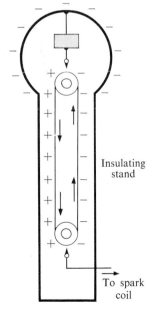

Insulating
stand

To spark
coil

FIG. 12–9.   Van de Graaff generator.

The electric field E_a in the air just outside the sphere will have the magnitude

$$E_a = \frac{k_e Q}{R^2},$$

since the field outside a spherical conductor is similar to that of a point charge. If we eliminate Q between these two equations, we get

$$V = RE_a. \tag{12-20}$$

Although dry air is normally a good insulator, its insulation properties disappear, through a chain reaction process of ionization, when the electric field strength exceeds 30,000 volts per centimeter or 3×10^6 volts per meter. Thus if $R = 3$ m, V cannot exceed 9×10^6 volts. For various technical reasons the limit reached might be half of this potential, but even a p.d. of 4.5×10^6 volts is sufficient (1) to cause impressive effects that simulate lightning and (2) to accelerate atomic particles to speeds in excess of 10^7 m/sec.

12–6 The Millikan oil-drop experiment

We are now in a position to understand one of the great experiments of all time, one which firmly established the atomicity of electricity and the size of the elementary charge. This experiment was performed by the American physicist Robert A. Millikan (1868–1953), and for his work he later received the Nobel Prize.

Millikan's apparatus is shown in Fig. 12–10. Two parallel horizontal metal plates are separated about 1 cm by insulators and shielded from air currents by

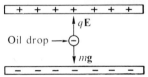

FIG. 12–10.   Millikan's oil-drop experiment.

an enclosing box. Oil is sprayed as fine droplets into the region between the plates. This region is brightly illuminated and viewed against a dark background through a telescope. The oil drops appear as tiny bright stars.

First a variable p.d. ΔV is applied to the plates. The oil drops are frictionally charged by the spraying process. Let q be the charge on a certain drop of mass m. The weight of the drop is mg downward. The electric force on the drop $F_e = qE$, where E is the magnitude of the electric field due to ΔV. The direction and magnitude of this field may be adjusted so that the electrical force is upward and just balances the weight of the drop. Then for the suspended drop we have

$$qE = mg. \tag{12-21}$$

In this formula, E may be computed from the formula $E = \Delta V/d$, Eq. (12-4), by measuring ΔV (with a voltmeter) and the plate separation d. The mass of the drop must be determined from its size and density. The density of the oil may easily be found, but the drops are too small for one to measure their diameters directly. Millikan found that he could measure the radius of a drop very accurately by timing its rate of fall when the electric field was turned off. The drops very quickly reach a limiting velocity of fall which is determined by their size, their density, and the viscosity of the air. (The correct formula relating these quantities had been worked out by a theoretician named Stokes.) After finding mg for a drop Millikan corrected for the buoyancy of the air.

Millikan's results showed that for every drop q was a whole number multiple of the charge $\pm e$, where e is evidently the fundamental quantity of charge out of which all larger charges are built. His drops had charges such as $+4e$, $-5e$, $+2e$, but never charges like $+3.72e$, or $-0.64e$.

The measured value of e is

$$e = 1.60 \times 10^{-19} \text{ coul.} \tag{12-22}$$

12–7 Capacitance

The *electric capacitance* C measures the ability of a conductor to hold charge. When used for this purpose, the conductor is called a *capacitor*. Let Q be the charge on the conductor when it is raised to a potential above ground and all neighboring conductors (if any are present) are grounded. Then the capacitance C is defined as

$$C = \frac{Q}{V}. \tag{12-23}$$

Capacitance is the charge on the conductor per unit potential, from which it follows that the mks-coulomb unit of capacitance is the coulomb per volt. This unit is also called the *farad*, so that

$$1 \text{ farad} = 1 \text{ coulomb/volt.} \tag{12-24}$$

Actually this unit is very large for practical purposes and fractions of it, such as the microfarad ($1\mu f = 10^{-6}$ f) and the micromicrofarad ($1\mu\mu f = 10^{-12}$ f), are used commercially, but when numerical values are substituted in formulas, C must be expressed in farads.

As charge is added to a conductor, the potential of the conductor rises above that of its surroundings. There is always a limit to how high this potential difference can be. If for each of a group of radio capacitors the safe upper limit for the potential above ground is, say, 400 volts, then the capacitor that can hold 10^{-6} coul/volt ($C = 10^{-6}$ farad) can hold at the most 400×10^{-6} coul, while the capacitor that can hold 2×10^{-6} coul/volt ($C = 2 \times 10^{-6}$ farad) can hold at the most 800×10^{-6} coul. This shows in what manner C measures the capacity to hold charge.

ILLUSTRATION 1.   *Charged sphere.* From Eq. (12–19) and Eq. (12–23) we have

$$C = \frac{Q}{k_e Q/R} = \frac{R}{k_e} \tag{12-25}$$

for the capacitance in air of a spherical conductor of radius R. Since $k_e = 9 \times 10^9$ mks-coulomb units, we see that even a large sphere with a radius of a meter has a capacitance of only a little more than 10^{-10} farad.

ILLUSTRATION 2.   *Parallel plate capacitor.* We shall compute the capacitance of a plate of area A that is at a distance d from a parallel grounded plates. From Eq. (12–15) we have

$$\Delta V = \frac{4\pi k_e d}{A} Q$$

for the p.d. between the plates. Equation (12–23) then tells us that

$$C = \frac{Q}{\Delta V} = \frac{A}{4\pi k_e d}. \tag{12-26}$$

Note that C may be increased by decreasing the separation d, but d must not be made so small that the charge on the insulated plate can jump to the grounded one.

A thin sheet of paper, or better still, mica, will serve to maintain a very small separation and at the same time act as an insulator between the plates. Furthermore, the introduction between the plates of a medium other than air has another good effect in that it reduces the electric field for given charges Q and $-Q$ on the plates. For example, with mica the field might be one-fifth what it would be for air, and this in turn means that ΔV would be one-fifth as much for mica as for air [see Eq. (12–11)]. A smaller ΔV for the same charge Q implies a correspondingly greater capacitance. Thus a mica capacitor has about five times the capacitance of an air capacitor of the same A and d. This factor 5 represents the value in the case of mica of what is termed the *dielectric constant*.

The physical explanation of the reduction in the electric field between charged plates due to the presence of a *dielectric* medium, such as mica, is that the molecules of the medium become *polarized*. By this we mean that the electric field displaces

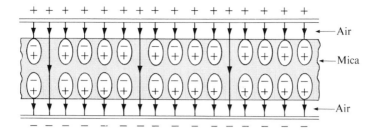

Fig. 12–11.   Electric field in a dielectric medium is reduced due to polarization of the medium.

the positive nuclei in the molecules of the medium in the direction of the field, while the negative electrons bound to the nuclei are displaced in the opposite direction. The electric field maintains a temporary separation of charge in the molecules, a separation that disappears when the field is removed. The result of this polarization is to produce a positive charge at the surface of the medium facing the negative plate and a negative charge at the surface opposite the positive plate, thus some of the lines of force that leave the positive plate end shortly on the negative surface charges of the dielectric medium and so do not continue through this medium. As a result, the field in the medium is reduced (see Fig. 12–11).

12–8 Energy of the electric field

To set up an electrostatic field requires work, for unlike charges must be separated. The conservation of energy principle tells us that the work done in producing the field must be stored as potential energy which can be recovered when the unlike charges are allowed to neutralize one another.

We may think of this energy as being associated with the charges, or as being stored in the region containing the field. Actually we do not measure this energy while it is stored, but only during the process of storing it, or when it is converted into some other form of energy. However, we do know that energy can be transported through space by electromagnetic waves, such as radio waves, so it is a useful concept to think of energy as residing in an electrostatic field.

PROBLEMS

1. Two charged balls 4 cm apart repel each other with a force of 36×10^{-5} n. What will the force be if (a) the same charges are placed on balls 3 cm apart, and (b) the separation is 6 cm and each charge is doubled?

2. Two identical conducting balls attract each other with a force of 27×10^{-5} n when 4 cm apart. The balls are touched together and again placed 4 cm apart; they now repel each other with a force of 9×10^{-5} n. (a) Why did the force change from attraction to repulsion? (b) Find the final charge on each ball. (c) Find the original charge on each ball.

3. Find the electric field E at the point $x = 0$, $y = 0$ when a charge of $+64 \times 10^{-9}$ coul is at $x = 0.4$ m, $y = 0$ and a charge of -27×10^{-9} coul is at $x = 0$, $y = 0.3$ m.

4. Taking $V = 0$ at infinity, find V at the point $x = 0$, $y = 0$ in problem 3.

5. For the charges in problem 3 find the location of the point(s) on the line passing through the charges at which (a) $\mathbf{E} = 0$, (b) $V = 0$.

6. Parallel plates are separated by 8 mm. If the upper plate is charged to 40 volts and the lower plate is grounded, find (a) the field E between the plates, (b) the positions of the equipotential surfaces for which $V = 10$, 20, and 30 volts, respectively.

7. Find for a point charge $q = 6 \times 10^{-9}$ coul the radii of the equipotential surfaces for which $V = 10$, 20, 30, and 40 volts, respectively.

8. Show the general pattern of the field due to two equal charges of the *same* sign separated by a distance d.

9. Show that if the electric field is horizontal and decreasing in the positive x-direction, then there must be a negative space charge in the region.

10. An electron ($q' = -1.6 \times 10^{-19}$ coul) is placed in the field between the plates of problem 6. (a) What is the force on the electron? (b) How much work is needed to move the electron from the positive to the negative plate? (c) What K.E. will the electron gain in traveling from the negative to the positive plate? (d) If in (c) the electron ($m = 9 \times 10^{-31}$ kg) starts from rest, with what speed will it strike the positive plate?

11. An *electron-volt* is a small unit of energy convenient for atomic physics; it is defined as the energy acquired by an electron that is accelerated through a p.d. of 1 volt. Show that 1 electron-volt $= 1.6 \times 10^{-19}$ joule.

12. Prove that a volt per meter equals a newton per coulomb.

13. A parallel-plate capacitor is charged to a potential of 100 volts and then the charging source is disconnected. If the separation of the plates is now increased from 0.5 cm to 2 cm, what (neglecting edge effects) will be (a) the potential across the plates, and (b) the electric field between the plates? (c) Did the field change? (d) Did the electric energy increase and, if so, where did the added energy come from?

14. Same as problem 13 except that the charging source remains connected to the capacitor.

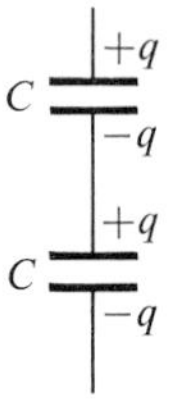

FIG. 12–12.   Capacitors in series.

15. (a) Show that the combined capacitance of two equal capacitors in series (negative plate of the first is connected to positive plate of the second, as in Fig. 12–12) is one-half that of either alone. (b) How should the capacitors be connected so as to give a total capacitance equal to the sum of the separate capacitances?

16. A hollow conductor bears a net charge Q_1. A charge Q_2 is placed on an insulated body inside the conductor. Find the charge on (a) the inside surface, and (b) the outside surface of the conductor.

17. Draw the contour lines of an imaginary topographic map. Let your map include a mountain that is conical in shape except for one sharp ridge and a ravine. Indicate some of the fall lines.

EXPERIMENT 16

FIELDS

Object: To study, as typical fields, the magnetic fields of magnets and the earth.

Problem: Physicists construct in their minds certain concepts and pictorial models, such as the planetary model of the atom, the concept of molecules in motion, and the concept of a field represented by lines of force. These concepts serve to tie together (some say "explain") a lot of experimental facts, and they may suggest new experiments to try, leading to new discoveries.

The concept of a *field* was invented to describe (or explain) action at a distance. Thus since gravitational, electric, magnetic, and nuclear forces may exist between particles in a vacuum, we speak of gravitational fields, electric fields, etc.

Here we shall study magnetic fields because they are the easiest to set up and measure. However, since we shall be dealing with steady magnetic fields due to permanent magnets, there will be a complete analogy between our magnetic fields and certain electric fields. If you wish, you may call all north poles "positive charges" and all south poles "negative charges" and you will have the electrical analogue. Hence imagine lines of force to radiate out from north poles toward south poles. Remember that the intensity of the field due to a point charge falls off inversely with the distance; this is true also for the magnetic field due to a magnetic pole. Since fields have direction, they must be added vectorally. A magnetized iron filing or a small magnetic compass should align itself with the resultant field. The compass is more sensitive, but iron filings give us quickly a picture of the whole field pattern in regions where the field is strong enough to magnetize the filings.

Procedure:

Step 1. Using iron filings, form in turn the magnetic fields listed below and make a sketch of each. Place the magnets on the table, separated about 5 cm, place a sheet of cardboard over them, sift filings onto the cardboard and tap.

(a) Magnets end to end, unlike poles adjacent. Investigate only the field between the magnets.

(b) Magnets end to end, like poles adjacent.

(c) Magnets in T-formation, pole of one about 5 cm from middle of other magnet.

Step 2. (a) Fasten down a sheet of paper about 2 ft square. Using a compass, try to find a location where the earth's field is fairly uniform. Place a magnet near one end of your sheet and outline it on the paper, marking the poles. Indicate at one corner the general direction of the earth's field.

(b) To trace a line of force, put a dot on the paper, set the case of the compass so that the dot is at the edge of the case directly in line with the needle, make a dot close to the case at the other end of the needle. Make use of the second dot to locate a third, and so on.

(c) Enough lines must be traced to show the form of the field over the entire paper. Trace a line until it either runs off the paper or into the magnet, but also try and let the spacing of your lines be in accordance with the *strength* of the field as indicated by how violently the compass oscillates when shaken. Put arrows on each line to show the *direction* of the field.

Step 3. (a) Look for a region where the field has almost zero intensity. Try to explain this vectorally.

(b) Check by vector addition the direction of the field at two other points.

Question: What is the polarity of the earth's equivalent magnetic pole up in the arctic?

EXPERIMENT 17

COULOMB BALANCE
(Determination of the Coulomb Law Constant k_e)

Object: To observe the existence of an electric force, to measure this force, and so to determine the proportionality constant involved.

Problem: According to Coulomb, two charges, q and q', a distance r apart repel one another with a force F_e given by

$$F_e = k_e \frac{qq'}{r^2},$$ (1)

where k_e is a constant of proportionality similar to G in Newton's law of gravitation. We wish to measure k_e experimentally.

Since it is difficult to work with point charges of known value, we shall measure the force between two charged parallel plates (see Fig. 12–13). For such plates the electric force in newtons may be computed from Coulomb's law:

$$F_e = \frac{A(\Delta V)^2}{8\pi k_e d^2},$$ (2)

where A = area of each plate in square meters, ΔV = voltage difference between plates, and d = separation of plates in meters. By measuring F, A, and ΔV, one may determine k_e for the system of units used. Here we use the mks-coulomb system, for which the accepted experimental value for k_e is close to 9×10^9 n-m²/coul² (1 coulomb = 1 ampere-second).

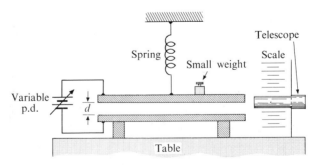

FIG. 12–13. Coulomb balance.

Procedure:

Step 1. With a small weight of mass m (say 50 mg), but no voltage, on the upper movable plate sight your telescope on this plate's bottom edge. (Remember that the field of view in a telescope is reversed.)

Step 2. Gently remove the weight. The upper plate will rise. Now gradually increase ΔV until the electric force F_e replaces the weight mg and the bottom edge of the upper plate is again lined up with the crosshairs of your telescope. Then $F_e = mg$. Record ΔV.

Step 3. It remains to measure the diameter of the plates, so as to compute A, and their separation d at the start and/or finish. The latter may be done best by using a telescope that slides on a vertical scale and reading the scale first with the crosshairs on the bottom of the upper plate and then on the top of the bottom (fixed) plate. Now you may compute k_e. Make several trials, average your values of k_e, and find your actual percent error.

Step 4. Try to justify your error by considering all possible sources of error.

CHAPTER 13

Ampere's Law of Magnetic Force

13–1 The electric current

A succession of moving charges constitutes an electric current. The most common example of such a current is that due to the flow of electrons in a wire. In such a case we define the *electric current I* at a given point in the wire as the time rate of passage of charge through a section of the wire at that point. Let Δq be the charge passing in the time interval Δt. Then, by definition,

$$I = \frac{\Delta q}{\Delta t}. \tag{13–1}$$

It is conventional to take the positive direction of the current to be opposite to the way the electrons flow; as has been said, this convention results from Franklin's choice (long before the discovery of the electron) of positive for the charge left on glass rubbed with silk. In electrolytes and ionized gases an electric current may arise from the combined motions of positive charges in what we call the direction of I and of negative charges moving in the opposite direction.

The mks-coulomb unit of current, called the *ampere* (or *amp*) is defined as

$$1 \text{ ampere} = 1 \text{ coulomb/second}. \tag{13–2}$$

The electric current at a point may be steady or variable with time. The *instantaneous current* is defined in a manner similar to the way we defined instantaneous speed, that is, as the value of the ratio $\Delta q/\Delta t$ for a very short time interval, or the time derivative of q, so that

$$I(\text{instantaneous}) = \lim_{\Delta t \to 0} \left(\frac{\Delta q}{\Delta t} \right) = \frac{dq}{dt}. \tag{13–3}$$

Currents usually flow in completely closed circuits with a constant value of I around the circuit; such a circuit is like an endless rotating belt. A current may, however, lead to or from the plate of a capacitor that is being charged or discharged; this is analogous to water flowing into or out of a storage tank. We shall consider presently the relation of a single moving charge to a current circuit. When a charged particle spins about its own axis, as most elementary particles are believed to do, each element of its charge constitutes a small circular current circuit.

Suppose that we have a wire of cross section A in which there are n electrons of charge $-e$ that are free to move per unit volume. Let $\bar{v}$ be the average drift speed

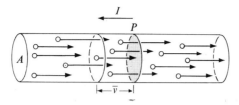

FIG. 13–1.   Motion of free electrons in a wire.

of the electrons along the wire and I the resulting current. If we take a section through the wire at some point P (Fig. 13–1), we may say that all of the moving electrons that are drifting toward this section and are not more than a distance $\bar{v}$ from it will, on the average, cross this section in unit time. Measuring back a distance $\bar{v}$ along the wire, we see that there are $n\bar{v}A$ electrons in this length $\bar{v}$ of the wire, and they will cross our section in unit time, so that charge of magnitude $\Delta q = n\bar{v}Ae$ passes P in the time interval $\Delta t = 1$. Hence the current I (in the direction opposite to that in which the electrons are drifting) will be given by

$$I = \frac{\Delta q}{\Delta t} = n\bar{v}Ae. \tag{13–4}$$

Now consider a *current element*, i.e., a small length Δl of the current-carrying wire. The volume $A\,\Delta l$ of this current element must contain $nA\,\Delta l$ drifting electrons. The magnitude of the total moving charge q in the current element is

$$q = (nA\,\Delta l)e. \tag{13–5}$$

From Eq. (13–4) we see that $nAe = I/\bar{v}$, so that we may write

$$q = \frac{I\,\Delta l}{\bar{v}}. \tag{13–6}$$

If the wire is thin and Δl is very small, the electrons whose charges add up in magnitude to q will all be so close together that they may be regarded as equivalent to a single negative charge $-q$ moving with the speed v in the direction opposite to the current I, or equivalent to a charge $+q$ moving with the speed v in the direction of the current I.

Let $\mathbf{v}$ be the vector with magnitude v and direction of the conventional current and let $\Delta\mathbf{l}$ be the vector with length Δl and the direction of the current and $\mathbf{v}$. Then from these definitions and Eq. (13–6) we have

$$I\,\Delta\mathbf{l} = q\mathbf{v}. \tag{13–7}$$

Reading this equation backwards, we see that it states that a charge q moving with the velocity $\mathbf{v}$ is equivalent to a current I flowing in the section $\Delta\mathbf{l}$ of a circuit. Thus a moving charge is equivalent to the current element whose $I\,\Delta\mathbf{l}$ equals the product $q\mathbf{v}$ for the charge.

EXAMPLE 1. A wire whose cross section is 1 mm^2 carries a current of 1 amp. Assume that $n = 8.0 \times 10^{28}$ free electrons/m^3, a reasonable value for copper. (a) Find the average drift speed of the free electrons. (b) What length of the current-carrying wire would constitute a current element equivalent to a single proton moving with a speed of 10^6 m/sec?

Solution.   (a) Here $I = 1$ amp, $A = 10^{-6}$ m^2, $n = 8.0 \times 10^{28}$/m^3, $e = 1.6 \times 10^{-19}$ coul. From Eq. (13–4) we find for $\bar{v}$, the magnitude of the average drift velocity,

$$\bar{v} = \frac{I}{n\,Ae} = \frac{1 \text{ coul/sec}}{(8 \times 10^{28}/\text{m}^3) \times (10^{-6} \text{ m}^2) \times (1.6 \times 10^{-19} \text{ coul})}$$

$$= 7.8 \times 10^{-5} \text{ m/sec.}$$

(b) Here $v = 10^6$ m/sec. From Eq. (13–7)

$$\Delta l = \frac{qv}{I} = \frac{(1.6 \times 10^{-19} \text{ coul}) \times (10^6 \text{ m/sec})}{1 \text{ coul/sec}}$$

$$= 1.6 \times 10^{-13} \text{ m.}$$

Note the very low value of the drift velocity. Free electrons in a conducting wire do *not* move with anything like the speed of light, or with the speed of atomic particles. Frequent collisions with the atoms of the wire prevent the free electrons from picking up much speed down the wire. It is the tremendous number of free electrons per unit volume that accounts for the large currents of an ampere or more that are frequently sent through electrical lines. From the electrostatic point of view, an ampere *is* a large current because it involves the passage through a section of the wire of a coulomb every second, whereas a static charge of 10^{-6} coul is relatively large. However, it should be realized that an electric current in a wire does not involve *separation* of positive and negative charges, whereas static electrification does. In a wire the free electrons simply move *between* the positive ions formed by the atoms that have contributed these free electrons to the wire. Such a wire does not bear a net charge.

EXAMPLE 2. In a copper sulfate (CuSO$_4$) solution, through which a current passes, the current is carried by positive copper ions, each bearing a charge of $2e$, which move in the direction of I. The copper ions give up their charges to the negative plate and are deposited thereon; the supply of copper ions is replenished by the passage of new copper ions into solution at the positive plate.

The atomic weight of copper is 63.54, so that it takes 6×10^{26} atoms of copper to give a deposit of 63.54 kg (6×10^{26} is Avogadro's number N_0, the number of atoms in a mass in kg equal to the molecular weight). These 6×10^{26} atoms would have to be deposited by an equal number of ions; the charge on each ion being $2e$, the total charge carried by 63.54 kg would be $12 \times 10^{26}e$.

Let m be the mass in kilograms deposited by a current I in the time Δt. Then $m/63.54$ is the fraction of 6×10^{26} ions deposited, and hence the charge Δq carried through the solution must be

$$\Delta q = \frac{m}{63.54} \times 12 \times 10^{26} e.$$

But from the definition of current we have

$$\Delta q = I \Delta t.$$

If we equate these two expressions for Δq, we get

$$12 \times 10^{26} \, me = 63.54 \, I \Delta t.$$

Since m and Δt are easily measured, this expression may be used to compute e if I is read on a calibrated ammeter (a meter that reads current in amperes), or, if one assumes the value of e found by other methods, one may compute I and calibrate a meter placed in the circuit. (See Experiment 19 at end of chapter.)

13–2 The magnetic force

The earliest recorded magnetic phenomena are those that the Greeks discovered in connection with the ore named magnetite, so called because it was found near the city of Magnesia in Thessaly. Magnetite is now known to be iron oxide (Fe_3O_4). The Greeks, and later the Chinese, found that pieces of magnetite attract to themselves unmagnetized iron, the attraction being most pronounced at certain regions called *poles*. It was observed that in this way pieces of iron could be permanently magnetized, and that when a rod of magnetized iron was suspended about a vertical axis, it would align itself in a north-south direction. The north-seeking pole was called the *north pole*, the other the *south pole*. The ancients were thus led to use the magnetic compass in navigation.

Later the forces between magnets were observed and studied. Such *magnetic* forces, which occur between uncharged magnets, are obviously different from electrostatic forces. Coulomb made a careful quantitative study of the forces between magnetic poles and arrived at another general law, very similar to his law of electrostatic force, which states the following.

Like poles repel, unlike poles attract, the force being proportional to the product of the pole strengths and inversely proportional to the square of their distance of separation.

This relation was used to define a unit of pole strength.

For over a century this law of Coulomb was taken to be one of our fundamental laws and pole strength was considered a fundamental concept. Now, however, a better way of describing the electric and magnetic properties of the physical world has been adopted and this way will be described.

The discovery in 1800 by Volta in Italy that an electric current will flow continuously in a wire joining strips of, say, copper and zinc dipped into an acid or salt solution, opened up the possibility of studying the properties of electric currents. One important such property was discovered in 1819 by the Danish

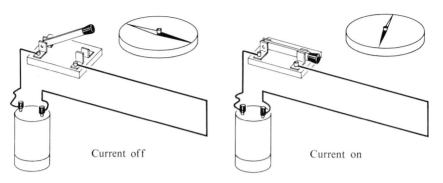

Current off   Current on

FIG. 13–2. Oersted's experiment.

scientist Oersted. Oersted observed that a pivoted magnet was deflected when in the neighborhood of a current-carrying wire (see Fig. 13–2). The importance of this discovery lies in the fact that it showed for the first time an interrelation between electricity and magnetism; it showed that a force can exist between electric currents and magnetic poles. In present-day theory this force is regarded as being of the same fundamental nature as that which exists between neighboring poles, i.e., a *magnetic* force.

If a magnetic force exists between a magnetic pole and an electric current, is it not a logical step to look for a magnetic force between neighboring currents? Such an effect was soon found, and a careful experimental study of it led the French physicist Ampere (1775–1836) to the statement of the general expression for the magnetic force between two current elements. Due to the equivalence between current elements and moving charges, Ampere's law can equally well be taken as the statement of the relationship between the magnetic force, exerted by one moving charge on another, and the magnitudes, velocities, and separation of the two charges.

The final step in the development of our present-day theory of magnetic forces has been to drop the concept of magnetic poles as separate entities, comparable with electric charges. On the one hand, positive and negative charges *can* be completely separated, and there are atomic particles, such as electrons and protons, that have a net charge of one sign or the other. There are conducting media in which charged particles can move and so give rise to an electric current. On the other hand, magnetic north and south poles always occur in pairs and *cannot* be completely separated and isolated. There is no magnetic equivalent of the electron and there are no magnetic conductors in which poles can move and produce magnetic currents. It is possible to show that the magnetic forces which magnets exert on one another may be attributed to magnetic forces between charges moving within the magnetized bodies. The force between an electric current and a magnetic compass is similarly attributed to the forces between the charges moving within the magnet and the moving charges that constitute the electric current. Thus we postulate that all magnetic effects are electrical in origin and are due, not to electrostatic forces and fields, but to those resulting from the motion of charges.

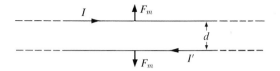

FIG. 13-3.   Magnetic force between long parallel current circuits.

13-3 Ampere's law of magnetic force. Fundamental Law VIII

Ampere was interested in describing the magnetic force between neighboring current circuits. He found experimentally that this force depends not only on the electric current in each circuit, but also on the size, shape, and relative positions and orientations of the two circuits. The general problem seemed hopelessly complex, so Ampere and his contemporaries (notably Biot and Savart) turned to the special case of two long straight wires carrying currents I and I', respectively (see Fig. 13-3). They found that the magnetic force is attractive when the currents are in the same direction and repulsive when the currents are opposite, and that the magnitude of the force is proportional to the product of the currents. (A current may be divided into equal parts by sending it through two or more identical wires in parallel, and in this way a scale of currents may be established, just as Coulomb established a scale of charges.)

When the separation of two parallel current circuits is much less than their length, the force is found to be inversely proportional to the separation, but, as will be shown later, this is just the relationship that would result if the force between neighboring current elements were an *inverse square force*. So we may say that the magnitude F_m of the magnetic force between two neighboring parallel current elements, $I\,\Delta l$ and $I'\,\Delta l'$, a distance r apart (Fig. 13-4), is given by

$$F_m = k_m \frac{(I\,\Delta l)(I'\,\Delta l')}{r^2}, \qquad (13\text{-}8)$$

where k_m is the constant of proportionality. We shall consider this to be a form of *Ampere's law*. Equation (13-8) applies only to adjacent parallel current elements each perpendicular to the line joining them, as in Fig. 13-4. Ampere found that for such an orientation of the current elements, the magnetic force is a *maximum*, and that for other orientations, Eq. (13-8) must be replaced by a more complicated formula. We shall not give, or try to explain, this general formula because it is much better to adopt the field point of view when summarizing Ampere's discoveries, as we shall presently do.

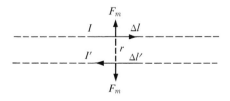

FIG. 13-4.   Magnetic force between current elements.

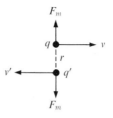

FIG. 13–5.   Magnetic force between two moving charges.

The current elements in Fig. 13–4 are equivalent to two charges, q and q', moving in parallel but opposite directions with the speeds v and v', respectively (as in Fig. 13–5), provided that

$$qv = I\,\Delta l \qquad \text{and} \qquad q'v' = I'\,\Delta l'$$

(see Eq. 13–7). If we substitute these expressions in Eq. (13–8), we get, as another form of Ampere's law,

VIII. $$F_m = k_m \frac{(qv)(q'v')}{r^2} \tag{13–9}$$

for the magnitude of the magnetic force between two charges that are moving in parallel directions and are at their distance of nearest approach, or directly opposite one another. The force is attractive for like charges moving in the same direction and repulsive for like charges moving in opposite directions. This is a special case of our *Fundamental Law VIII*, but it is for this case that one can most easily compare the magnetic with the electric force. However, before we can do this we must discuss the value of the constant of proportionality, k_m.

When we came to Coulomb's law in the last chapter, we assumed that the units of force, distance, time, and charge had already been chosen and that the equation $F_e = k_e\, qq'/r^2$ defines k_e, leaving its value to be determined experimentally. Now we proceed differently, because we are going to use Eq. (13–9), or some other form of Ampere's law, to define our unit of charge, the coulomb. This means that we cannot also use Eq. (13–9) to define k_m, but we must define k_m in advance.

While the value of k_m may be chosen quite arbitrarily, we might as well use some judgment in our choice. In the past, physicists have been tempted to put $k_m = 1$, but in so doing they forced upon themselves a set of *electromagnetic units* which do not coincide with the practical units. Fortunately the electrical engineer's units were so chosen that if we use mks mechanical units and choose

$$k_m = 10^{-7}\ \text{n-sec}^2/\text{coul}^2, \tag{13–10}$$

all of our electrical units will be the same as the *practical* or *electrical engineering units*.

We may now define the *coulomb* as that charge such that if two charges, each 1 coul and each moving side by side at a speed of 1 m/sec in parallel directions, are

1 m apart, then the magnetic action and reaction between them is 10^{-7} n. From this point we may proceed to define the other mks-coulomb units; e.g., 1 amp = 1 coul/sec, 1 volt = 1 j/coul, etc.

13–4 Comparison of the magnetic with the electric force

For the charges in Fig. 13–6, we may say that as far as the *magnetic force* alone is concerned, *like charges attract and unlike charges repel one another.* Equation (13–9) gives the magnitude of this force. Now, although current elements do not normally bear a net charge and so do not experience a Coulomb electric force, two moving charges *do* experience an electric force $\mathbf{F}_e$ in addition to the magnetic force $\mathbf{F}_m$. For the *electric force*, the rule is *like charges repel, unlike attract*, so that, when charges are moving in parallel directions, the magnetic force and the electric force on each charge are opposite.

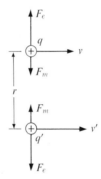

FIG. 13–6.   Electric and magnetic forces between "like" charges.

How do the two forces $\mathbf{F}_e$ and $\mathbf{F}_m$ compare in magnitude? For our special case (Fig. 13–6) we have

$$\frac{F_m}{F_e} = \frac{k_m}{k_e}\, vv'. \tag{13–11}$$

We just saw that putting $k_m = 10^{-7}$ n-sec^2/coul^2 leads to the mks-coulomb system in which k_e has the measured value of $k_e = 9 \times 10^9$ n-m^2/coul^2. Therefore

$$\frac{k_m}{k_e} = \frac{10^{-7}\ \text{n-sec}^2/\text{coul}^2}{9 \times 10^9\ \text{n-m}^2/\text{coul}^2} = \frac{1}{9 \times 10^{16}}\ \frac{\text{sec}^2}{\text{m}^2},$$

and

$$\frac{F_m}{F_e} = \frac{vv'}{9 \times 10^{16}\ \text{m}^2/\text{sec}^2} = \frac{vv'}{c^2}, \tag{13–12}$$

where

$$c = \sqrt{k_e/k_m} = 3 \times 10^8\ \text{m/sec}. \tag{13–13}$$

Not only does $\sqrt{k_e/k_m}$ turn out to have the units of velocity, but it has the magnitude of a very important velocity, namely that of *light* in empty space.

Is this a coincidence or is there a connection between electromagnetic (electric and magnetic) forces and light? This question was answered by Maxwell, and his theory will be discussed in Chapter 15. However, we may say here that physicists always suspect that coincidences such as the above have an underlying significance and are not the result of mere chance.

If we assigned a different value to k_m than 10^{-7} n-sec^2/coul^2, we would obtain a different experimental value for k_e, but the ratio k_e/k_m would not change. The important quantity is neither k_e nor k_m, individually, but their ratio. We are en-countering in $c = \sqrt{k_e/k_m}$ a universal constant of the physical world. This con-stant does not appear in Newtonian mechanics, but it plays an important role in the relativistic mechanics of Einstein, according to which (Chapter 16) no material object can have a speed equal to or greater than c.

13–5 The magnetic field

It is when one comes to a complete description of Ampere's law that the ad-vantages of the field point of view become most apparent.

Two current elements $I \Delta l$ and $I' \Delta l'$ can interact even when located in a vacuum. Here again is "action at a distance"; therefore let us follow a procedure analogous to that in Section 12–3.

Ampere's experimental work on the magnetic force and our *Fundamental Law VIII* may be summarized as follows.

(a) Around every current element (or moving charge) there exists a *magnetic field*, which is a vector quantity different from the electric field **E**.

(b) The *direction* of the magnetic field is represented by the way one's fingers curl when one grasps the current element in one's *right* hand and lets one's thumb point in the direction of the positive current (Fig. 13–7).

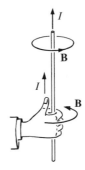

FIG. 13–7. Right-hand fist rule for finding the direction of the magnetic field **B** around a current carrying wire.

(c) The *strength* of the magnetic field (also called the *magnetic induction*) at a distance r in a direction making an angle θ with that of a current element $I \Delta l$, due to $I \Delta l$, is

$$\Delta B = k_m \frac{I \Delta l}{r^2} \sin \theta, \qquad (13\text{–}14)$$

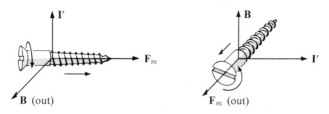

FIG. 13–8. Right-hand screw rule for finding the direction of the magnetic force $\mathbf{F}_m$ on current carrying wire in a magnetic field $\mathbf{B}$.

where $k_m = 10^{-7}$ n-sec²/coul² and $\Delta\mathbf{B}$ will represent the magnetic field due to a current element, and $\mathbf{B}$ that due to a complete circuit or a moving charged particle.

(d) The *force* of a magnetic field $\mathbf{B}$ on a current element $I' \Delta\mathbf{l}'$ placed in the field (but not contributing to it) has the magnitude

$$F_m = I' \Delta l' B \sin \theta', \tag{13-15}$$

where θ' is the angle between the direction of $\mathbf{B}$ and that of the current element $I' \Delta l'$.

(e) The magnetic force is in the *direction* of advance of a right-hand screw rotating from the direction of the positive current in $I' \Delta l'$ to the direction of $\mathbf{B}$ (Fig. 13–8).

If this seems complicated it is because magnetic fields *are* complicated! They are not central (directed radially out from a source) and they are not as independent of direction as are electric or gravitational fields. First consider postulate (c) above. It states that a magnetic field falls off inversely as the square of the distance from its source and that at a given distance the magnetic field is a maximum if $\theta = 90°$ and zero if $\theta = 0°$ (see Fig. 13–9). The inverse square relationship is a familiar one, but the fact that there is no magnetic field in the line of a current element or moving charge is surprising.

Postulate (d) enables us to compute the magnetic force once we have calculated $\mathbf{B}$. Here again there is a direction dependence. If the current element or moving charge *on which* $\mathbf{B}$ acts (*not* that producing $\mathbf{B}$) and $\mathbf{B}$ are directed at right angles to

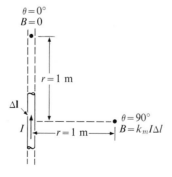

FIG. 13–9. Dependence of magnetic field on direction.

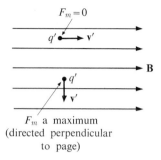

F_m a maximum
(directed perpendicular
to page)

FIG. 13–10.   Dependence of magnetic force on direction of motion of charge.

one another ($\theta' = 90°$), then the force is a maximum, while if they are directed parallel ($\theta' = 0°$), the force is zero (see Fig. 13–10). Equation (13–15) is frequently used to compute B when F_m, I', θ', and $\Delta l'$ are known. For instance, if F_m is the force on a long straight wire of length l' carrying the current I' perpendicular to a uniform magnetic field, then for this field

$$B = \frac{F_m}{I'l'} . \qquad (13–16)$$

On the other hand, if F_m is the force on a charge q' moving with speed v' across the magnetic field, then

$$B = \frac{F_m}{q'v'} , \qquad (13–17)$$

a formula to be compared with Eq. (12–5), $E = F_e/q'$, for the electric field. We must divide F_m by v' as well as by q' because the magnetic force is proportional to v' as well as to q' and B is independent of the moving charge used to measure it (B).

Postulate (e) states the fact that *the magnetic force is always perpendicular to the plane containing* **B** *and the direction of the current or the velocity of the moving charge* on which the magnetic field acts. Thus in Fig. 13–10 the force on the lower charge is perpendicular to the page; whether it is in or out is often of minor importance, although this may be determined from the right-hand screw rule.

The reader may check the above postulates by showing that they lead to an attractive force given by Eq. (13–8) for the case of like current elements side by side. [To be logical, the force in (13–15) should be labeled ΔF_m, since it refers to a current element, and the force in (13–8) should be labeled $\Delta(\Delta F_m) = \Delta^2 F_m$, since it refers to an interaction between *two* current elements; but, for the sake of simplicity, we have dropped the Δ's in front of F_m.]

Ampere made the further postulate that the magnetic field due to two or more current elements is the vector sum of the individual fields, so that the magnetic field **B** at a point P due to a complete current circuit is given by

$$\mathbf{B} = \text{vector sum over circuit } I \text{ of } \Delta\mathbf{B} \text{ in (b) and (c).} \qquad (13–18)$$

The mks-coulomb unit for **B** follows from its definition above; it must be such that with l' in meters and I' expressed in amperes, F_m must come out in newtons.

Hence from Eq. (13–16) our unit for **B** is the newton per ampere-meter (n/amp-m), which is also called the weber per square meter (w/m²). The last statement amounts to a definition of the *weber*. Thus

$$1 \text{ w/m}^2 = 1 \text{ n/amp-m},$$
$$1 \text{ w} = 1 \text{ n-m/amp}.$$

Faraday introduced the concept of magnetic lines of flux, analogous to the electric lines of force discussed in the last chapter. It is customary to take a scale such that there are *B* lines per square meter through a surface normal to **B**; that is, *B* determines the *concentration of the flux*. Thus it is logical to express **B** in terms of something per unit area, that something being flux. Therefore *the weber is the mks-coulomb unit of flux.** Flux will be represented by the symbol Φ.

In the above summary of Ampere's law the calculation of magnetic forces is broken down into two steps, as follows.

Step 1. *Calculation of the magnetic field* **B** *due to a given current circuit.* This involves the application of Eqs. (13–14) and (13–18).

Step 2. *Calculation of the force due to a given magnetic field* **B** *on a current circuit* (other than the one producing **B**), or on a moving charged particle.

Let us consider illustrations of each of these steps.

ILLUSTRATION 1. *A circular current circuit.* We shall compute the magnetic field **B** at the center *P* of a circular coil of radius *R* carrying a current *I* (Fig. 13–11).

Take the current element $I \Delta l$ shown in Fig. 13–11. We see that the angle θ between its direction and that from it to the center of the circuit is 90°, so that $\sin \theta = \sin 90° = 1$. Here $r = R$ for all successive current elements around the circuit, and I and k_m are constant for all such current elements. Therefore at P

$$\Delta B = \frac{k_m I}{R^2} \Delta l,$$

$$B = \sum_{\text{circuit}} \Delta B = \frac{k_m I}{R^2} \sum_{\text{circuit}} \Delta l$$

$$= \frac{k_m I}{R^2} 2\pi R$$

$$= \frac{2\pi k_m I}{R}, \qquad (13\text{–}19)$$

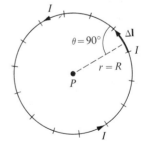

FIG. 13–11. Circular current circuit.

since $\sum \Delta l$ is just the total length of the circuit, which is the circumference of a circle of radius *R*. The direction of **B** is out from the page.

---

* Other magnetic units used in the earlier literature (and in some current articles), together with their relation to our mks-couloumb units, are the following: 1 gauss = 10^{-4} w/m² and 1 maxwell = 10^{-8} w. Thus 1 w/m² = 10,000 gauss and 1 weber = 10^8 maxwells.

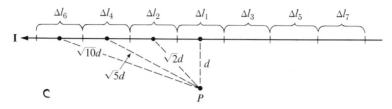

FIG. 13–12.   Long straight current circuit.

ILLUSTRATION 2.   *A long straight current circuit.* We wish to know the value of
B at a distance d from a long straight wire carrying the current I (Fig. 13–12). This
problem can be solved exactly only with the aid of the integral calculus, but let
us attempt an approximate solution.

Consider the segment Δl_1, of length d in Fig. 13–12. For this segment $\sin \theta = 1$
and r^2 is approximately equal to d^2 (it averages slightly more), so that

$$\Delta B_1 \doteqdot \frac{k_m I}{d^2} \cdot d = \frac{k_m I}{d}.$$

For the segment Δl_2, also of length d, $\sin \theta = \sin 45° = 0.7$ and $r^2 = 2d^2$ at
the midpoint, so that substitution in Eq. (13–14) tells us that

$$\Delta B_2 \doteqdot \frac{k_m I d}{2d^2} \times 0.7 = \frac{0.35 k_m I}{d}.$$

The segment Δl_3 is symmetrically located on the other side of Δl_1, so that

$$\Delta B_3 = \Delta B_2 \doteqdot \frac{0.35 k_m I}{d}.$$

For the segments Δl_4, Δl_5, Δl_6, and Δl_7 similar calculations show that

$$\Delta B_4 = \Delta B_5 \doteqdot \frac{0.09 k_m I}{d}, \qquad \Delta B_6 = \Delta B_7 \doteqdot \frac{0.03 k_m I}{d}.$$

We see that the successive contributions to **B** at P drop off rapidly for segments
farther and farther away. For our seven segments

$$\sum_1^7 \Delta B = \frac{1.94 k_m I}{d}.$$

The application of a more precise analysis shows, as one may have guessed, that
the total contribution of all the segments in a very long wire to the magnetic field
at P is

$$B = \frac{2k_m I}{d}. \tag{13–20}$$

The direction of **B** at P is out from the page.

ILLUSTRATION 3. *Force between parallel current circuits.* Let us find the force per unit length on a long straight current circuit with current I' that is parallel and at a distance d from the current circuit in Fig. 13–12 (see Fig. 13–13).

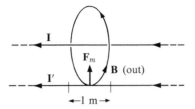

FIG. 13–13.   Magnetic force between parallel current circuits.

Now we use Eq. (13–15), in which B has the value given by Eq. (13–20), $\theta' = 90°$, $\sin \theta' = 1$. Substitution of these values shows that

$$\frac{F_m}{\Delta I'} = I' \times \frac{2k_m I}{d} \times 1 = \frac{2k_m I I'}{d}. \tag{13–21}$$

From postulate (e) above, the direction of this force is toward the wire carrying the current I. As has been stated earlier, these results were first discovered experimentally. Equation (13–21) also furnishes us with a practical method of measuring electric currents in terms of our definitions of k_m, the coulomb and the ampere (see Experiment 18 at end of the chapter). *One ampere is that current which, when flowing in each of two parallel wires 1 m apart, results in a magnetic interaction of 2×10^{-7} newtons per meter.*

ILLUSTRATION 4.   *A rectangular current carrying coil in a uniform magnetic field.* Consider a rectangular coil of one turn suspended so that its plane is parallel to the magnetic field **B**, as in Fig. 13–14. Let the length of the coil perpendicular to

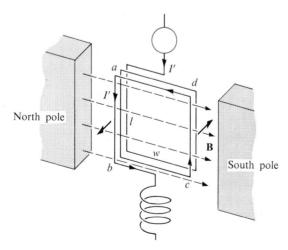

FIG. 13–14.   Torque on a galvanometer coil.

the field be l and its width w, and let the current in the coil be I'. Such a coil is found in *galvanometers*, which are devices for measuring small currents, and in ammeters (which measure larger currents), and voltmeters (which measure potential differences).

The force $\mathbf{F}_m$ on the top (ad) and bottom (bc) of the coil is zero, since for these two sides the current I' flows parallel or antiparallel to $\mathbf{B}$ and $\sin \theta' = 0$. For the side ab, which is perpendicular to $\mathbf{B}$, $\sin \theta' = 1$ and the force $\mathbf{F}_m$ will be $I'lB$ normal to the plane of the coil. On the opposite side cd the force will have the same magnitude, but the opposite direction. The result is a twisting action, or *torque*, as it is called. The effectiveness of this kind of action is measured by the product of the magnitude of either of the two oppositely directed forces and the separation of the forces; in our present problem this product is $I'lBw = I'AB$, where A is the area of the coil. Should the coil have N turns, the torque would be given by $NI'AB$. The important result is that the twisting effect is linearly proportional to the current in the coil and so gives us a simple method of comparing electric currents.

13–6 Properties of magnetic fields contrasted with those of electric fields

Let us summarize for future reference some of the important properties of electric and magnetic fields and then compare them.

(a) Electric lines of force diverge from positive charges and converge on negative ones. If one takes a closed surface S and counts the net electric flux (normal component of field times area) coming out across the whole surface, this net flux out will be proportional to the net charge (positive less negative) enclosed within the surface S. This was stated by Eq. (12–6).

If the magnetic pole concept is dropped and all magnetic fields are attributed to moving charges or currents, then magnetic lines of force have nothing on which to start or end; they cannot diverge or converge. Therefore, a magnetic line of force that enters a closed surface S must also leave S, and hence the net magnetic flux across a closed surface must *always* be zero.

(b) Electric lines of force due to *static* charges do *not* form closed paths, while magnetic lines of force always *do* form closed paths around currents.

(c) Electrostatic fields are conservative and make it practicable to define a potential function V that has a definite value at one point relative to its value at some other point. This is because the work to take a test charge from one point to another in an electrostatic field is independent of the path taken.

The statements in the last paragraph do *not* hold true for magnetic fields. The magnetic field due to a long straight current circuit is directed in circles about the circuit, as in Fig. 13–7. Consider two points on opposite sides of the wire; a path taken between the points will be in opposition to the field if it is followed around the left side of the circuit and it will be in the sense of the field if followed around the right side. This is analogous to the situation in which there is a circular wind pattern, such as around a low-pressure area, and a plane may fly to one side and have a tailwind, while if it flew to the other side it would have a headwind, so that the work done by its engines would not be independent of the path taken between two cities on opposite sides of the low-pressure area. Thus in the case of magnetic fields it is not practicable to introduce a potential function analogous to the electric potential V.

(d) The facts stated in (b) and (c) may be expressed as follows. Take a closed path s and call the displacement along a small piece of the path Δs. Multiply Δs by the component of the field in the direction of Δs. Add for all the segments Δs around the closed path and call the sum

$$\sum_{\text{closed path}} F_s \, \Delta s,$$

where F_s denotes the component of the field along the path. Then for an electrostatic field $\mathbf{E}$,

$$\sum_{\text{closed path}} E_s \, \Delta s = 0,$$

while for a magnetic field

$$\sum_{\text{closed path}} B_s \, \Delta s \neq 0$$

if the path encloses a current.

13–7 The action of electric and magnetic fields on charged particles

Electric and magnetic fields have been and are being used to accelerate and deflect elementary particles and atomic ions. Such experiments usually enable one to determine (a) the speed v, and (b) the charge-to-mass ratio q/m, of the particle in terms of the E and B values of the applied fields.

The force $\mathbf{F}_e$ due to an electric field $\mathbf{E}$ acting on a particle of charge q is

$$\mathbf{F}_e = q\mathbf{E}, \tag{13–22}$$

while the force $\mathbf{F}_m$ due to a magnetic field $\mathbf{B}$ acting on a particle of charge q moving with a velocity v has the magnitude

$$F_m = qv \, B \sin \theta, \tag{13–23}$$

where θ is the angle between $\mathbf{v}$ and $\mathbf{B}$;* $\mathbf{F}_m$ has the direction of advance of a right-hand screw rotating from $\mathbf{v}$ to $\mathbf{B}$. The statements about the magnetic force follow from Ampere's law if, in the postulates (d) and (e) of Section 13–5, one replaces $I'\Delta l'$ with qv and considers the direction of motion of a positive charge to be equivalent to that of a positive current (and that of a negative charge to be the opposite).

It is a good thing to remember in connection with experiments involving charged particles and fields that (1) gravitational forces are negligible, (2) an electric field $\mathbf{E}$ in the direction of motion will speed up or slow down the particle, depending on the sign of its charge, (3) an electric field $\mathbf{E}$ transverse to the motion will deflect the particle, (4) a magnetic field $\mathbf{B}$ parallel to $\mathbf{v}$ will have *no effect* at all, and (5) a magnetic field $\mathbf{B}$ transverse to the motion will deflect the particle, but not alter its speed.

---

* Primes have been dropped, since only one charge is involved here.

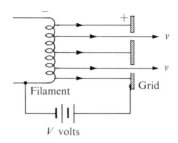

FIG. 13–15.   Acceleration of electrons to a positive grid.

(a) *Determination of v.* The three most commonly used methods of determining the speed of a particle are the following.

Method 1.   Acceleration of a charged particle through a known p.d. without collisions. In a vacuum tube, electrons that, in a sense, "boil off" from a hot filament may be accelerated toward a positive grid or tunnel-shaped electrode. Some of the electrons will strike the electrode and be captured, but others will shoot through the holes of the grid, or the tunnel, into the region beyond (Fig. 13–15). Let the potential of the grid (or tunnel) be V volts above that of the filament, so that the work done by the electric field on the electron (of charge $-e$) is

$$W = eV.$$

If the electron starts practically from a state of rest and does not suffer any collisions, we may equate W to its gain in K.E., so that we have

$$eV = \tfrac{1}{2}mv^2,$$

$$v = \sqrt{\frac{2eV}{m}}, \tag{13–24}$$

where v is the final speed and m the mass of the electron.

This same method may be applied to other particles of charge q (instead of e), provided that one knows that they are accelerated practically from rest.

Method 2.   Balancing a moving charged particle in crossed electric and magnetic fields. Let a particle of charge q and mass m move horizontally into a region where an electric field $\mathbf{E}$ exerts an upward force $\mathbf{F}_e$ and a magnetic field $\mathbf{B}$ simultaneously exerts a downward force $\mathbf{F}_m$ on the particle. If $\mathbf{F}_e$ and $\mathbf{F}_m$ are equal in magnitude, as well as opposite in direction, the net force on the particle will be zero and it will pass undeflected through the region of the fields. The necessary condition for this to happen is that

$$F_e = F_m,$$
$$qE = qvB \sin \theta.$$

The q may be cancelled on each side of the last equation. If the magnetic force is to be directed downward on a particle moving, say, to the north, then $\mathbf{B}$ must be to the east if q is positive (and to the west if q is negative). Here $\mathbf{v}$, $\mathbf{E}$, and $\mathbf{B}$ are

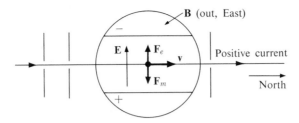

FIG. 13–16.   Crossed electric and magnetic fields.

mutually perpendicular (Fig. 13–16) and $\sin \theta = 1$.   Therefore

$$v = \frac{E}{B}.$$
(13–25)

Method 3.   Deflection of a moving charged particle in a transverse magnetic field only.   Let the particle of charge q, mass m, and velocity $\mathbf{v}$ move at right angles to a uniform magnetic field $\mathbf{B}$.   Since $\mathbf{F}_m$ is normal to $\mathbf{v}$, the latter will change in direction, but not in magnitude.   In other words, the particle will undergo centripetal acceleration and move in a circular path whose radius we shall call R. $\mathbf{F}_m$ now provides the centripetal force $\mathbf{F}_c$ required for this circular motion.   We therefore put

$$F_c = F_m,$$

$$\frac{mv^2}{R} = qvB,$$

$$v = \frac{qBR}{m}.$$
(13–26)

The paths of charged particles may be made visible in several ways; the paths may be photographed in cloud and bubble chambers.*   In this way R may be measured.   A known magnetic field may be generated by sending a known current through one or more circular coils and then computing B with the aid of a formula derived from Ampere's law, such as Eq. (13–19).   If the nature of the particle is known, then its q/m ratio may be taken from tables and v computed from Eq. (13–26).

(b) *Determination of q/m.*   Suppose now that the q/m ratio of a certain particle has not yet been determined and we wish to measure its value.   How would we proceed?

Many ingenious methods of measuring q/m for particles have been devised.   The simplest ones involve a combination of two of the three methods just described for finding v, so that between two of the equations

$$v = \sqrt{\frac{2qV}{m}}, \qquad v = \frac{E}{B}, \qquad v = \frac{q}{m}BR,$$

we may eliminate v and solve for q/m.

---

* See texts on modern physics.

The charge q is usually known; it is most often one or two electron units (1.6×10^{-19} coul) so that the determination of q/m leads to that of m. Such devices for determining m are called *mass spectrographs*.

13–8 The cyclotron and its successors

The cyclotron was invented by the American physicist E. O. Lawrence (1901–1958). It is a device for imparting a very high energy W to a charged particle by giving it many small increments in energy, such as 100 increments each equal to $W/100$. By this method the high potential differences and resulting insulation problems of Van de Graaff and transfomer-rectifier devices are avoided.

The cyclotron (see Fig. 13–17) employs a magnetic field to bend the charged particles in a circular path inside an evacuated "tank." Within the tank are two hollow D-shaped electrodes which are connected to a source of alternating potential of high frequency and fairly high voltage. There is thus an alternating electric field $\mathbf{E}$ across the gap between the "dees." Suppose that a particle is accelerated across the gap and then, after completing a semicircular path under the influence of the applied magnetic field $\mathbf{B}$, it again reaches the gap just when the electric field has been reversed. Such a particle will receive a second accelerating boost from the electric field. Then (and here is the important point) the particle will continue to be boosted every successive time it crosses the gap, as long as its mass remains constant and $\mathbf{B}$ does not change. The proof of this statement follows.

We have seen that for charged particles moving across a magnetic field $\mathbf{B}$ the radius of curvature R of their path must be given by Eq. (13–26), or

$$R = \frac{vm}{qB}. \tag{13–27}$$

The time t required for a half-revolution in a circular orbit of radius R will be

$$t = \frac{\pi R}{v} = \frac{\pi m}{qB}, \tag{13–28}$$

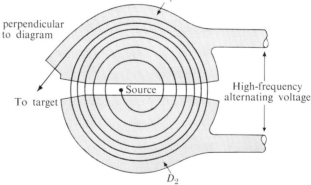

FIG. 13–17.   Schematic diagram of a cyclotron.

a time that is not dependent on the speed v or radius R. (In a larger orbit the particle just goes proportionately faster.)

The particles spiral outward until they near the outer wall where, having attained their maximum energy, they are deflected toward some target.

We shall see in Chapter 16 that at speeds of over one-tenth the speed of light the mass of a particle is *not* constant, but increases. This increases the time t in Eq. (13–28), so that the particle arrives at the gap between the dees *after* the accelerating electric field has passed its maximum value. To compensate for this effect, one may (1) allow **B** to increase with m, or (2) allow the frequency of the alternating field to decrease with $1/m$ for a pulse of accelerating particles; after such a pulse has reached the target, the process may be repeated. Such devices are called *synchrocyclotrons*, since accelerations are synchronized with the relativistic mass increase.

To give heavy particles still higher energies, physicists have been forced to build larger and larger accelerators, since R in Eq. (13–27) increases first with v and then with m. It is much too expensive to build a cyclotron-type magnet with solid cylindrical poles many feet in diameter (the largest is 15 ft), and so in the large *synchrotrons or bevatrons* (which impart billions of electron-volts of energy to particles) it has been necessary to use ring-shaped magnets to supply the deflecting magnetic field. If particles are preaccelerated up to speeds close to that of light, their speed will not undergo much further change, and so if the particles are held in a fixed orbit, the time for a revolution will also remain nearly constant. Then the magnetic field need be applied only at this orbit and not throughout its entire area. The magnetic field must, however, be increased periodically as pulses of particles are brought up to the maximum energy. The synchrotron at the Brookhaven National Laboratories on Long Island, New York, is 840 ft in diameter and accelerates protons up to energies of 30 billion electron-volts. Still larger accelerators are planned in the United States, in the U.S.S.R. and perhaps elsewhere.

EXAMPLE. Protons are accelerated to a speed $v = 0.1c = 3 \times 10^7$ m/sec. Find their energy and the radius of curvature of their path in a magnetic field $B = 0.8$ w/m^2 = 0.8 n/amp-m = 0.8 n-sec/coul-m.

Solution. Since $v = 0.1c$, we may neglect (but just barely) relativistic effects. Then $m = 1.6 \times 10^{-27}$ kg for protons. The K.E. of each proton will be

$$\text{K.E.} = \tfrac{1}{2}mv^2$$

$$= \tfrac{1}{2}(1.6 \times 10^{-27} \text{ kg}) \times (3 \times 10^7 \text{ m/sec})^2$$

$$= 7.2 \times 10^{-13} \text{ joule}$$

$$= \frac{7.2 \times 10^{-13} \text{ j}}{1.6 \times 10^{-19} \text{ j/electron-volt*}} = 4.5 \times 10^6 \text{ electron-volts.*}$$

---

* See problem 11 of Chapter 12.

In Eq. (13–27) we have $m = 1.6 \times 10^{-27}$ kg and $q = 1.6 \times 10^{-19}$ coul for protons, so that

$$R = \frac{vm}{qB}$$

$$= \frac{(3 \times 10^7 \text{ m/sec}) \times (1.6 \times 10^{-27} \text{ kg})}{(1.6 \times 10^{-19} \text{ coul}) \times (0.8 \text{ n-sec/coul-m})}$$

$$= 3.75 \times 10^{-1} \text{ m}$$

$$= 37.5 \text{ cm.}$$

PROBLEMS

1. What is the magnitude and direction of the current due to a discharge through air in which 6×10^{17} electrons of charge $-e$ pass downward and 2×10^{17} ions of charge $+e$ pass upward through a given area in 0.1 sec?

2. The belt of a Van de Graaff generator is 40 cm wide and travels at a speed of 20 m/sec. If 5×10^{-6} coul of charge is sprayed on every square meter of the outside face of the upgoing belt and -5×10^{-6} coul/m^2 on the outside of the downgoing belt, what is the current (useful plus leakage) that will flow from the upper plate to ground?

3. How long will it take a current of 1 amp to deposit 1 gm of copper from a copper sulfate solution?

4. Show that the direction of the magnetic force on a charged particle moving perpendicular to an applied field **B** is toward the region where the magnetic field of the particle is opposite to **B**.

5. Show that the path of a charged particle moving obliquely to a magnetic field **B** is a helix, or spiral, about a magnetic line of force.

6. If charged particles from outer space, such as (1) electrons from solar disturbances, or (2) primary cosmic ray particles, enter the earth's magnetic field, to what areas of the earth's surface will such particles arrive in the (a) greatest number, (b) least number?

7. Look up and explain the relationship of problem 6 to the occurrence of Northern Lights.

8. Two parallel current circuits, each 30 cm long and 1 cm apart, carry the same current I. Compute the force between the circuits, both in newtons and in gram-weight, when $I = 5, 10, 15,$ and 20 amp, respectively.

9. Derive Eq. (13–20) as exactly as you can without using calculus.

10. Find **B** on the axis of a circular current circuit of radius R and at a distance $R/2$ from the plane of the coil.

11. Through the corners of a square and perpendicular to its surface pass four wires, each carrying an upward current of 10 amp. If the square is 2 cm on a side, what is the magnitude and direction of the net force per meter on one wire? This is the "pinch effect" observed in the parallel motion of charged particles in a plasma.

12. Two cylinders are wound with wire carrying a current. If the cylinders are placed end-to-end on the same axis and the current in each circulates the same way, will the cylinders attract or repel one another? Show that each cylinder behaves magnetically like a bar magnet.

13. A wire carries an electron current of 1 amp. If an observer moves parallel with the wire at the same speed as the average drift velocity of the electrons, what current will he observe in the wire? Explain.

14. A beam of alpha particles, which are known to be doubly charged helium ions, passes undeflected through crossed electric and magnetic fields. The electric field is produced by using parallel plates 2 cm apart with a p.d. of 200 volts. The magnetic field is that inside a long helical coil with 318.4 ($=1000/\pi$) turns/m and carrying a current of 2.5 amp. For such a helical coil or "solenoid" the magnetic induction B inside, as computed from Ampere's law, is given by the formula $B = 4\pi k_m NI/l$, where N/l represents the turns per meter of length and I the current. Compute E, B, and the speed of the alpha particles.

15. The alpha particles in problem 14 are allowed to pass on into a region where their path is perpendicular to a second magnetic field of 0.5 w/m^2; the radius of their circular path is 40 cm. (a) Find q/m for the particles. (b) Assume $q = 2e$ and find m. (c) Through what p.d. would one have to accelerate a helium ion from rest to give it the speed found in problem 13?

16. Show that for a circular path of *any* radius about a long straight wire carrying a current I

$$\sum_{\text{closed path}} B_s \, \Delta s = 4\pi k_m I.$$

EXPERIMENT 18

AMPERE BALANCE

(Ampere's Law and Calibration of an Ammeter)

Object: To observe the magnetic force between adjacent currents and to calibrate an ammeter.

Problem: According to Ampere's law the magnetic force F_m between two parallel conductors each of length L, separated by a distance d, and each carrying the current I is

$$F_m = 2k_m I^2 L/d. \tag{1}$$

The logical procedure followed has been to define k_m as 10^{-7} n/amp^2 and to use this equation to define the *ampere*. By measuring F_m, L, and d one may compute the value of I in a given case, pass this same current through an ammeter, and so calibrate the ammeter.

Procedure:

Step 1. The Ampere balance* consists of a delicately balanced metal rod which may be located just above a similar fixed rod. Following a procedure similar to that of Experiment 17, one starts with a small mass m on the upper rod, which is adjusted so that with the weight mg acting downward, the two rods have a suitable separation, say about 1 cm. The weight is removed and the balance restored at the same separation by substituting for mg a magnetic force of attraction F_m just equal to mg. This is done by gradually increasing the current I through the two rods and watching the position of the movable rod through a telescope until it is seen to return to its original position. Then

$$F_m = 2k_m I^2 L/d = mg. \tag{2}$$

---

* Purchasable from the W. M. Welch Mfg. Co., 1515 Sedgwick St., Chicago 10, Ill.

Step 2. The length L and separation d must be measured. For the latter it is best to find the diameter of each conducting rod with calipers and the air gap separation of the rods with a telescope and scale. Then d is the center-to-center separation of the rods.

Step 3. By placing an ammeter in series with the Ampere balance, so that the same current I passes through each, one may check the scale reading of the ammeter for each value of I computed from Eq. (2). To obtain different currents one may alter either the mass m or the separation d. In so doing one may observe the relation between F_m and each of these factors.

EXPERIMENT 19

ELECTROLYSIS
(Determination of the Electronic Charge e)

Object: To measure the atomic unit of charge.

Problem: The smallest positive charge obtainable is believed to be that on an object that has lost one of its normal quota of electrons. We shall call this charge $+e$. If a neutral body gains an additional electron, the body will have a charge of $-e$. Millikan measured such charges on small oil drops, but this experiment is beyond the scope of this course. Chemists have proven that copper atoms in copper sulfate are bivalent, or that in a solution of this salt the sulfate ion takes two electrons from the copper atom and so each copper ion has a charge of $2e$. Here we shall measure the charge per copper ion and so find e.

Chemists have measured the atomic weight of copper to be 63.54 and so 63.54 kg of copper equal one kg-mole. A kg-mole of any substance contains the same number (N_0) of atoms. What is N_0 called? N_0 may be determined independently in a number of ways, such as by means of x-ray diffraction, radioactivity, sedimentation, etc., and the value found for it is 6×10^{26}. A simple, though rough, method of determining N_0 is outlined in Experiment 24 at the end of Chapter 18. Knowing N_0, we can compute how many copper ions there are in a given mass (m) of copper.

By means of an electric current, one can cause m kg of copper to be electroplated out in a given time. From the definition relating current to charge, the charge q carried to an electrode by a current I flowing for t seconds is

$$q = It.$$

By measuring m, one may compute how many copper ions it took to transport this charge and hence find the charge per ion. But each ion carried a charge $2e$, so e can be computed.

Procedure:

Step 1. Derive the formula you will use to compute e in terms of N_0, m, I, t, and the atomic weight of copper.

Step 2. Clean the copper plate rubbing it well with sandpaper and rinsing with water and alcohol. After the plate is *completely dry*, weigh it carefully on the balance. Place the plate in the battery jar nearly filled with copper sulfate solution.

Step 3. Connect the cell in series with the ammeter, a knife switch, a rheostat, and a source of current. Be sure the weighted copper plate is the negative electrode. Before closing the switch have your connections checked by the instructor. Now close the switch noting the time and regulating the current until it is approximately 1 amp. Keep the current constant throughout the entire process by watching the ammeter carefully and changing the resistance if necessary. Allow the current to flow for 50 min. Remove the copper plate, after noting the final ammeter reading. Rinse the plate thoroughly and allow to dry before weighing. Weigh again very carefully to determine the amount of copper deposited.

Step 4. Compute e and compare your value with the accepted value of 1.6×10^{-19} coulombs. Can you justify your percent error?

EXPERIMENT 20

THE RATIO e/m FOR ELECTRONS

Object: To measure the charge to mass ratio for electrons and compute the mass of an electron using the Bainbridge tube.*

Problem: We know from Ampere's law and the field concept that a moving charge is acted on by the magnetic field of neighboring moving charges. The latter will in this experiment be the electrons carrying a current I in two coils of wire. These coils will be so wound and situated that their separation equals the radius of each, and they are then called Helmholtz coils. For such a pair of coils the magnetic field in the center region between the coils is very uniform and, moreover, the strength of the field may be computed from the formula

$$B = \frac{32\pi nI}{\sqrt{125a}} \times 10^{-7}, \tag{1}$$

where B is the magnetic field in w/m^2 (the mks-coulomb unit), n is the number of turns per coil, I is the current in amperes, and a is the mean radius of the coils.

When a charge e moves with speed v across a magnetic field B, a magnetic force F_m will act perpendicular to its motion. The particle then will travel in a circular path of radius R for which

$$\frac{e}{m} = \frac{v}{BR}. \tag{2}$$

The value of B may be computed from Eq. (1) and R may be measured, but how do we eliminate v? This is done as follows. We shall accelerate our electrons from rest to the speed v by pulling them through a known potential difference of V volts. As one volt = 1 j/coul, the work done on the electron will be eV joules. We equate this to the gain in kinetic energy and get

$$\tfrac{1}{2} mv^2 = eV \tag{3}$$

---

* This tube and the accompanying coils may be purchased from the W. M. Welch Mfg. Co., 1515 Sedgwick St., Chicago 10, Ill.

Between (2) and (3) we can eliminate v and get

$$\frac{e}{m} = \frac{2V}{B^2 R^2},$$ (4)

where V may be measured with a voltmeter.

Procedure:

Step 1. Derive Eq. (4) and then substitute in it for B from Eq. (1).

Step 2. Inspect apparatus and be sure of what each meter measures.

Step 3. Set the plate voltage at 30 volts and close the filament switch. The plate current should be 5 to 8 milliamp, filament current 4.2 to 4.3 amp; if this is not so *consult your instructor*, but *do not* try to change filament current yourself.

Step 4. Adjust the current in the coils so that the electron beam will be undeflected by the earth's magnetic field. This current reading must be subtracted from following readings.

Step 5. Increase the current in the coils until the electron beam is bent around so that its outer edge passes through the center of the prong nearest the filament; R is then 0.032 m.

Step 6. Repeat 5 for the next two prongs, for which $R = 0.039$ and 0.045 m, respectively.

Step 7. Set the plate voltage at 45 volts and repeat Step 6.

Step 8. After compensating for the earth's field in the coil current readings, calculate $V/I^2 R^2$ for each run and average your five values for this quantity. Use this average value of $V/I^2 R^2$ to compute e/m.

Step 9. Compare your value with the accepted value of 1.76×10^{11} coul/kg.

Step 10. From Experiments 19 and 20 compute your value for m, the mass of the electron.

CHAPTER 14

Faraday's Law of Electromagnetic Induction

14–1 Introduction

In Chapter 13 we assumed that we were dealing with magnetic fields which did not change with time, or whose time dependence could be ignored. Such steady magnetic fields are analogous to the fields of static charges in electricity. Hence Chapter 13 might have been entitled "magnetostatics." To complete our discussion of magnetic fields, in the present chapter we shall deal with the effects of changing magnetic fields.

From the work of Oersted, Ampere, and others, Faraday knew that electric currents could produce magnetic fields. With this knowledge he then began to look for the converse effect, i.e., currents produced *by* magnetic fields. While he found that a steady magnetic field passing through a stationary coil of wire connected to a galvanometer produced no current, he did observe a temporary current in the coil when the magnetic field linking it was changed. We now call this effect *electromagnetic induction*, and currents produced in this way are termed *induced currents*.

Faraday proceeded to investigate all the possible ways of producing induced currents and then he summarized his results in the law that bears his name. There are several different methods of inducing a current in a conducting circuit. First, the circuit may be rigid but moving in the magnetic field in such a way that the total magnetic *flux* (lines of magnetic field) through the circuit is changing with time, as when a coil is rotated in a magnetic field. Second, the circuit may be deformable and its area may be changing in such a way that the total flux through the circuit is varying. Third, the circuit may have constant area but include a changing path in a moving conductor (such as a rotating disc) which is moving across a magnetic field **B**. Fourth, the circuit may be stationary, but the magnetic field **B** directed through a surface enclosed by the circuit may vary with the time. Combinations of these methods are also possible. In general, we may classify the above processes into (a) those involving motion of all or part of the circuit, and (b) those involving a time rate of change of **B**. We shall find that in (a) the effects may be explained in terms of the expression for the magnetic force as given by Ampere's law, but that in (b) we are encountering something quite apart from either Ampere's or Coulomb's law.

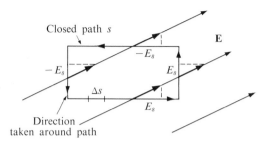

FIG. 14–1. Work done by an electrostatic field on a charge taken around a closed path is zero.

14–2 Definition of electromotive force

Let us call the electric fields due to stationary charges *electrostatic fields*. We have seen that if we imagine that an agent takes a small test charge around any closed path s in such a field (see Fig. 14–1), then the total work done by the field on the charge will be zero, since the field is conservative and the charge starts and ends at the same potential. If we break the path s up into a large number of directed line segments Δs and call E_s the component of the electrostatic field E in the direction of Δs, then since E is the force per unit charge and $E_s \Delta s$ represents work per charge,

$$\sum_{\text{closed path}} E_s \, \Delta s = 0 \tag{14–1}$$

expresses the fact that if a charge is taken around any closed path, the work done on it by an electrostatic field is zero.

If a conductor is placed in an electrostatic field, the charges in the conductor that are free to move will temporarily do so and redistribute themselves in such a way that at all points within the conductor the electric field is zero; all points within the conductor will then be at a common potential.

At ordinary temperatures the free charges in a conductor encounter resistance when they move through the conductor, which means that, when a steady current is maintained, electrical energy is continually being dissipated; a rise in the temperature of the conductor reminds us that this energy has become part of the internal energy of the conductor. This irreversible process is called the *Joule heating effect*, and it requires the presence of a device whereby energy may be taken from some outside source and continually converted into electrical energy. Such a device must produce an electric field E' for which the work done on a charge around a closed path is *not* zero, i.e.,

$$\sum_{\text{closed path}} E'_s \, \Delta s \neq 0.$$

This must be so in order that work may be done by the charge against resistance forces. The field E' will be called a *nonelectrostatic field;* a source of such a field is said to be the seat of an *electromotive force,* or *emf.* The electromotive force around a closed path (which is usually taken coincident with an electric circuit) will be designated as ε, and it is defined as

$$\varepsilon = \sum_{\text{closed path}} E'_s \, \Delta s. \tag{14–2}$$

This represents the work per charge done by the field; ε is expressed in volts (or newtons per coulomb), the same units as are used for electric potential.

If an electric current is to be maintained in a closed circuit, there must be an emf in the circuit, just as a closed water circuit needs a pump to maintain the flow against resistance and to maintain all the pressure drops in the various parts of the circuit. The emf of a circuit is usually localized, like the pump in a water circuit, but this need not be so.

ILLUSTRATION. *Joule's law of electric heating.* Let a current I flow in a circuit containing the emf ε. Then the work done by ε when a charge Δq passes around the circuit is $\varepsilon \, \Delta q$. The time rate of doing work, called the *power P*, is

$$P = \frac{\varepsilon \, \Delta q}{\Delta t} = \varepsilon \, \frac{\Delta q}{\Delta t} = \varepsilon I. \tag{14–3}$$

Now suppose that the current I is proportional to ε (this is the case for the commonly used metallic conductors, but not for vacuum tubes or transistors), so that we may write

$$\varepsilon = IR, \tag{14–4}$$

where R is a constant for our special case. Then we may eliminate ε in Eq. (14–3) and write

$$P = I^2 R. \tag{14–5}$$

With R constant we have the relation that *the power is proportional to the square of the current*, which is known as *Joule's law.* Of course one may always introduce and define R (it is called the *resistance*) by Eq. (14–4), but one cannot always assume that R is independent of the current. If R does depend on I, then P will not be proportional to I^2. The mks-coulomb unit for resistance is the volt per ampere, which is called the *ohm.*

Let us consider some sources of emf. The outside source of energy in a photocell is light, in a thermocouple it is heat, and in a battery it is chemical energy. In a generator, work is performed when a conductor is moved across a magnetic field and this work is converted into electrical energy. The expression for the resulting emf may be derived from Ampere's law. This emf is called a *motional electromotive force.*

14–3 Motional electromotive force

Let us take a simple example. In Fig. 14–2, let ab be a movable conductor of length l parallel to what we shall take to be the x-axis. To eliminate the effect of weight, picture the conductor riding on two frictionless horizontal tracks extend-

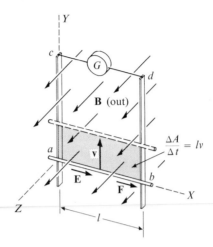

FIG. 14–2. Motional electromotive force.

ing in the y-direction. Assume that a uniform magnetic field **B** extends in the z-direction (out from the page in Fig. 14–2). Now let us suppose that the conductor is moved at a speed v in the positive y-direction. The free charge q in the wire will, according to Ampere's law, experience a force **F** given by Eq. (13–23), which tells us that the force is

$$\mathbf{F} = qvB \tag{14–6}$$

in the plus x-direction. Imagine a reference system moving with the conductor, so that in this system the free charge in the wire is a static charge experiencing the force **F**. Since a magnetic force does not act on a static charge, an observer in this moving reference system would say that an electric force, represented by an electric field, must be present. Whether this force is termed electric or magnetic depends on the choice of reference system to which it is referred. The important thing is that there is a force acting on the charge q and that this force can be used to drive a current around the circuit. The contact points at a and b will correspond electrically to the terminals of a battery. From the relation between electric force and field we have for the effective electric field (it is nonelectrostatic)

$$\mathbf{E}' = \frac{\mathbf{F}}{q} = vB$$

in the x-direction. This effective field exists only in the moving arm ab of length l. From Eq. (14–2), we have for the emf around the circuit

$$\mathcal{E} = \sum E'_s \, \Delta s = vBl. \tag{14–7}$$

Since vl is the area swept out by the moving arm per unit time, which we shall call $\Delta A / \Delta t$, we may write

$$\mathcal{E} = B \frac{\Delta A}{\Delta t}. \tag{14–8}$$

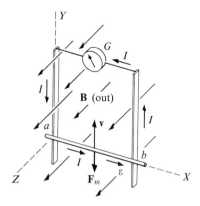

FIG. 14–3   Electric generator.

Note that if the entire circuit were moving in the y-direction with the speed v, the galvanometer arm cd would experience an effective $\mathbf{E}'$ from c toward d just equal to that in ab, and, as a result, the ε for the circuit would be zero. The galvanometer G would then show no deflection. Therefore what we detect in the case where only the arm ab moves is the relative motion of ab with respect to the rest of the circuit.

Figure 14–3 shows the same circuit as in Fig. 14–2; as before, ab is the moving arm. The induced current I, which is in the counterclockwise sense, is also indicated. The time rate of doing work by the field, or the power P, is given by Eq. (14–3), or

$$P = \varepsilon I.$$

Since this work is expended only when the conductor is moving across the magnetic field, the source of the energy must be the agent moving the wire, as we shall now show.

From Chapter 13 we know that a conductor of length l carrying a current I across a uniform magnetic field $\mathbf{B}$ experiences a force which, to distinguish it from the force $\mathbf{F}$ in Eq. (14–6), we shall call $\mathbf{F}_m$. From Eq. (13–15), we have

$$\mathbf{F}_m = IlB$$

in the direction of advance of a right-hand screw turning from the direction of $\mathbf{I}$ to that of $\mathbf{B}$, that is, in the negative y-direction. Since $\mathbf{F}_m$ is opposite to the direction of motion, moving the wire with the speed v involves expending power by the moving agent (say one's hand) at the rate

$$P = F_m v = IlBv. \tag{14–9}$$

Equating the two expressions for P, we again find that

$$\varepsilon = vBl,$$

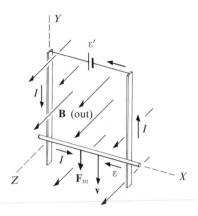

FIG. 14-4.   Electric motor.

which shows that the derivation of this equation based on Ampere's law and the concept of an electric field existing in a conductor that is moving across a magnetic field are consistent with the conservation of energy principle. This, then, is the theory of the *electrical generator*, through which mechanical energy is converted into electrical energy.

If we choose to move the conductor in the opposite direction, as in Fig. 14–4, the directions of the induced electric field and the emf ε will be reversed. To maintain the current I in the same sense as before, we must insert into the circuit a battery or generator whose emf ε' is opposite to, and greater than, the ε due to the moving conductor. In this case the force $\mathbf{F}_m$ will be the same as before (Fig. 14–3), but the conductor is now moving in the direction of $\mathbf{F}_m$. When an object moves in the direction of an applied force it receives mechanical energy.   The source of this energy must be in the electrical circuit, for the current I is moving against the induced emf. This energy source is the battery or generator inserted elsewhere in the circuit, of which the moving conductor is a part.   This is the principle of the *electric motor*, through which electrical energy is converted into mechanical energy.

EXAMPLE. A metal airplane with a wingspan of 60 m flies at 900 km/hr, cutting the vertical component of the earth's magnetic field, for which $B = 5 \times 10^{-5}$ w/m². What is the p.d. between the wingtips?

Solution. Here $v = 9 \times 10^5$ m/3600 sec and, since 1 w/m² = 1 n/amp-m, we have

$$\varepsilon = vBl$$

$$= \frac{9 \times 10^5 \text{ m}}{3600 \text{ sec}} \times \frac{5 \times 10^{-5} \text{ n}}{\text{amp-m}} \times 60 \text{ m}$$

$$= 0.75 \text{ n-m/amp-sec} = 0.75 \text{ j/coul} = 0.75 \text{ volts.}$$

One should realize that this value of ε would be much greater if the earth's field were comparable in strength with the magnetic fields of most magnets.

14-4 Magnetic flux

We found it convenient to picture an electric field by drawing lines of force to show the direction of the field, and to represent the strength of the field by the concentration of these lines. It was stated that we may do the same thing for a magnetic field. Let us arbitrarily take B lines of force per unit area through a surface whose normal is in the direction of **B**. (Because of the small numerical value of B when it is expressed in mks-coulomb units, lines of fractional value must be imagined.) In any event, we define the total *magnetic flux* Φ crossing a surface of area A perpendicular to **B** as

$$\Phi = \overline{B}A, \tag{14-10}$$

where $\overline{B}$ represents the average value of the magnetic field over A.

Let us recall that we may change the flux through a closed surface essentially in two ways, namely, (a) by moving the surface, and (b) by varying the field through a fixed surface. In the first case we may (1) move the whole of the circuit to a position where Φ has a different value, or (2) alter the size or shape of the circuit so as to vary the flux through it, or (3) both move and alter the circuit.

In case (a) above, whatever we do involves motion of the periphery of the circuit, and so we may apply Eq. (14-8), namely,

$$\mathcal{E} = \overline{B}\,\frac{\Delta A}{\Delta t}, \tag{14-11}$$

where $\overline{B}$ refers to the average magnetic field over the added area ΔA. Since in case (a) we assume that $\overline{\mathbf{B}}$ does not vary with the time, any change $\Delta\Phi$ in the flux must be the result of a change in the area A, so that

$$\Delta\Phi = \overline{B}\,\Delta A.$$

If we substitute $\Delta\Phi$ for $\overline{B}\,\Delta A$ in Eq. (14-11), we get

$$\mathcal{E} = \frac{\Delta\Phi}{\Delta t}, \tag{14-12}$$

or *the induced emf due to motion of a circuit is numerically equal to the time rate of change of magnetic flux through the circuit.* The motion referred to is that of all or part of the circuit relative to the observer; motion relative to the magnetic field has no meaning because a magnetic field is not a material object.

ILLUSTRATION 1. *Measurement of $\overline{B}$ with a search coil.* Figure 14-5 shows a coil of wire of N turns, the plane of the coil being parallel to a uniform magnetic field **B**. No magnetic flux passes through the coil because its area perpendicular to **B** is zero. Now let the coil rotate 90°, so that its area perpendicular to **B** is its actual geometric area A multiplied N times. (The effective area of the coil is the sum of the areas of all the turns, one on top of another.) The ΔA in Eq. (14-11) is thus

$$\Delta A = NA,$$

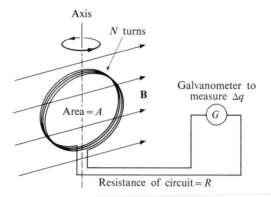

FIG. 14-5.   Search coil method of measuring **B**.

so that the average emf induced during the time Δt taken to turn the coil is

$$\varepsilon = BNA/\Delta t.$$

If the coil forms part of a closed circuit of resistance R, then during the time Δt the average induced current I will, according to Eq. (14-4), be

$$I = \frac{\varepsilon}{R} = \frac{BNA}{R\,\Delta t}.$$

Let Δq represent the total quantity of charge that flows around the circuit in the time Δt. Then

$$I = \frac{\Delta q}{\Delta t}.$$

If we equate the two expressions for I, we find that

$$\Delta q = \frac{BNA}{R},$$

$$B = \frac{R\,\Delta q}{NA}. \tag{14-13}$$

By measuring R, Δq (or $I\,\Delta t$), N, and A, one may compute B.

If the coil is turned 180° from the position shown in Fig. 14-5, ε and I will be zero. Why is this so? If the coil is placed with its plane perpendicular to **B** and then is rotated 180° about an axis perpendicular to **B**, one must take $\Delta A = 2NA$. Explain the factor 2.

In all of these so-called "search coil" experiments, the induced charge Δq is independent of the time Δt taken to flip the coil. Does this seem reasonable?

ILLUSTRATION 2. *Alternating current generator.* Suppose that the coil in Illustration 1 is rotated round and round in a uniform magnetic field. The sense of the flux and induced emf will then reverse in direction every time the coil rotates 180°. The resulting current will also flow alternately one way and then the other. In fact both the emf and the current, if plotted against the time, will yield graphs that have the shape of a sinusoidal wave. Such alternating currents are called A.C. for short, in contrast with the D.C. (direct current) output of an electric storage battery, or the generator of Fig. 14–3. Note that it is relatively easy to generate A.C., which is the type of current that our electric power stations generate.

14–5 Faraday's law of electromagnetic induction. Fundamental Law IX

This law is simply a generalization of Eq. (14–12) to cover *both* (a) moving circuits and (b) magnetic fields varying with the time. The extension of Eq. (14–12) to include (b) constitutes a new fundamental postulate quite apart from Ampere's law. Faraday made this postulate because it summarized the results of all of his experiments on electromagnetic induction.

Faraday's law states that *the emf induced in a circuit equals the time rate of change of magnetic flux through the circuit*, or

IX. $$\varepsilon = \frac{\Delta\Phi}{\Delta t},$$ (14–14)

whatever the reason for the flux change. This is our *Fundamental Law IX.*

For example, let a coil of wire be placed so as to intercept the magnetic field due to a current I in some other nearby circuit, then in the time Δt let the current I and the field due to it be reduced to zero. The average emf ε induced in the coil will be the same as when the coil is rotated 90° in the field, or jerked completely out of the field, in the time Δt. In other words, it is the value of the flux change, not the manner in which the flux change is produced, that is important.

For moving circuits and constant $\overline{\mathbf{B}}$, Eq. (14–14) is equivalent to Eq. (14–11). For fixed circuits through which $\overline{\mathbf{B}}$ varies with the time, we may deduce another special form of Eq. (14–14). Since $\Phi = \overline{B}A$, then if A does not change and $\overline{B}$ does, we have

$$\Delta\Phi = A\,\Delta\overline{B}$$

and

$$\varepsilon = \frac{\Delta\Phi}{\Delta t} = A\,\frac{\Delta\overline{B}}{\Delta t}$$ (14–15)

for a fixed circuit.

14–6 Lenz's law

This is really a part of Faraday's law. Expressions giving the *magnitude* of the induced emf ε have been stated, but nothing has been said about the *direction* of ε, except in Section 14–3. Lenz's law is the rule for finding this direction.

In Figs. 14–2 and 14–3 the induced emf and the resulting induced current are counterclockwise when **B** is directed out from the page and the area of the circuit

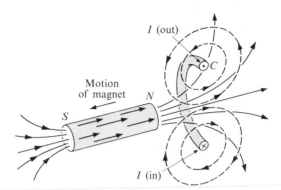

FIG. 14–6. Lenz's law. Field due to magnet is decreasing to the right inside coil; field due to induced current is to the right inside coil. (Only half of coil is shown.)

is decreasing. The flux through these circuits is decreasing in the outward direction. Now the induced current I produces its own magnetic field and we may use the right-hand fist rule to compute the direction of this field. The result is that the magnetic field due to the induced current is also directed outward within the circuit. It is as though nature, through this induced field, tried to compensate for the reduction in the flux due to the applied field **B**. This turns out experimentally to be a general rule, so that we may say that *the direction of the induced emf is always such as to result in opposition to the change producing it.* This is *Lenz's law.*

Were Lenz's law not true, a slight displacement of a current-carrying conductor in a magnetic field, in the direction of the magnetic force on the conductor, would result in an increase (instead of an actual decrease) in the current and an increased force. This would be an unstable situation as well as one in which the conservation of energy principle was disobeyed, for the increased magnetic force could be used to do useful work while at the same time electrical energy would be generated, all without supplying any energy to the system from outside. This sort of reasoning may be extended to other situations in which a system in equilibrium is displaced and the principle arrived at, which is really based on our Fundamental Laws IV and V, is the following.

When a system in equilibrium is displaced, the equilibrium is displaced in the direction which tends to undo the effects of the disturbance.

This generalization of Lenz's law is called the *principle of Le Chatelier;* it is sometimes referred to as the "law of the cussedness of nature." It is, however, fortunate that it exists, or we would live in a very strange and unstable world indeed!

ILLUSTRATION. *Coil and magnet in relative motion.* Figure 14–6 shows a magnet whose north pole is leaving a coil C. In our problem the applied field due to the magnet is to the right inside the coil. As the magnet leaves the coil, the field through the coil gets weaker so that Φ is decreasing to the right. The induced emf and current in the coil must then be in such a sense as to produce a field to the right,

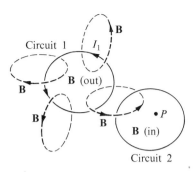

FIG. 14-7. Mutual inductance.

since such a field will help compensate for the decreasing applied field to the right. Application of the right-hand fist rule tells us that viewed from the side of the magnet, the induced current in the coil is clockwise.

It is important to bear in mind that the induced current will flow in a circuit only while the flux through the circuit is *changing*. After the magnet has been withdrawn to a great distance, so that the applied field has become and remains zero, the induced current must also be zero; thus a permanent change in the flux through the coil does finally result. While nature may try to oppose a change, man can still enforce the change upon nature.

If the magnet in Fig. 14-6 were moving toward the coil, the induced current in the coil would be counterclockwise, viewed from the magnet. A similar conclusion may be reached by saying that, if the induced current is counterclockwise, the coil is equivalent to a small magnet with its north pole to the left; such a magnet would oppose the approaching north pole of the moving magnet. Since this force of opposition is what Lenz's law predicts, our assumption as to the direction of the induced current must be correct.

14-7 Mutual inductance and self-inductance

Suppose that there is a steady current I_1 in what we shall call circuit 1 (see Fig. 14-7). At any point P in the neighborhood of this circuit, the resulting value of **B** will, according to Ampere's law, be proportional to I_1. Therefore the magnetic flux Φ_{21} through a nearby second circuit 2 due to the current I_1 in circuit 1 must be proportional to I_1, or

$$\Phi_{21} = MI_1, \qquad (14\text{-}16)$$

where the constant of proportionality M is called the *coefficient of mutual inductance* between the two circuits.

Equation (14-16) defines M, and so we may use it to determine the mks-coulomb unit of mutual inductance. Since the mks-coulomb unit for Φ_{21} is the weber and that for I_1 is the ampere, M must be expressed in webers per ampere. This unit is also called the *henry*, so that

$$1 \text{ henry} = 1 \text{ w/amp} = 1 \text{ volt-sec/amp.} \qquad (14\text{-}17)$$

The name of this unit honors an American physicist, Joseph Henry (1797–1879), who, while a schoolteacher at Albany Academy, discovered mutual inductance independently of Faraday.

Let the current I_1 in circuit 1 of Fig. 14–7 change with time, but so slowly that the value of **B** at P at any moment is very nearly the same as it would be if fields traveled with infinite speed and not (as we shall find in the next chapter) with the finite speed of light. Assume that in the time interval Δt, I_1 changes by ΔI_1 and Φ_{21} by $\Delta \Phi_{21}$. From Eq. (14–16) we have

$$\Delta \Phi_{21} = M \, \Delta I_1.$$

If we now substitute this value for the $\Delta \Phi$ in Faraday's law, we obtain for the induced emf ε_2 in circuit 2, resulting from the change ΔI_1 in I_1,

$$\varepsilon_2 = \frac{\Delta \Phi}{\Delta t} = M \frac{\Delta I_1}{\Delta t}. \tag{14–18}$$

Thus M also measures the emf induced in one circuit per unit rate of change of current in another circuit. Actually it does not matter which circuit we call 1 and which 2, for the same M also represents the flux through circuit 1 due to unit current in circuit 2. (This theorem is proved in more advanced books on electricity and magnetism.)

We may regard self-inductance as a special case of mutual inductance where circuit 2 becomes circuit 1. In other words, the magnetic field due to the current I_1 in circuit 1 must result in there being flux Φ_{11} through circuit 1. Let us define the *coefficient of self-inductance* L_1 of circuit 1 by writing

$$\Phi_{11} = L_1 I_1. \tag{14–19}$$

If we again let I_1 change by ΔI_1 in the time interval Δt and apply Faraday's law, we will find that the change $\Delta \Phi_1 = L_1 \Delta I_1$ in the flux through circuit 1, due to the variation in this circuit's own current, must result in an induced emf ε_1 in that circuit, where

$$\varepsilon_1 = L_1 \frac{\Delta I_1}{\Delta t}. \tag{14–20}$$

According to Lenz's law the direction of ε_1 must be such as to oppose the change producing it, or ε_1 must be directed opposite to the sense in which the current changes. If I_1 is increasing, ε_1 will be opposite to I_1, in which case it is often called the *back emf;* but if I_1 is decreasing, ε_1 will be in the same sense as I_1.

ILLUSTRATION 1. *Toroidal solenoid with two windings.* Consider a thin air-core ring solenoid with two windings, as shown in Fig. 14–8. Let N_1 represent the number of turns in one winding, and N_2 the number of turns in the other winding.

With a current I_1 in the first winding, we will have a magnetic field within that is proportional I_1 and also, since the contribution from two turns must be twice that from one, proportional to N_1. The resulting flux passes through each of the

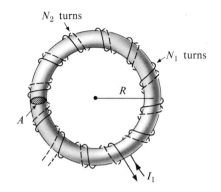

FIG. 14–8. Toroidal solenoid with two windings.

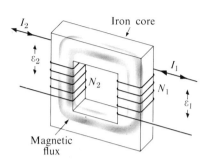

FIG. 14–9. A transformer.

N_1 turns of the first winding and through each of the N_2 turns of the second winding. Therefore

$$\Phi_{11} \propto N_1^2 I_1 \quad \text{and} \quad \Phi_{21} \propto N_1 N_2 I_1. \tag{14–21}$$

As a result we find that

$$L_1 \propto N_1^2 \quad \text{and} \quad M \propto N_1 N_2. \tag{14–22}$$

Similarly,

$$L_2 \propto N_2^2. \tag{14–23}$$

These relationships apply to air-core coils in general.

ILLUSTRATION 2. *The transformer.* This is a device similar to the two coils wound on a common core, but the core is usually made of soft iron. The effect of the iron is as follows. The magnetic field due to the current I_1 magnetizes the iron, which means that there is an alignment of the spinning electrons in the iron. The effect is the same as though currents many times greater than I_1 circulated around in the iron in the same sense as I_1 circulates in its coil. The result is a much greater magnetic flux inside the core when it is made of iron than when it is made of, say, air, wood, or brass. Actually the contribution made to the flux by the spinning electrons in the iron may be over 100 times that due to the free electrons drifting through the exernal winding. The self-inductance of a coil with an iron core may be as large as a henry or so.

In an iron-core ring or rectangular yoke (Fig. 14–9) the magnetic flux due to the iron, which is practically the whole flux, is constant around the closed core, so that the winding of circuit 2 may just as well be placed on the side opposite circuit 1. The emf applied to circuit 1 will be opposed by the approximately equal back emf in that circuit, given by

$$\varepsilon_1 = N_1 \frac{\Delta \Phi}{\Delta t},$$

where here $\Delta\Phi/\Delta t$ is the time rate of change of flux per turn. Similarly, the induced emf in circuit 2 is given by

$$\mathcal{E}_2 = N_2 \frac{\Delta\Phi}{\Delta t}.$$

If we divide one equation by the other we find that

$$\frac{\mathcal{E}_1}{\mathcal{E}_2} = \frac{N_1}{N_2}. \tag{14-24}$$

Transformers are used to "step up" or "step down" the voltage in an alternating-current line. The effect on the current is the inverse of that on the voltage; since the power output of a transformer cannot exceed the power input, and some of the input electrical energy is dissipated thermally, we may say that

$$\mathcal{E}_2 I_2 = \mathcal{E}_1 I_1 - \text{a dissipation factor.}$$

If the dissipation factor is negligible,

$$\frac{I_2}{I_1} = \frac{\mathcal{E}_1}{\mathcal{E}_2} = \frac{N_1}{N_2}. \tag{14-25}$$

Electric power is transmitted cross-country at high voltages and low currents so as to reduce the Joule heating effect, Eq. (14–5), and then the voltage is stepped down for the consumer of the electric power. This can, of course, only be done with alternating currents and constitutes a great advantage of alternating over direct currents.

14–8 Energy stored in a magnetic field

When we build up a current in a circuit, an external source of emf must do work against the induced back emf. Work is also expended in heating the wire, but such work need not concern us here. The rate at which work must be done *against* the back emf $\mathcal{E}$ is

$$P = \mathcal{E}I,$$

where I represents the instantaneous current. Let the current rise steadily from zero to a final value I_f in the time interval Δt, so that

$$\mathcal{E} = L\frac{\Delta I}{\Delta t} = \frac{LI_f}{\Delta t},$$

where L is the coefficient of self-inductance of the circuit. The work done in building the current up to I_f equals the average value of the power (work per second) multiplied by the time Δt, or

$$W = \bar{P}\,\Delta t.$$

The average power is $\bar{P} = \mathcal{E}\bar{I}$, where the average current $\bar{I}$ is *half* the final current

TABLE 14–1

CORRESPONDING MECHANICAL AND ELECTRICAL CONCEPTS

Mechanical		Electrical	
Concept	Symbol	Concept	Symbol
Displacement	s	Charge	q
Velocity	v	Current	I
Force	F	Emf or p.d.	ε or V
Compliance of a spring	$C = s/F$	Capacitance of a capacitor	$C = q/V$
Mass	m	Inductance	L
Resistance	$r = F/v$	Resistance	$R = V/I$
Work	$W = Fs$	Work	$W = qV$
Power	$P = Fv$	Power	$P = \varepsilon I$

I_f, if I increases steadily from 0 to I_f. Therefore,

$$W = \frac{\varepsilon I_f}{2} \times \Delta t$$

$$= \frac{L I_f}{\Delta t} \times \frac{I_f \, \Delta t}{2}$$

$$= \tfrac{1}{2} L I_f^2. \tag{14–26}$$

Since the work represented by Eq. (14–26) may be recovered by letting the current decrease back to zero, we must consider it as being stored somewhere while the current is flowing. Analogous to the interpretation of the energy of an electrostatic field, we may think of this energy either as being associated with the charges comprising the current, or as being stored in the region containing the magnetic field resulting from the current. According to the first viewpoint, the stored energy is in the conductor and in a kinetic form, while in the field point of view we think of the energy as traveling out into space while the field is being established and returning to the wire when the field collapses. We shall adopt this latter viewpoint for the same reasons as were given in Section 12–7. We shall see that time-dependent fields travel through space with the speed of light, and that such fields may transmit energy to a distant receiver. However, it is interesting to note that in circuit theory the self-inductance L plays a role analogous to inertia, or mass, in mechanics. Because of self-inductance, work is required to increase the current in a circuit, just as it takes work to increase the speed of a mass particle, or any object with inertia. Coils with iron cores and large L values are called *choke coils* because they tend to prevent sudden changes in the currents passing through them; their "electrical inertia" is a stabilizing influence.

The analogy between mass and inductance is only one example of the analogy between mechanical and electrical concepts summarized in Table 14–1.

14–9 Faraday's law applied to fields in free space

So far we have considered the application of Faraday's law to closed circuits in which the induced emf produces an induced current. The presence of a conducting circuit is necessary as far as motional emf is concerned, which is not surprising since the expression for motional emf can be derived from Ampere's law for the force on a moving charge. When, however, one turns to where Faraday's law makes its new contribution, the postulate that a time-changing magnetic field may also induce an emf, then one finds that Faraday's law tells us something important about the interrelationship between electric and magnetic fields in general.

To Faraday the emf given by Eq. (14–15) and the motional emf of Eq. (14–11) were both illustrations of the same physical law, namely, that an emf is present in a circuit whenever the magnetic flux linking the circuit is changing. This approach has the advantage of simplification, one of the aims of theoretical physics, but at the same time it obscures the important point that a changing magnetic field gives rise to a nonelectrostatic field *whether or not a conductor is present.*

Referring back to the definition of emf, Eq. (14–2), we see that it is defined as the sum of the products $E'_s \Delta s$ taken around a closed path "which is usually taken coincident with an electric circuit," but need not be so taken. The important thing about the emf concept is its relation to a nonelectrostatic field, i.e., an electric field whose lines of force *do* form closed curves. Around any path that follows a closed electric line of force an emf exists, whether or not a conductor is present. Faraday's law states that such an emf exists around a path inside of which the magnetic flux is changing. Hence Faraday's law says that around a region where **B** is changing with the time one will find a nonelectrostatic field **E'** whose lines of force form closed paths.

A changing magnetic field induces a nonelectrostatic electric field. Let us express this relationship mathematically.

Consider a small area A through which the average flux density or magnetic induction $\overline{\mathbf{B}}$ is directed normally. Let $\overline{\mathbf{B}}$ change in magnitude by $\Delta \overline{B}$ in the time Δt. Then the resulting flux change $\Delta \Phi$ through A is

$$\Delta \Phi = A \, \Delta \overline{B}$$

and the induced emf ε around the periphery of A is

$$\varepsilon = \frac{\Delta \Phi}{\Delta t} = A \, \frac{\Delta \overline{B}}{\Delta t}.$$

If we use Eq. (14–2), which defines ε, we may write

$$\sum_{\text{closed path}} E'_s \Delta s = A \left(\frac{\Delta \overline{B}}{\Delta t} \right), \tag{14–27}$$

where the closed path encloses the area A. This is the *field form of Faraday's law.* However, this is not a complete statement of Faraday's law unless we relate the

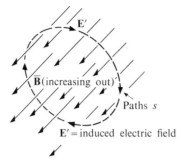

FIG. 14-10. Induced electric field due to a changing magnetic field.

direction of the induced electric field to the direction in which $\overline{\mathbf{B}}$ is changing. To do this we use Lenz's law.

In Fig. 14-10 let $\overline{\mathbf{B}}$ be increasing in strength in the outward direction so that more and more flux threads the dotted closed path in the outward direction. If the closed path *were* a conducting circuit (here it is not), the induced current in it would be clockwise, because the magnetic field of such a current would be directed inwardly within the circuit, thus opposing the change in flux. Such a current would result from an electric field $\mathbf{E}'$ directed clockwise around the circuit. Therefore, *in a region where* $\mathbf{B}$ *is increasing in strength toward the observer, the induced electric field around this region is clockwise.*

Note that Faraday's law does not involve any new constant to correspond with k_e in Coulomb's law, or k_m in Ampere's law. This fact and the fact that a special case of Faraday's law (that of motional emf) is derivable from Ampere's law are related. A formula derived from previous laws may contain combinations of the constants in those laws, but it cannot contain any new independent constant.

ILLUSTRATION. *The betatron.* This is an interesting application of Faraday's law in atomic physics. We saw in Chapter 13 that an electron may be accelerated in an electric field, while a steady magnetic field may be used to deflect, but not to

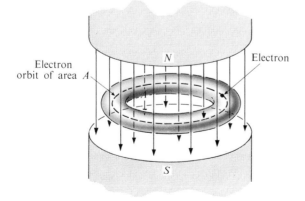

FIG. 14-11. Schematic diagram of a betatron.

speed up, a beam of charged particles. We have just seen that a changing magnetic field produces an electric field; thus we have another method of speeding up charged particles. In the betatron this principle is used to accelerate electrons to very high energies.

Electrons from a hot filament are injected into an evacuated doughnut-shaped tube of mean radius R and area A (see Fig. 14–11). An alternating magnetic field is applied parallel to the axis of the tube. This field serves two purposes: (1) an emf tangential to the tube is produced by the changing magnetic flux, thus speeding up the electrons, and (2) a radial force (see Ampere's law) acts on the electrons as they move across the magnetic field, a force which may be used to keep the electrons in the circular path of the tube. To accomplish this, the magnetic induction must be a certain function of r, the distance from the axis, so the field must be produced by placing the tube between specially shaped poles of an electromagnet. Of course, the electrons can be kept in the tube and accelerated in one direction during only one-quarter of each cycle of the alternating field.

PROBLEMS

1. Show that $\sum E_s \Delta s = 0$ around a rectangular path in a uniform electric field **E**. Can you prove the theorem for *any* path in a uniform field?

2. Show that in the neighborhood of an electrostatic charge $\sum E_s \Delta s = 0$ around a path, two of whose sides are circular arcs (with the charge at the center of curvature) and whose other two sides are directed radially toward or away from the charge.

3. The plates of a 6-volt battery are 2 cm apart. What is (a) the nonelectrostatic field between the plates, and (b) the net electric field between the plates when the battery is supplying current to an external circuit?

4. Suppose that in a conductor $I = 1$ amp when $\mathcal{E} = 5$ volts and $I = 2$ amp when $\mathcal{E} = 10$ volts. Find the electrical energy expended in 1 min when (a) $I = 1$ amp, (b) $I = 2$ amp. (c) Is Joule's law obeyed here? Explain.

5. Repeat problem 4 for another conductor for which $I = 1$ amp when $\mathcal{E} = 5$ volts and $I = 1.5$ amp when $\mathcal{E} = 10$ volts.

6. In Fig. 14–3 let ab be 0.5 m, $B = 0.2$ w/m², $v = 40$ m/sec, and $I = 3$ amp. Compute (a) the motional emf, (b) the power generated, (c) the force on ab, (d) the work done per second against this force.

7. A coil has 100 turns, each of 0.5-m² area. It is placed horizontally in a region where the earth's magnetic field has a vertical component of 5×10^{-5} w/m². Compute the induced emf if the coil is turned over in (a) 0.1 sec, (b) 0.2 sec.

8. In problem 7 compute Δq in each case, assuming $R = 20$ ohms.

9. A straight wire of length l is rotating at n revolutions/sec in a plane perpendicular to a magnetic field **B**. Find, in terms of l, n, and B, the emf induced between the ends of the wire when the axis of rotation passes through (a) one end, (b) the center.

10. Two coils, with self-inductance of 0.2 henry and 0.3 henry, respectively, lie side by side. Their mutual inductance is 0.1 henry. When the current in the first coil is increasing counterclockwise at the rate of 100 amp/sec and that in the second is increasing clockwise at the rate of 60 amp/sec, what is the magnitude and direction of the emf induced in each coil?

11. If the coils in problem 10 are coaxial, or one above the other, what is the magnitude and direction of the emf induced in each coil.

12. A circular coil of N_1 turns and radius a lies near the center and in the plane of a large circular coil of N_2 turns and radius b. Find M, the coefficient of mutual inductance, assuming $b \gg a$.

13. Show that when two coils are connected in series, the self-inductance of the combination is $L = L_1 + L_2 \pm 2M$. Explain which connection leads to the plus and which to the minus sign in the last term.

14. A transformer has 5 turns in its primary winding and 100 turns in its secondary. If the primary voltage is 110 volts and the primary current is 10 amp, find the secondary voltage and current, assuming (a) no dissipation of electrical energy, (b) 10% loss of electrical energy in the transformer.

15. Let $\Delta \bar{B}/\Delta t = 5$ w/m²-sec through an area $A = 0.01$ m². Take a circular path of radius 0.5 m around, and symmetric with respect to, A and compute the induced electric field **E'** at any point on this path.

16. An electron of charge $-e$ and mass m is traveling clockwise in a circular orbit of radius R about a nucleus. The electron makes n revolutions/sec when there is no external field. A magnetic field **B** is now applied in a direction from the observer to the orbit. Assume that R does not change but that n changes by a small amount Δn. Show that $\Delta n = +eB/4\pi m$, if terms in $(\Delta n)^2$ are neglected.

EXPERIMENT 21

JOULE HEATING
(The Mechanical Equivalent of Heat)

Object: To transfer a measured amount of electrical energy to a given mass of water and to measure the number of joules equivalent to one calorie.

Problem: If a current I amps is passed for t seconds through a coil of wire across which the p.d. is V volts (see Fig. 14–12), then $W = ItV$ joules of energy will be transferred to the coil. This follows from the definition of the ampere (= coul/sec) and the volt (=j/coul). When this energy is given to m kg of water the temperature of the water will rise, say by $\Delta T°$K. We are to determine the ratio J, where

$$J = \frac{It\,V}{m\,\Delta T}.\qquad(1)$$

The energy needed to raise 1 kg of water at room temperature by 1°K is called the *calorie*. Joule determined this directly in terms of work by stirring water with paddles, measuring the applied force and the distance moved, as well as the product $m\,\Delta T$. The experimental value of the calorie is 4185 joules; you may take this as the accepted value of J. If time and opportunity permit, you should repeat Joule's experiment. However, J may easily be determined electrically, using Eq. (1) above, the only problem being that I and V must be read on previously calibrated meters. We saw in Experiment 18 how an ammeter may be calibrated absolutely. If J can be found by other methods, electrical heating may be used to calibrate a voltmeter, rather than to find J. Let us say that if your measured value of J comes out close to 4185 joules/calorie, then your voltmeter must be correctly calibrated; otherwise either your voltmeter or your measurements of I, T, m, and ΔT are in error.

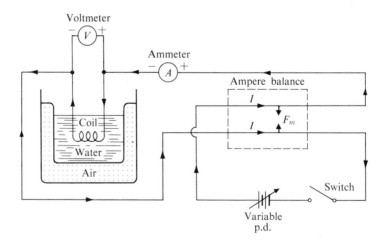

FIG. 14–12. Joule heating and the calibration of a voltmeter and ammeter.

Procedure:

Step 1. Heat a known mass of water from about 10° below to about 10° above room temperature (to equalize heat exchange with the room). Use current and voltage that best employ the full ranges of your ammeter and voltmeter. (Why?) Record I, V, t, m, and ΔT, and the possible error in each. The value of m should include the "water equivalent" of the container cup; for example, 11 gm of copper or brass have the same heat capacity as 1 gm of water. Compute J.

Step 2. Find the percent error in your computed value of J. Figure the total possible error and compare your actual with your possible error.

EXPERIMENT 22

FARADAY'S LAW
(Lenz's Rule)

Object: To verify Faraday's induction law and Lenz's rule for the direction of the induced emf.

Problem: Faraday discovered that a changing magnetic field generates an electric field, which may be used to drive a current. If the magnetic flux Φ through a coil of wire changes by $\Delta\Phi$ in the time Δt, then the emf $\mathcal{E}$ induced in the coil is given by

$$\mathcal{E} = -\frac{\Delta\Phi}{\Delta t}. \tag{1}$$

In a circuit of resistance R the induced current I will be

$$I = -\frac{1}{R}\frac{\Delta\Phi}{\Delta t}. \tag{2}$$

The minus sign here means that I itself is in such a direction that its own magnetic field will oppose the change $\Delta\Phi$ producing I; this is *Lenz's rule.*

The flux change $\Delta\Phi$ may be produced in many ways, several of which you will try. To verify Eq. (1), you will also vary $\Delta\Phi$ and Δt. To verify Lenz's rule, you will have to establish clearly the directions of $\Delta\Phi$ and of I. Knowing the direction of I, you may use the right-hand fist rule to find the direction of I's magnetic field, which should come out *opposite* to the direction in which Φ is *increasing*, or the *same* as the direction in which Φ is *decreasing*.

Procedure:

Step 1. Note how the coils are wound. Is there an extra half turn over the *top*, so that the entering current goes first over the top, or does the entering current have to go first around the bottom?

Step 2. Connect a high resistance in series with a dry cell and table galvanometer. Put a key switch in the circuit. Determine the polarity of the cell. Close the switch *momentarily* and note the direction of the throw of the arm of the galvanometer when the current enters at a given terminal. Now you can tell from the right or left deflections of the galvanometer the direction of the induced currents in the remainder of the experiment. (Disassemble circuit.)

Step 3. Connect one coil to the galvanometer with a resistance box in series. The resistance box is used to control the sensitivity of the galvanometer. Use the resistance box only to keep the deflections from going off sale and record resistance used in such cases. (a) Bring up the *N*-pole of the magnet slowly and take it away slowly. (b) Repeat (a) with the *S*-pole. (c) Repeat (a) with the *N*-pole but bring it up faster and take it away faster. Note direction of current in the coil in each case and compare deflections (or currents) in (a) and (c).

Step 4. (a) With one coil connected to the galvanometer and resistance box and the other coil to the dry cell, bring up one coil fast and take it away fast. (b) Reverse the direction of the current and repeat (a). Note the direction of current flowing through the coils.

Step 5. Connect as in Step 4 but put a switch in the dry cell circuit and place the coils together. Make and break the current flowing in the dry cell circuit.

Step 6. Repeat Step 5 with an iron core through the coils.

Step 7. Write a brief summary of the results, indicating how Faraday's law and Lenz's rule were verified. Include diagrams showing clearly the directions of $\Delta\Phi$, *I*, and the magnetic field due to *I*.

CHAPTER 15

Maxwell's Law of Magnetoelectric Induction

15–1 Historical introduction

Faraday was a brilliant experimental physicist, whereas the Scottish scientist James Clerk Maxwell (1831–1879) was a gifted theoretical physicist. Maxwell first read about and studied the work of Coulomb, Ampere, and Faraday and then proceeded to formulate their laws in terms of the vector calculus. He noted a certain lack of symmetry in the resulting equations, part of which he could attribute to the fact that nature provides us with free electric charges, but not with free magnetic poles. However, Maxwell was particularly struck by the fact that Faraday's law could be interpreted as saying that a changing magnetic field induces an electric field whereas the converse effect had not been observed or postulated. It would be simple if we could just say that Maxwell thereupon made the postulate that a changing electric field induces a magnetic field and added the corresponding term to his equations. In effect he did do this, but in the process of doing so he attempted to give his postulate a firmer foundation than the mere assumption that because one thing is true its converse must also be true. Furthermore, before Maxwell could express his postulate mathematically he had to determine whether an electric field changing at a given rate induces a strong or a weak magnetic field. Since no one had observed such an effect directly, before or during Maxwell's lifetime, it seemed pretty certain that in practical situations the magnetic field was weak. But how weak? Evidently Maxwell had to determine the value of a numerical factor. As we shall show, this factor turns out to be k_m/k_e, or $1/c^2$, where c is the speed of light.

How did Maxwell proceed? He showed that the equations expressing Coulomb's, Ampere's, and Faraday's laws were not compatible with the equation expressing the principle that electric charge can neither be created nor destroyed. He saw that the equations describing the behavior of electric and magnetic fields were consistent with the equation of charge conservation only for a steady state (in which all quantities are independent of the time) and not when the charge in a given region was changing with time. Maxwell found that to remove this inconsistency in the case of a nonsteady state it was only necessary to add to the equation summarizing Ampere's law an additional term, one involving the time rate of change of the electric field $\mathbf{E}$. With the addition of this new term, Maxwell's field equations became a concise summary of the laws of electromagnetism. The introduction of the new term amounted to postulating a law which, except for a numerical constant, is the converse of Faraday's law, but Maxwell called it the "displacement current" term, for reasons that will be explained.

Maxwell's greatest contribution to physics was his electromagnetic theory of light. Elimination of either **E** or **B** between his field equations led him to equations of the same form as those describing sound or water waves. The wave equations for **E** and **B** indicated that an electric and a magnetic field should be propagated through empty space as transverse waves with the speed $v = \sqrt{k_e/k_m}$, that is, with the speed of light, and that these waves should have the other properties of light, except, perhaps, visibility. Maxwell was thus led to make the very educated guess that electromagnetic waves and light are one and the same thing, or, to put it another way, that electromagnetic waves furnish a good model for describing the behavior of light while it is being propagated from where it is emitted to where it is absorbed.

Experimental confirmation of Maxwell's postulate did not come until 15 years after he published his work. In 1887–1888 another brilliant experimenter, Heinrich Hertz of Germany, succeeded in producing and detecting electromagnetic waves of the kind we now call radio waves. By 1901 Marconi had sent radio waves across the Atlantic Ocean. Now, of course, we use electromagnetic waves not only in radio transmission, but in television, radar, and the study of molecular vibrations.

The points mentioned in the above outline will now be explained in more detail.

15–2 The conservation of charge

It is an experimental fact that so far no case has been observed in which the net amount of charge (positive less negative) in our world has been altered.

Charges of one sign may move through a region filled with charges of the opposite sign, as electrons do in a wire, but these moving charges never suddenly vanish.

Charges of one sign may be separated from charges of the opposite sign and accumulated on a capacitor. If a region A contains a net charge Q and a charge ΔQ is taken away from A and put in another region B with an original charge Q', then the charge in region A will become $Q - \Delta Q$ and that in B will be $Q' + \Delta Q$. If the charges in regions A and B are added, they will still equal $Q + Q'$, so that the world as a whole has neither gained nor lost charge.

In recent years it has been found possible to create out of energy a particle called a *positron*, which is similar to an electron except that it bears a charge of $+e$. Whenever a positron is created, one finds that an ordinary negative electron with a charge of $-e$ is born at the same time. Similarly, a proton (charge $+e$) and an antiproton (charge $-e$) may be produced as a pair, but not separately. Again we see that such pair production does not alter the net charge in our world.

The converse of pair production is pair annihilation in which a particle of charge $+e$ and one of the same mass but bearing a charge $-e$ come together and vanish into radiant energy. The charges of such particles neutralize each other, regardless of what happens to the particles themselves.

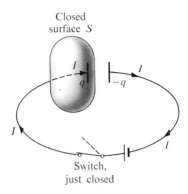

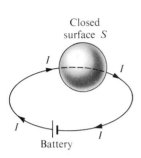

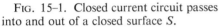

FIG. 15–1. Closed current circuit passes into and out of a closed surface S.

FIG. 15–2. Closed surface S contains one plate of a capacitor that is being charged.

It may seem logical to consider the conservation of charge principle as one of our fundamental laws. It certainly has the necessary universality and may be called a fundamental principle if one so wishes. However, in this book we are endeavoring to describe the behavior of our physical world in terms of a *minimum* number of laws, and it turns out that if we postulate the laws of Coulomb, Ampere, and Faraday and add to these the postulate that Maxwell made, then the conservation of charge principle may be deduced from the above laws as a theorem. The reader will recall that the conservation of momentum principle was similarly deduced from Newton's laws I and II. We shall see that we must adopt Maxwell's postulate anyway, since without it there would be no explanation of electromagnetic waves. Thus we take the conservation of charge to be a derived principle.

How is the conservation of charge principle expressed mathematically? Perhaps the simplest way is as follows. Consider a closed surface S which at a given moment contains the net charge q. This charge may change with time, say at the rate $\Delta q/\Delta t$, because of electric currents passing into or out of the region. We are most familiar with currents that flow around closed circuits, like endless belts, as in Fig. 15–1. Such currents take out charge from S at the same rate they bring it in. On the other hand, S may contain one plate of a capacitor, as in Fig. 15–2, and a current may flow into S and end on this plate, which means that charge is then building up in S. In a similar manner charge might flow off the plate and out of S. In any event the conservation of charge principle states that *the net rate of flow of charge into a region S equals the time rate of increase of net charge in the region.* Let I_{out} represent the net current *out* of S. Then since a positive value of I_{out} would mean a decrease in the net charge q inside, we have

$$I_{\text{out}} = -\frac{\Delta q}{\Delta t} \tag{15–1}$$

as a simple mathematical expression of the conservation of charge principle. This equation, expressed in terms of the calculus, is called the *equation of continuity*.

EXAMPLE. A box measures 20 cm × 40 cm × 50 cm and charge is entering across three faces at the rates 2 coul/sec, 4 coul/sec, and 5 coul/sec, respectively, while charge is leaving across the other faces at the rates 1 coul/sec, 2 coul/sec and 6 coul/sec, respectively. Find the time rate of change of (a) charge, (b) charge density ρ (charge per unit volume), in the box.

Solution. The net time rate of increase of charge in the box is $2 + 4 + 5 - 1 - 2 - 6 = 2$ coul/sec. The volume of the box is $0.2 \times 0.4 \times 0.5 = 0.04$ m³. The time rate of change in the charge density ρ is thus

$$\frac{\Delta\rho}{\Delta t} = \frac{2 \text{ coul/sec}}{0.04 \text{ m}^3} = 50 \text{ coul/m}^3/\text{sec}.$$

15–3 Extension of Coulomb's law to a nonsteady state

Consider a point charge q at the center of a spherical surface S of radius r (Fig. 15–3). Then at any point on S, the electric field strength E is, according to Coulomb's law,

$$E = \frac{k_e q}{r^2}. \tag{15–2}$$

The area of the surface S is $A = 4\pi r^2$, so that for the product EA we have

$$EA = 4\pi k_e q, \tag{15–3}$$

regardless of the radius r of the surface. Equation (15–3) may be extended so as to apply to any closed surface S surrounding a charge q, provided that one simply breaks the surface up into small areas, multiplies each such area by the component of the electric field perpendicular to that area, and adds all such products to obtain the quantity equal to $4\pi k_e q$. The proof of this goes back to the lines-of-force picture of the field, in which only so many lines diverge from a given charge and hence must cross any surface, S or S', enclosing that charge (see Fig. 15–3). The product EA may be thought of as *electric flux*, just as BA represents magnetic flux.

Let us now suppose that there is a net current I_{out} leaving the region inside S. Then, according to the conservation of charge principle, q must be changing, say

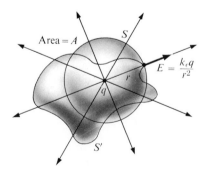

FIG. 15–3. Same electric flux crosses any closed surface surrounding a given charge q.

at the rate $\Delta q/\Delta t$, as given by Eq. (15–1). According to Eq. (15–3), a change in q must mean a change in the product EA, that is, a change in the electric flux crossing S. Since we are concerned with a fixed surface, A does not change with time, and so the change in the product EA must be due entirely to a change ΔE in the electric field strength. Thus

$$\Delta(EA) = (E + \Delta E)A - EA = (\Delta E)A = A(\Delta E).$$

If this occurs in the time Δt, the time rate of change of EA is

$$\frac{\Delta(EA)}{\Delta t} = A \frac{\Delta E}{\Delta t}. \tag{15–4}$$

From Eq. (15–3) we see that the time rate of change in EA must equal that of $4\pi k_e q$ or, since $4\pi k_e$ is a constant,

$$\frac{\Delta(EA)}{\Delta t} = 4\pi k_e \frac{\Delta q}{\Delta t}. \tag{15–5}$$

If we combine Eqs. (15–4) and (15–5), we get

$$A \frac{\Delta E}{\Delta t} = 4\pi k_e \frac{\Delta q}{\Delta t}. \tag{15–6}$$

Finally, we substitute $-I_{out}$ for $\Delta q/\Delta t$, according to Eq. (15–1), and obtain

$$A \frac{\Delta E}{\Delta t} = -4\pi k_e I_{out},$$

or

$$\frac{A}{4\pi k_e} \frac{\Delta E}{\Delta t} + I_{out} = 0. \tag{15–7}$$

In Eq. (15–7) it is understood that $A \Delta E$ is the change in *outward* electric flux just as I_{out} is the *outward* current through S, that is, *out* is taken as the positive direction on S.

15–4 Maxwell's displacement current

Let us consider the surface S to enclose just the positive plate of a capacitor that is being charged by a current of magnitude I, as in Fig. 15–4. Since the current is in and not out, we must call it $-I$ in Eq. (15–7). On the other hand the electric flux runs outward through S toward the other plate and so the first term in Eq. (15–7) is positive. Thus we have

$$\frac{A}{4\pi k_e} \frac{\Delta E}{\Delta t} = I. \tag{15–8}$$

From this last equation we see that the term on the left not only must have the same units as electric current, but that it is numerically equal to the line current I.

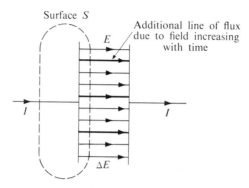

FIG. 15–4. Conduction current I enters S and an increasing electric field leaves S.

Maxwell saw that if one regards

$$\frac{A}{4\pi k_e} \frac{\Delta E}{\Delta t}$$ (15–9)

as representing the equivalent of a current between the plates of the capacitor, then the result is the same as though the current I flowed continuously without a break through the circuit containing the capacitor. If this is so, then in the conducting part of the circuit the current I is due entirely to the motion of free charges, while between the plates the current I continues as what Maxwell called a *displacement current*, due to the time rate of increase of the electric field.

Maxwell suggested that a strain equivalent to a limited but increasing displacement of charge takes place within the medium between the plates while E is increasing. But what is this medium and what charges are displaced? We assumed the space between the plates to be empty. Does empty space possess some sort of elastic properties? If we assume that this is so, we shall in effect be adopting the old *ether theory*, a theory which was unfruitful and did not grow gracefully, as we shall discover in the next chapter.

The real justification for our regarding $A \,\Delta E/4\pi k_e \,\Delta t$ as equivalent to the current I must be based on the fact that they each give rise to a magnetic field as postulated by Ampere's law. Maxwell's fundamental hypothesis was that this is so. In other words, he postulated that *the magnetic field between the plates is the same as though the current $A \,\Delta E/4\pi k_e \,\Delta t$ actually flowed between the plates.* Since Maxwell did not know this to be an experimental fact, it was a bold guess on his part, but its consequences turned out to be important and experimentally verifiable.

15–5 Maxwell's postulate. Fundamental Law X

We saw in Chapter 13 that around a long straight wire carrying a current I there is a magnetic field directed in circles around the wire. At a distance r from the axis of the wire the magnetic induction is

$$B = k_m \frac{2I}{r}.$$ (15–10)

If we follow the field around a closed path of length s, we have for the product of B and the path length $s = 2\pi r$,

$$B \cdot s = \sum_{\text{closed path}} B \, \Delta s = k_m(4\pi I), \qquad (15\text{–}11)$$

where I is the current linking the path. This turns out to be a general statement of Ampere's law.

Maxwell's postulate was that the quantity I in Eq. (15–11) must include any displacement current present as well as ordinary conduction currents. This is the same as saying that if I is taken to include *only* conduction currents, then in general one must add the term in (15–9) to I and modify Eq. (15–11) so that it becomes

$$\sum_{\text{closed path}} B \, \Delta s = 4\pi k_m \left[I + \frac{A}{4\pi k_e} \frac{\Delta E}{\Delta t} \right]$$

$$= 4\pi k_m I + \frac{k_m}{k_e} A \frac{\Delta E}{\Delta t}. \qquad (15\text{–}12)$$

In empty space, where there are no charges or conduction currents, $I = 0$ and Eq. (15–13) becomes

X.
$$\sum_{\text{closed path}} B \, \Delta s = \frac{k_m}{k_e} A \frac{\Delta E}{\Delta t}, \qquad (15\text{–}13)$$

which is the mathematical statement of Maxwell's postulate that a changing electric field gives rise to a magnetic field. This is our *Fundamental Law X.*

With the addition of Maxwell's postulate, we recognize that *electric fields* can be produced (a) by the presence of charges and (b) by changing magnetic fields, and that *magnetic fields* can be produced by (a) the motion of charged particles and (b) by changing electric fields.

15–6 Comparison between Maxwell's and Faraday's laws

To present-day physicists, Maxwell's postulate is interpreted as stating an effect that is the converse of Faraday's law. Let us compare the two.

The field form of Faraday's law is Eq. (14–27), or

$$\sum_{\text{closed path}} E'_s \, \Delta s = A \frac{\Delta B}{\Delta t}, \qquad (15\text{–}14)$$

while Maxwell's law is expressed in Eq. (15–13). The analogy between these equations is striking, yet there are important points in which the analogy breaks down. First, Eq. (15–13) contains the constant factor $k_m/k_e = 1/c^2$, which Eq. (15–14) does not have. Since $1/c^2$ is a very small quantity, one must conclude that, measured in mks-coulomb units, the magnetic fields induced by changing electric fields are numerically much smaller than the electric fields induced by changing magnetic fields. Furthermore, weak electric fields may be detected by the weak currents they can set up in a conducting circuit, whereas we cannot look for a weak

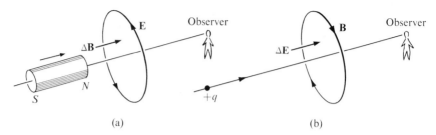

FIG. 15–5.   Directions of induced electric and magnetic fields.

"magnetic current" because neither free poles nor conductors for them exist. All of this explains why Maxwell's law was the last of the four fundamental laws of electromagnetism to be discovered.

A second important difference between Faraday's and Maxwell's laws concerns the *directions* of the induced fields. We saw in the last chapter that if **B** is increasing in strength toward the observer, the induced electric field is clockwise, as in Fig. 15–5(a). On the other hand, since the magnetic field induced by a changing electric field is equivalent to that of a positive current in the direction of positive Δ**E**, one may apply the right-hand fist rule to determine the direction of the induced magnetic field; the result is that *in a region where* **E** *is increasing toward the observer, the induced magnetic field around the region is counterclockwise*, as in Fig. 15–5(b). We recall that when comparing the magnetic with the electric force between charges moving in parallel paths, we found the forces to be opposite in direction and that F_e/F_m also contained the factor $1/c^2$, so perhaps the conclusions above should not surprise us.

EXAMPLE. Two parallel plates are 1 cm apart. With air between the plates, the maximum possible electric intensity is found to be 3×10^6 n/coul or volts/m; this is called the *dielectric strength* of air, or the value of **E** at which the medium becomes conducting. We may, then, let the p.d. between our plates increase to 30,000 volts. Suppose that this is accomplished in 0.01 sec. Then

$$\Delta E/\Delta t = 3 \times 10^8 \text{ volts/m-sec.}$$

Let the plates have a radius of 5 cm, so that the area A across which the field passes is $\pi(0.05 \text{ m})^2 = 0.0025\pi$ m². Take a circular path of 6-cm radius around and outside of the region between the plates. This path will correspond to a line of force of the induced magnetic field **B**; its positive sense is shown in Fig. 15–6. The length of the path is $2\pi \times 0.06$ m $= 0.12\pi$ m. If we now substitute in Eq. (15–13), we find that

$$B \times 0.12\pi \text{ m} = \frac{1}{9 \times 10^{16} \text{ m}^2/\text{sec}^2} \times 0.0025\pi \text{ m}^2 \times 3 \times 10^8 \frac{\text{volts}}{\text{m-sec}}$$

$$= 7 \times 10^{-11} \text{ volt-sec/m} = 7 \times 10^{-11} \text{ w/m}^2,$$

which is indeed a very weak field (about one-millionth that of the earth). It is understandable why Maxwell's postulate was confirmed indirectly long before it was verified directly.

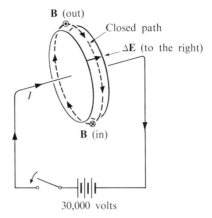

FIG. 15–6. Calculation of induced magnetic field around plates between which E is increasing.

15–7 Electromagnetic waves

We turn now to the great prediction of Maxwell's theory. Coulomb, Ampere, and Faraday arrived at their fundamental postulates as a result of experimentation and the inductive process of seeking a statement that summarizes a host of different observed facts. Maxwell, on the other hand, did not summarize any new experimental facts, but he did make predictions that were eventually found to be true and thus justified his theory. Let us consider in a qualitative way how his theory predicts that electric and magnetic fields may be propagated through space as transverse waves.

A simple generator of electromagnetic waves is shown in Fig. 15–7; a source of alternating emf is connected to two metal rods that form an antenna. Suppose that at the instant shown, electrons are flowing downward, or the direction of the positive current I is upward, and that positive charges are accumulating on the upper wire and negative charges on the lower wire. The electric field E will be similar to that of a dipole (Fig. 12–5), as shown by solid lines. The magnetic

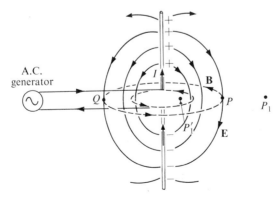

FIG. 15–7. Antenna approaching state of maximum charge.

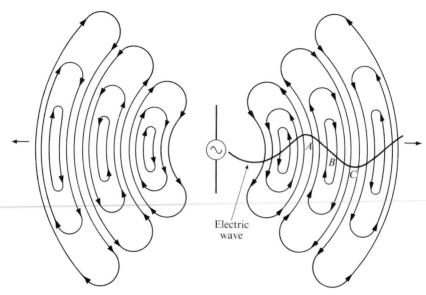

Electric
wave

FIG. 15–8. Pulses of electric field spreading out from an antenna with oscillating polarity. At *A* the magnetic field is out, at *B* it is zero, at *C* it is in.

field **B** will be in circles about the antenna and its direction, according to the right-hand fist rule of Ampere, will be into the page at *P* and out at *Q*, as shown by the dotted curve. Thus at *P* and *Q* the fields **E** and **B** are at right angles.

Next consider how these fields are changing with the time. The charges on the wires are increasing so that, according to Coulomb's law, their electric field will spread out farther, say to P_1. Since the charges on the wires are approaching their peak values, after which they will decrease in magnitude, the current *I* must be decreasing toward zero, after which it will be downward. A decreasing *I* means that at *P* the magnetic field **B** is decreasing with the time; according to Faraday's and Lenz's laws, if **B** is in and decreasing (or out and increasing), there must be an induced electric field **E**′ directed in loops about the changing magnetic field. The direction of this new electric field will be downward at P_1 and upward at P_1', so that it will reinforce **E** at P_1 and oppose it at P_1'. Thus the region where the electric field is strongly downward moves out away from the wire, as in Fig. 15–8.

Finally, consider the magnetic effect of the changing electric field. As the pulse of the electric field moves outward, the wires reach their maximum charge and then their charges begin to decrease. As a result of this decrease in charge on the wires, plus the fact that **E**′ opposes **E** (first at P_1' and then later at *P* in Fig. 15–7), the electric field at *P* will decrease in the downward sense. According to Maxwell's postulate, an electric field decreasing downward (or increasing upward) at *P* will give rise to a magnetic field that is directed in loops that go into the page at P_1 and come out at P_1'. Thus at P_1 an inwardly directed wave of the magnetic field accompanies the downward wave of the electric field that is in motion away from the antenna. This wave of inward **B** and downward **E** will be followed by one of

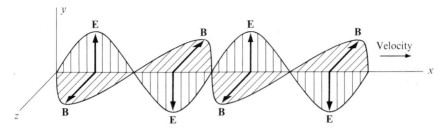

FIG. 15-9. Relationship between the directions of the electric field, the magnetic field and the direction of propagation in an electromagnetic wave.

outward **B** and upward **E**. As the polarity of the antenna is periodically reversed, a continuous wave of electric and magnetic fields will, according to the four laws of electromagnetism, be radiated outward. These waves are transverse with respect to both **E** and **B**. The direction of propagation is the direction of advance of a right-hand screw rotating from **E** to **B**, as shown in Fig. 15-9.

Out in space, far from the transmitting antenna, electromagnetic waves are self-propagating. The changing electric field induces a new magnetic field which, in turn, also changes and induces a new electric field. The ingredients necessary for the propagation of a mechanical type of wave are "springiness" and inertia in the transmitting medium. Electromagnetic waves do not require a material medium for their propagation because they contain, in a sense, the same necessary ingredients as built-in properties, according to Faraday's and Maxwell's laws. Mechanical waves consist of oscillating particles whose energies are both kinetic and potential. By analogy, one may think of a capacitor as an electric spring, (the more one charges it the greater its tendency to discharge), and the electric energy of a charged capacitor as potential energy stored in its electric field. As mentioned earlier, self-inductance is analogous to mass, and the energy stored in the magnetic field due to a current in a coil is analogous to kinetic energy. Thus an electromagnetic wave contains the equivalent of K.E. and P.E.

When electromagnetic waves pass into matter they encounter electrons, such as the bound electrons orbiting in atoms and the free electrons in conductors. As the alternating electric field **E** passes an electron, the electron is urged alternately one way and the opposite way. When **E** is, say, upward the electron is urged downward, and when **E** is downward the force on the electron is upward. The moving electron is also affected by the magnetic field **B** in the wave. The result of the interaction between an electromagnetic field and the electrons in matter is that the electrons absorb energy from the field. This absorbed energy may (1) be turned into internal thermal energy of the absorber, (2) be reradiated in different directions, (3) give rise to alternating currents in a receiving antenna and connecting circuit. For process (3) to be most efficient, the receiving circuit must be "tuned" to resonance with the frequency of the waves that are being sent out and picked up, i.e., the frequency of the transmitter.

It is unfortuante (for the purposes of this book) that one cannot prove without employing higher mathematics that the speed of an electromagnetic wave in free space is equal to $\sqrt{k_e/k_m} = 3 \times 10^8$ m/sec, which is the speed of light, but this is indeed true, both theoretically and experimentally. We have already seen that the ratio k_e/k_m, or its reciprocal, is the most important constant in the theory of electromagnetism.

15–8 Some pure speculation

This section is just to show that even though the subject of electromagnetism has been wrapped up into a neat package by the theory of Maxwell and his predecessors, there is still plenty of opportunity left, here and elsewhere in physics, for a person with a creative mind to exercise his imagination.

The constancy of the speed of light appears to be firmly established; at least there is not sufficient evidence to indicate a change in its value during the past 60 years or more. However, one may still make all sorts of *speculations* about what has happened in the course of geological history, or in the time since the solar system was formed, or even in the time since our present universe was created (perhaps 10^{10} years ago). In such long periods of time universal constants *may* have changed in value. It is possible that gravitational and electromagnetic forces were once more nearly of the same order of magnitude and that (a) G has been decreasing and gravity "losing its grip," or (b) k_e, $\sqrt{k_e/k_m}$, and the speed of light have been increasing! The worth of such speculations will depend on whether they meet the tests of a good theory by being (1) simple, (2) comprehensive, (3) fruitful, and (4) adaptable to modification.

PROBLEMS

1. Explain why the equation that expresses the principle that *fluid* cannot be created or destroyed has the same form as Eq. (15–1). What do I_{out} and q stand for in this case? Can you think of any situation where the conservation of fluid principle and the equation expressing it do not hold?

2. Discuss the similarities and differences between the flow of charge or a fluid and the conduction of heat.

3. Suppose that charge is flowing in the x-direction and the flow per unit area per second is propotional to $+x^2$. For what values of x will the charge density be (a) increasing, (b) decreasing, (c) steady?

4. An electromagnetic wave strikes a surface at right angles to the direction in which the wave is traveling. If the wave carries energy to the surface at the rate of 0.06 watts/m^2, how much energy must each cubic meter of the electromagnetic field contain?

5. Describe the patterns of the electric and the magnetic fields near a bar magnet that is insulated and charged positively. If, as Maxwell's theory predicts, energy is propagated in the direction of advance of a right-hand screw rotating from **E** to **B**, will such a charged magnet gain or lose energy? Explain.

6. A steady current flows up in a long straight wire in which **E** is in the upward direction. Does the wire gain energy from, or lose energy to, the electromagnetic field?

7. What does the product BA add up to over a closed surface S? Compare with Eq. (15–3) and explain the lack of similarity.

8. Compute the displacement current in the Example at the end of Section 15–6.

CHAPTER 16

The Relativity Principle

16–1 Introduction

The fundamental laws of physics that we have considered so far all date from before the year 1900, whereas those discussed in this and the following chapters were only discovered in the present century. The physics of the period prior to 1900 is frequently referred to as "classical physics," and we have seen that it succeeded in discovering the laws and building the theories in terms of which the ordinary occurrences of our physical world can be explained. The reason that so much could be accomplished without the use of the principles of 20th-century "modern physics" is that these latter principles are only significant when we extend our investigations from the realm of man's ordinary macroscopic world to that of the microscopic world of atoms and nuclei, or to the astronomical world of the cosmos.

It is not that the relativity and quantum principles fail to apply to such everyday phenomena as the motion of a baseball or a car, for they do apply, but the point is that they do not *have* to be applied. We shall see that when the expressions of the relativity theory differ from those of Newtonian theory, the former reduce to the latter when the speed of the material objects with which we are concerned is considerably less than c, the speed of light. The newer theory embraces the older one as a special case; this case, however, includes most common occurrences because the speed of light happens to be very great. If the speed of light were infinite, those effects peculiar to the relativity theory would not occur; we would then always be able to use Newtonian theory, which is simpler and easier to apply.

The quantum theory bears the same relationship to classical theories; its fundamental constant is Planck's constant h and it is because h is so *small* that quantum effects do not appear in the macroscopic world. If h were zero, we would not need the quantum theory at all; as our world exists, h represents a product of energy and time that is negligible compared with, say, the product of the energy of a baseball and its time of flight.

16–2 Inertial systems

By a *reference system* we shall mean a frame of reference, such as a set of x-, y-, z-axes and a clock, stationary with respect to the axes, for measuring the time t at which an event occurs. By an *inertial system* we shall mean a reference system S relative to which Newton's laws of motion take their customary form, or any other system S' that is moving relative to S with *unaccelerated* motion. Since the earth is rotating, it does not constitute a true inertial system, but in laboratory experiments the effects of the earth's rotation are negligible and the ground or walls of a building serve sufficiently well for an inertial system. Newton believed an ideal inertial system to be one that is absolutely at rest. A large group of so-called "fixed stars" are relatively at rest, and these are sometimes taken as defining an "absolute" system. However, we shall see that the term "absolutely at rest" has no meaning and that all motion is relative. It is unimportant to ask which one of two or more inertial systems is at rest.

Suppose that a certain law is deduced and its predictions are found to hold true experimentally by observers in one inertial system, say that of the laboratory. Now consider a second set of observers who are investigating the same law on a space ship that is moving at a large but constant velocity relative to the laboratory. If both sets of observers conclude that the law, in the same form, holds true, then the law is said to be *relativistically invariant*. Newton believed that his laws possessed this property.

16–3 The principle of relativity.   Fundamental Law XI

We are familiar with the situation in which two trains pass each other slowly and steadily on parallel tracks and a passenger looks out of the window of one train and sees only the other one; the passenger cannot say what the speed of either train is relative to the ground, he can only measure the relative motion of the two trains. Or suppose, for example, that we are enclosed in a large box without windows, such as a freight car or an elevator, and that this box can move smoothly and quietly relative to the ground; again we will not be able to detect or measure the motion if it is *unaccelerated*. Of course accelerated motion is detectable because when a car speeds up we are thrown backwards, and when a car is centripetally accelerated on a curved track we are thrown to one side; in an elevator we are aware of acceleration because of the apparent change in our weight.

Einstein's *special theory of relativity*, which is what we shall discuss, was proposed in 1905 and deals with unaccelerated motion. Later he developed the more *general theory* that is concerned with accelerated systems and gravity, a theory that requires for its understanding an advanced training in mathematics as well as physics.

In a generalization of what has been said above regarding our inability to detect unaccelerated motion, Einstein made the following postulate.

There is no physical experiment that can be performed relative to one inertial system only by means of which the uniform velocity of that system relative to another inertial system can be detected.

This is Einstein's *principle of relativity* and our *Fundamental Law XI*. We shall break this principle down into two parts, as follows.

(1) *The speed of light in vacuo as measured relative to any inertial system is always the same;* that is, it is independent of the motion of the source and that of the observer. The speed, relative to the ground, of a bullet fired from a moving plane

depends on the speed of the plane; the speed of sound, relative to the ground, depends on the speed of the air that carries the sound; but nothing "carries light" in empty space. We shall show that this postulate is verified experimentally by the Michelson-Morley experiment and leads mathematically to the Lorentz space-time transformation equations.

(2) *The fundamental laws of physics have the same form, or are invariant, for all inertial systems.* Some time before Einstein announced his theory of relativity, H. A. Lorentz showed that the equations expressing the laws of electromagnetic fields are invariant if one assumes the same space-time transformations referred to in (1). Einstein proved, as we shall show, that the invariance of Newton's laws of motion also follows from the same space-time transformations if one assumes that the mass of a body varies with its energy. The consequences of this assumption have been fully tested experimentally, as witness the atomic bomb.

The Lorentz space-time transformation equations plus Einstein's mass-energy equivalence relation, $E = mc^2$, thus summarize Einstein's principle mathematically.

16–4 The Michelson-Morley experiment

To make the meaning of this experiment clearer, the following analogy is frequently presented.

Suppose that in Fig. 16–1, A and B are two points on opposite banks of a stream which is flowing in the x-direction with the speed v relative to the ground. Let l be the width of the stream and let C be a point a distance l upstream from A. We imagine a race between two identical swimmers, each of whom swims with the speed c in still water, one swimmer being told to swim across the stream to B and back to A, while the other must swim upstream to C and then back to A. How will the times of the two swimmers compare?

Consider the first swimmer, who must cross the stream. In order to allow for the drift current $\mathbf{v}$, he must aim diagonally upstream so that the component of his effective velocity across the stream, say c_c, is only one component of the vector $\mathbf{c}$, the other being equal and opposite to the current $\mathbf{v}$ (see Fig. 16–2). Then

$$c_c = \sqrt{c^2 - v^2}.$$

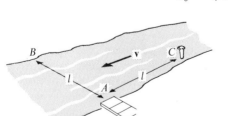

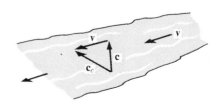

FIG. 16–2. The swimmer's effective velocity c_c across stream is less in magnitude than his speed c in still water.

FIG. 16–1. Race between two swimmers in a flowing stream.

The distance across and back is $2l$, hence the time t_1 for this swimmer will be $2l/c_c$, or

$$t_1 = \frac{2l}{\sqrt{c^2 - v^2}} = \frac{2lk}{c},\tag{16-1}$$

where

$$k = \frac{1}{\sqrt{1 - v^2/c^2}}.\tag{16-2}$$

The other swimmer makes slow progress upstream, his effective speed being $c - v$, but he has the current with him on the return leg, when his resultant speed is $c + v$. His total time t_2 will thus be $l/(c - v)$ up plus $l/(c + v)$ back, or

$$t_2 = \frac{l}{c - v} + \frac{l}{c + v} = \frac{2lc}{c^2 - v^2}.$$

We shall change the form of this equation so that we may more easily compare t_2 with t_1. To do so we divide numerator and denominator on the right-hand side by c^2 and get

$$t_2 = \frac{2l}{c} \times \frac{1}{1 - v^2/c^2} = \frac{2lk^2}{c}.\tag{16-3}$$

We must take $c > v$, or the second swimmer could not reach the point C. Then $k > 1$, $k^2 > k$, and hence $t_2 > t_1$. The first swimmer wins, but the difference in times, involving only terms in the square and higher powers of v/c, will be small if $v \ll c$. Note that by measuring t_1, t_2, and l, we can determine the drift velocity v.

Let us assume that the two swimmers are accurately timed. Suppose (this is a purely hypothetical case) that the two times were found to be exactly the same, what explanations might be offered? We might conclude that (1) the ratio v/c is zero and $k = 1$, within the limits of measurement, or (2) that the distance from A to C was inaccurately measured and that it is actually less than the distance across the stream. Conclusion (1) implies either no appreciable current ($v = 0$), or very fast swimmers ($c \rightarrow \infty$). Conclusion (2) would necessitate a shortening of the distance $\overline{AC}$ to l/k, where l is the width of the stream; with l/k in place of l in the expression for t_2, we see that we would have $t_2 = t_1$.

The reason that t_1 and t_2 are different is because the current, which carries the swimmers along, affects them differently. In the same way, sound waves carried by the air travel faster with the wind than across or against the wind. In the time of Maxwell much thought was given to the question of whether there was any medium which carried light. Some physicists suggested that there was such a medium, pervading all space, which they called the *ether*, and they regarded it as an absolute frame of reference. If such an ether existed, the earth could not always be at rest relative to the ether, since in six months' time the motion of the earth in its orbit is reversed. Suppose that the earth is moving through the ether;

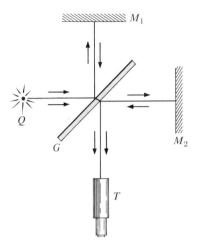

FIG. 16–3. The Michelson-Morley experiment.

then this relative motion, called *ether drift*, should affect the motion of light just as the current of the stream was seen to alter the effective speeds of the two swimmers.

Maxwell suggested a crucial experiment for testing the ether theory. This experiment was performed by Michelson, who was shortly aided by Morley, and it is called the *Michelson-Morley experiment*.   The apparatus employed was essentially a Michelson interferometer floating on a pool of mercury. The interferometer, diagrammed in Fig. 16–3, is the optical analog of the case of the stream and the two swimmers. A beam of light from a source Q strikes a half-silvered glass plate G, so that part of the light is reflected to the mirror M_1 and part passes through G and is reflected by the mirror M_2. Upon returning to G the two beams are again partly reflected and partly transmitted. The transmitted part of the beam from M_1 joins the reflected part of the beam from M_2 and the combined light passes into the telescope T. The optical lengths l of the two paths are made the same.   Then if there is an ether drift v parallel to GM_2, the light from M_2 will be, with respect to phase, a little behind that from M_1. A pattern of interference fringes is observed through the telescope T.

The crucial part of the experiment comes when the whole apparatus is rotated 90° about a vertical axis, so that any ether drift originally parallel to GM_2 will now be parallel to GM_1, causing a shift in the relative phases of the two combining beams.   During the rotation the observer must watch for a resulting shift in the interference pattern seen through the telescope. Taking for v the earth's orbital velocity of 30 km/sec, Michelson and Morley computed for their apparatus a shift of about half a fringe, according to the ether theory. Actually they found no significant shift, although they believed that a shift of 1/100 of a fringe could have been observed. This experiment has been repeated many times since Michelson first attempted it in 1880, and it is now generally agreed that the earth's motion through space cannot be detected as a motion through the ether.

As in the case of the two swimmers, the null result in the Michelson-Morley experiment may be interpreted as indicating (1) that the drift current is effectively zero, or (2) that distances parallel to the drift current are effectively shorter by a factor $1/k$ than they appear to be to an observer moving with the apparatus. As we have said, the earth moves in different directions at different times of the year, and therefore if there were an ether throughout space the earth could not always be at rest relative to it. The possibility that the earth carries with it an envelope of ether, stationary relative to the earth, has been ruled out by other experimental evidence. Conclusion (1) then necessitates giving up the ether drift hypothesis. The Irish physicist Fitzgerald suggested possibility (2), which amounts to the following.

Suppose that an observer measures the length of an object to be l' when he is moving with the object, but he finds the same length to be $l = l'/k$ (which is less than l') when the object is moving longitudinally with a speed v relative to the observer. In the Michelson-Morley experiment the observer is moving with the apparatus and he claims that the apparent length l' of the longitudinal path is equal to the length l of the transverse path. An observer at rest relative to the fixed stars would say that the longitudinal path is shorter. Since any measuring stick placed alongside the Michelson apparatus will undergo the same contraction, an observer moving with the apparatus cannot measure the motion of the apparatus relative to the ether. Be this so, the experiment still proves that motion of the source of light and the observer does not affect the measured speed of light.

We shall next show that the above argument may be reversed and that assumption of the constancy of the speed of light leads to the Lorentz space-time transformation, from which Fitzgerald's proposed contraction follows as a corollary.

16–5 Relativity derivation of the Lorentz space-time transformation

Let x, y, z, t refer to an event, such as a flash of light, occurring in the inertial system S at x, y, z at the time t, and x', y', z', t' to the same event in the inertial system S'. Take the x-axis and x'-axis to coincide and let S' be moving relative to S with the speed v in the x-direction (Fig. 16–4).

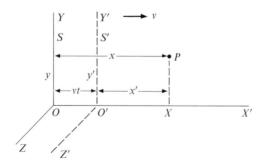

Fig. 16–4.   Two inertial systems in relative motion.

Let the two sets of axes coincide at the time we shall take to be $t = 0$ and $t' = 0$; starting at this time, let a spherical light wave spread out from the origin. At the time t in S this wave will reach some point P whose coordinates are x, y, z. Let the wave reach P at the time t' as measured by observers in the system S' and call the coordinates of P in this system x', y', z'. Since speed of propagation equals distance traveled divided by the time taken, we have

$$c = \frac{\sqrt{x^2 + y^2 + z^2}}{t},$$

or

$$x^2 + y^2 + z^2 - c^2t^2 = 0. \tag{16-4}$$

Similarly, we may write for observations made in S'

$$x'^2 + y'^2 + z'^2 - c^2t'^2 = 0, \tag{16-5}$$

where the c is *not* primed since, according to Einstein's postulate, c is the *same* in S' as in S.

From symmetry considerations it seems reasonable to try putting $y = y'$ and $z = z'$, since the relative motion of the systems is in the x- or x'-direction and not in the y- or z-directions. Combining Eqs. (16–4) and (16–5), we then get

$$x^2 - c^2t^2 = x'^2 - c^2t'^2. \tag{16-6}$$

We seek the transformation relations between x', t' and x, t which satisfy this equation by reducing it to an identity.

In accordance with Galilean-Newtonian theory, we would naturally assume the transformation equations to be

$$x' = x - vt,$$
$$t' = t, \tag{16-7}$$

which are called the *Galilean*, or *Newtonian, space-time transformation equations*. These equations are in agreement with observations involving familiar moving systems, such as trains or airplanes, for which $v \ll c$. One can see by substitution that these equations do not satisfy Eq. (16–6). We must look for a set of equations which (1) will satisfy Eq. (16–6), (2) reduces to (16–7) when $v \ll c$, and (3) is as simple as possible. Therefore let us try the linear transformations

$$x' = k(x - vt),$$
$$t' = k(t - bx), \tag{16-8}$$

where k and b are independent of x and t and are to be determined. Presumably $k \to 1$ and $b \to 0$ as v/c approaches zero [see (2) above].

If we substitute Eqs. (16–8) in Eq. (16–6), we get

$$x^2 - c^2t^2 = k^2(x^2 - 2vxt + v^2t^2) - c^2k^2(t^2 - 2bxt + b^2x^2). \tag{16-9}$$

For Eqs. (16–8) to satisfy Eq. (16–6) this last equation must be an identity, i.e., it must hold for all values of x and t, such as $x = 1, t = 0$, or $x = 0, t = 1$, etc. This means that the coefficients of the x^2 terms must be the same on each side, and so must the coefficients of the t^2 terms, or

$$1 = k^2 - c^2k^2b^2, \qquad \text{(coefficients of } x^2\text{)},$$
$$-c^2 = k^2v^2 - c^2k^2, \qquad \text{(coefficients of } t^2\text{)}.$$

From the second equation we find (after dividing by c^2 and rearranging terms) that

$$k^2(1 - v^2/c^2) = 1, \qquad k = \frac{1}{\sqrt{1 - v^2/c^2}},$$

so that this is the same k as we defined in Eq. (16–1). Substitution for k^2 in the first equation above will show that

$$b = v/c^2.$$

Note that as $(v/c) \rightarrow 0$, $k \rightarrow 1$, and $b \rightarrow 0$, and also that the coefficient of the xt term in Eq. (16–9) vanishes, as should be the case.

If we substitute the values found for k and b in Eq. (16–8), we get

$$x' = \frac{x - vt}{\sqrt{1 - v^2/c^2}}, \qquad t' = \frac{t - vx/c^2}{\sqrt{1 - v^2/c^2}}, \qquad (16\text{–}10)$$

which are the so-called *Lorentz space-time transformation equations* required by Einstein's postulate that the speed of light is the same in any inertial system. The most remarkable feature of these equations is the interrelationship between space and time in the two systems. The following three sections will illustrate this point.

16–6 The Lorentz-Fitzgerald contraction

Suppose that we have a rigid meter stick which when at rest in the laboratory is checked against a standard meter bar. Call the laboratory, or ground, the system S. For the system S' we shall take a very fast train which is moving in the x-direction with the speed v. Let the meter stick ride on the train with its length parallel to the direction of motion (see Fig. 16–5). An observer on the train checks the meter stick against a standard bar that he is carrying, and finds the length of the stick still to be one meter.

Observers on the ground set up telescopes along the tracks so that they can observe where, relative to S, the two ends of the stick are at some time t. The ground observers must first check their clocks with each other to be sure that they agree on the time t. They then say that they will observe the two ends of the moving meter stick at the *same* time t, or, as they say, "simultaneously." Observer A at x_a finds the front end of the moving stick to be passing the point x_a on the ground at the same time that B at x_b finds the other end passing the point x_b.

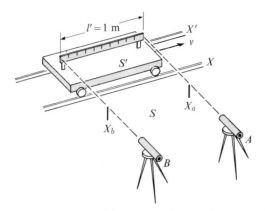

FIG. 16–5. A moving meter stick appears shortened to ground observers.

Substituting in the Lorentz equation $x' = k(x - vt)$, we have for the conditions above

$$x'_a = k(x_a - vt), \qquad x'_b = k(x_b - vt),$$

where the t is the same in each case. Subtraction yields

$$x'_a - x'_b = k(x_a - x_b),$$

or

$$x_a - x_b = \frac{1}{k}(x'_a - x'_b) = (x'_a - x'_b)\sqrt{1 - v^2/c^2}. \qquad (16\text{--}11)$$

Now $(x'_a - x'_b)$ is the length of the stick as checked by the observer on the train, and hence is exactly one meter. Then the length measured by the ground observers is *less* than one meter by the factor $1/k$.

Since motion is relative, the system S may be thought of as moving relative to S' with the velocity $-v$. Therefore we may turn the experiment around and have observers C, D, etc., on the train measure, *at their same time t'*, the length of an object on the ground. The result would be

$$x'_a - x'_b = (x_a - x_b)\sqrt{1 - v^2/c^2}$$
$$= (x_a - x_b)/k.$$

We see that this apparent shortening effect is reciprocal. *The measured length of an object is less when the object and the observer are in relative motion than when they are at rest with respect to each other.* Thus we have derived the *Lorentz-Fitzgerald contraction* from Einstein's postulate.

16–7 Simultaneity and relativity

The Lorentz-Fitzgerald contraction becomes less mysterious when we understand that two events which are simultaneous in one inertial system may not be simultaneous in another.

Let us return to the case of the ground observer A who makes a measurement at $x = x_a$ at the time t, while his friend B makes an observation at $x = x_b$ at the "simultaneous" time t. Let an observer C, traveling as before on a fast train, note the times t'_a and t'_b when, according to his clock, observers A and B make their respective measurements. From the Lorentz equation $t' = k(t - vx/c^2)$ we have

$$t'_a = k(t - vx_a/c^2), \qquad t'_b = k(t - vx_b/c^2). \qquad (16\text{--}12)$$

If we take $x_a > x_b$, we see that $t'_b > t'_a$. Observer C then claims that by his clock B was a little later than A in making his observation. Observer C might then argue that since B looked at the moving meter stick later than A did, B would see the back end at a point farther along the track than he would have if he had looked at his end just when A was looking at the front end. The result of B's lateness would be to make the back end position seem nearer that of the front end, i.e., the length would come out short of its true value.

We see that *two events, at x_a and x_b, which occur simultaneously in the system S, are not observed to be simultaneous in the system S'.* This theorem is also a reciprocal one.

EXAMPLE. Find the length of a meter stick, as measured by ground observers, when the stick is moving with a speed $v = 0.6c$ relative to the ground. Show that the apparent shortening may be explained, by an observer moving with the stick, as being due to non-simultaneous measurements by the ground observers.

Solution. We have $x'_a - x'_b = 1$ m and

$$1/k = \sqrt{1 - v^2/c^2} = \sqrt{1 - 0.36} = 0.8.$$

Hence From Eq. (16–11) we get

$$x_a - x_b = (x'_a - x'_b)/k = 0.8 \text{ m}.$$

Subtracting the first equation in (16–12) from the second gives

$$t'_b - t'_a = \frac{kv}{c^2}(x_a - x_b) = \frac{v}{c^2} \times (1.0 \text{ m}).$$

The ground observers report that the moving stick appears to them to be 0.8 m long. In communicating this information to the moving observer, the ground observers hold up a stick of their own which they have cut to be 0.8 m long. The moving observer looks at this stick and concludes that it is $0.8/k = 0.64$ m long and that the ground observers missed the length of the moving stick by 0.36 m. The moving observer explains this as the result of B's reading being made $(v/c^2)(1.0$ m) sec later than A's reading. The moving observer points out that in this time the back end of his stick would advance a distance

$$v(t'_b - t'_a) = \frac{v^2}{c^2} \times (1 \text{ m}) = 0.36 \text{ m},$$

which is what the moving observer believes to be the error made by the ground observers.

16–8 The apparent slowing of moving clocks

In the last section we took $x_a > x_b$, $t_a = t_b$, and found that $t_b' > t_a'$. Now we shall take $x_a = x_b$ and $t_b > t_a$.

Let observer A at $x = x_a$ flash one signal at the time $t = t_a$ and another signal at $t = t_b$. The signals might be one minute apart by A's clock. Suppose that a group of observers in the moving system S' have synchronized their clocks and that the observer passing A at the time of the first flash looks at his clock and records the time t_a' of the flash. Another observer in S' similarly records the time t_b' of A's second flash as he passes A. From the Lorentz equations, we have

$$t_a' = k(t_a - vx_a/c^2), \qquad t_b' = k(t_b - vx_a/c^2),$$

where $x = x_a$ in each case. Subtraction yields

$$t_b' - t_a' = k(t_b - t_a). \tag{16–13}$$

Since $k > 1$, the time between A's flashes is found to be longer by observers in the S' system than it is according to A (who is in the system S). Conversely, due to the relativity of motion, the time between two events occurring at the same place in S' is found to be longer by observers in S than by observers in S'. We may sum up by saying that *a clock will be found to run more and more slowly the greater the relative motion between the clock and the observer.*

This effect becomes important in the case of high-energy cosmic particles of low mass, such as mesons, whose speeds relative to the ground may be only slightly less than that of light. These particles are observed to have short lifetimes, but with their high speeds they may travel considerable distances during their lifetimes. Since the speed of a meson gradually decreases as it loses energy in the earth's atmosphere, the velocity of the ground relative to the meson also changes. Hence for a given meson the lifetime usually referred to is that for a system in which the meson is at rest. Calling this lifetime τ_0 and letting τ represent the lifetime observed in the earth system, relative to which the meson is moving, the apparent distance traveled by the meson will be the value of $\bar{v}\tau$, where $\bar{v}$ is the average speed over the apparent lifetime τ. Mesons with low speeds can be created in the laboratory so that the lifetime τ_0 of a given type of meson can be measured. However, it is found that even if a cosmic meson is assumed to have a speed $\bar{v}$ nearly equal to that of light, the distance $\bar{v}\tau$ that it travels is greater than $c\tau_0$, so that τ must be greater than τ_0. Here is direct experimental proof of the apparent slowing of the passage of time in a moving system.

EXAMPLE. A meson has a speed $v = 0.8c$ relative to the ground. Find how far the meson travels relative to the ground if its speed remains constant and the time of its flight, relative to the system in which it is at rest, is 2×10^{-8} sec.

Solution. Since $v = 0.8c$, $1/k = 0.6$, $k = 5/3$. Relative to the earth the time of flight is

$$\tau = k \times 2 \times 10^{-8} = 3.33 \times 10^{-8} \text{ sec.}$$

The apparent distance traveled is then

$$\Delta x = v\tau = (0.8 \times 3 \times 10^8 \text{ m/sec}) \times (3.33 \times 10^{-8} \text{ sec})$$
$$= 8.0 \text{ m}.$$

Note that this is greater than the distance the meson could travel in 2×10^{-8} sec even if its speed were that of light.

―――――――――

The same line of reasoning has been applied in a speculative way to the problem of interstellar space travel. How much we would like to know whether other stars have planetary systems and whether life exists on any of them! The nearest star is Alpha Centauri and it is about 4 light-years distance; the brightest star, Sirius, is about twice as far away. A *light-year* is the distance traveled by light in one year, which is about 6×10^{12} miles or 10^{16} meters. We shall see that, according to the relativity theory, we cannot hope to travel at speeds equal to, or greater than, the speed of light. Suppose, however, that we could launch a space ship at a speed $v = 0.8c$ relative to the earth and follow its progress through a telescope. We would find that it took $4/0.8 = 5$ years to reach the neighborhood of Alpha Centauri according to *our* clocks, but the people on the space ship would say that, according to *their* clocks, our 5 years was

$$\frac{5}{\sqrt{1 - (0.8)^2}} = \frac{5}{0.6} = 8\tfrac{1}{3} \text{ years,}$$

during which time they could travel well beyond Alpha Centauri. To reach Alpha Centauri the space travelers would only have to exist for $0.6 \times 5 = 3$ years of their lives in their ship. (Since moving clocks run slow, we would call these three years five of our years.) Another way of putting it is to say that to the moving space travelers the distance to Alpha Centauri would appear shortened from the 4 light years measured by earth observers to $0.6 \times 4 = 2.4$ light years, which could be covered in 3 years by a ship moving at eight-tenths the speed of light. There will thus be a double advantage in performing space voyages at speeds as close to that of light as possible.

Should a person travel to Alpha Centauri and right back at the speed $v = 0.8c$, he would arrive home 6 years older, while his friends on earth would have aged by 10 years! The reason that there is a reciprocity between observations made of a system S' from a system S and observations made of S from S', but not in the case of the returning space traveler and his earthbound friends, is that the space traveler *turned around* in order to return to earth. The space traveler did not stay in the same inertial system S', but the earth inhabitants did remain in their system S. This method of out-living your contemporaries is referred to as the *twin paradox*, since a twin who takes a fast trip should return home younger than his twin brother or sister who does not go away. As George Gamow has pointed out, if the speed of light were only 20 mi/hr, a postman bicycling around on his route all day every day might eventually be younger than a sedentary grand-daughter!

If all of this sounds quite preposterous it is because it is unfamiliar. In our daily lives we do not encounter the length shortening and time slowing effects because at ordinary speeds these effects are far too small to measure. However, this does not mean that they do not exist; when dealing with high-speed particles for which the effects are measurable, we find that the predictions of relativity theory are true, so the theory must be accepted along with other successful ones. There is, however, great doubt that its extension to distant space travel will ever be practicable according to the present state of our knowledge. Problems 12 and 13 at the end of the chapter will help to make this point clear.

16–9 The transformation and addition of velocities

As before, take the system S' to be moving in the x-direction with the speed v relative to S, or S to be moving in the negative x'-direction with the speed v relative to S'. Consider an object which is moving relative to both systems, calling the velocity components V_x, V_y, V_z rleative to S, and V_x', V_y', V_z' relative to S'. Let $x = 0$ and $x' = 0$ at $t = 0$ and $t' = 0$. Let the object move to where its x-coordinate is x and its x'-coordinate is x' in the time t (as measured in S), or the time t' (as measured in S'). From the definition of velocity we have

$$V_x = \frac{x}{t}, \qquad V_x' = \frac{x'}{t'}.$$

From the Lorentz transformation equations,

$$x' = k(x - vt), \qquad t' = k(t - vx/c^2),$$

we see that

$$V_x' = \frac{x - vt}{t - vx/c^2} = \frac{(x/t) - v}{1 - vx/c^2 t}$$

$$= \frac{V_x - v}{1 - vV_x/c^2}. \qquad (16\text{–}14)$$

The corresponding equation for V_x in terms of V_x' may be obtained by changing the sign of v, since S is moving in the (positive) x'-direction with the speed $-v$ relative to S'. Thus

$$V_x = \frac{V_x' + v}{1 + vV_x'/c^2}. \qquad (16\text{–}15)$$

For the inertial systems we have been considering, $y' = y$, so that

$$V_y' = \frac{y'}{t'} = \frac{y}{k(t - vx/c^2)} = \frac{y/t}{k(1 - vx/c^2 t)}$$

$$= \frac{V_y}{k(1 - vV_x/c^2)}, \qquad (16\text{–}16)$$

and

$$V_y = \frac{V_y'}{k(1 + vV_x'/c^2)}. \qquad (16\text{–}17)$$

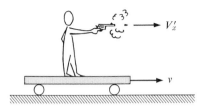

FIG. 16-6.   Addition of velocities.

Suppose now that a bullet is fired in the forward direction from a train whose speed is v (Fig. 16-6). The muzzle velocity of a bullet is measured relative to the gun, and since the gun moves with the train, we may let V'_x be the muzzle velocity. Then V_x is the velocity of the bullet relative to the ground. We shall show that V_x cannot exceed c so long as V'_x and v are less than c. We may write Eq. (16-15) as

$$V_x = \left[\frac{(V'_x/c) + (v/c)}{1 + (v/c)(V'_x/c)}\right]c = \left[1 - \frac{(1 - V'_x/c)(1 - v/c)}{1 + (v/c)(V'_x/c)}\right]c. \qquad (16\text{-}18)$$

Since each factor in brackets on the right is less than unity, we must have $V_x < c$.

EXAMPLE.   Given $v = 0.9c$ and $V'_x = 0.9c$; find V_x.

Solution.   From Eq. (16-18), we find that

$$V_x = \left[1 - \frac{(0.1)(0.1)}{1 + 0.81}\right] = 0.9945c,$$

whereas according to the Galilean transformations the answer would be $V_x = 1.8c$.

Since the relativistic composition of velocities makes it impossible to build up a velocity greater than c out of two velocities each less than c, we see that *the velocity of light in vacuo is the maximum attainable velocity for a material object.*

16-10 Relativistic dynamics and the variation of mass with velocity

We turn now to the second part of Einstein's relativity principle, which states that the laws of physics are the same, or invariant, in any inertial system. In particular we shall consider the invariance of Newton's law of motion and Newton's action-reaction law.

Newton's law of motion in its most general form states that

$$\mathbf{F} = \frac{\Delta\mu}{\Delta t} = \frac{\Delta(m\mathbf{v})}{\Delta t}, \qquad (16\text{-}19)$$

or the time rate of change of the momentum of a system equals the net force acting on the system.

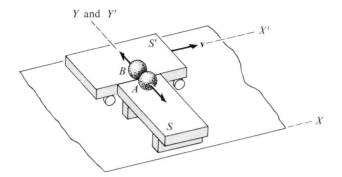

FIG. 16-7. Two observers verifying the conservation of momentum principle.

Newton's action-reaction law tells us that when two bodies A and B interact, as in a collision, the action of A on B is equal and opposite to that of B on A.

If we consider A and B as a closed system, with no forces acting from outside, then because of the action-reaction law $\mathbf{F} = 0$ and, from the law of motion, $\Delta\mu = 0$. Thus the conservation of momentum theorem depends on both of the above laws. Therefore, if Newton's laws are invariant, so must the conservation of momentum theorem also be invariant.

Consider the following hypothetical thought experiment. Objects A and B weigh the same on the same scales and so must have the same mass m_0 when at rest in the laboratory. Object A is at rest on a frictionless table that is bolted to the floor; B is at rest on another frictionless table, but B's table is mounted on a track so that it may be moved past A with constant velocity $\mathbf{v}$ (see Fig. 16–7). Let the system S be the laboratory and S' be B's platform. Take the x-axis and the x'-axis to be in the direction of $\mathbf{v}$. At the moment when B passes closest to A let the two objects (or people) interact, say by a slight glancing collision, or by having a compressed spring put between them, or by pushing against each other in some other way so that A and B move away from each other with a small speed $u \ll v$.

Before the collision, A and B together had no momentum perpendicular to the x- and x'-directions, so that there was no y-component of momentum in either system. After the collision the transverse momentum of A in system S is m_0u. From symmetry considerations and the action-reaction law the transverse momentum $m_0V'_y$ of B in system S' must also be m_0u, but in the opposite direction. Thus $V'_y = u$. An observer in the laboratory system S looks at B and observes it to have the transverse speed

$$V_y = \frac{V'_y}{k} = \frac{u}{k} = u\sqrt{1 - v^2/c^2}$$

[see Eq. (16–17), in which $V'_x = 0$ for B]. The laboratory observer would conclude that the transverse momentum of B is the product of B's mass and V_y, a product that cannot equal in magnitude the transverse momentum m_0u of A unless B's mass is no longer equal to m_0. Call m the *apparent mass* of B as measured by a

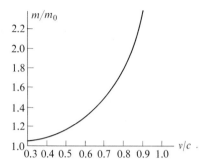

FIG. 16–8.   Variation of electron's mass with speed.

laboratory observer who believes in the invariance of the conservation of momentum theorem. Then this observer must assign to m a value such that

$$m V_y = m_0 u,$$

$$mu\sqrt{1 - v^2/c^2} = m_0 u, \tag{16-20}$$

$$m = \frac{m_0}{\sqrt{1 - v^2/c^2}}.$$

If this relation is true, then in either system, S or S', A and B together will have no momentum in the y-direction after the collision, since the momentum of one will be equal and opposite to that of the other. As A and B had no momentum in the y-direction before the collision, observers in either system will agree that momentum was conserved during the collision. Therefore, to preserve the invariance of the conservation of momentum principle and Newton's laws (from which the momentum principle follows), we must assign to a body moving relative to our system an apparent mass m that is greater than the *rest mass* m_0 we assign to the same body when at rest. The relation given by Eq. (16–20) is a general one.

While the mass of a body is evidently a function of its speed relative to the observer, this dependence of m on v is not significant until v reaches values of over 1% that of light, i.e., over 1800 mi/sec or 3×10^6 m/sec. The variation of mass with speed is shown graphically in Fig. 16–8. It is really only in the atomic world that we encounter speeds of $0.5c$ and greater, but experiments with high-energy electrons in an x-ray tube, and with still more energetic electrons from radioactive materials, have enabled physicists to verify Eq. (16–20) for values of v in excess of $0.99c$.

EXAMPLE. Find m/m_0 when $v = 0.99c$.

Solution. From Eq. (16–20) we have

$$\frac{m}{m_0} = \frac{1}{\sqrt{1 - (0.99)^2}} = \frac{1}{\sqrt{0.02}} = 7.09.$$

This represents an increase in mass of over 600% of the rest mass!

16–11 Einstein's mass-energy relationship

We saw in Chapter 9 that the kinetic energy (K.E.) of a body is calculated by computing the work required to accelerate the body from rest to its given state of motion at some speed v. Work is measured by the product of force times distance. If the mass of a body increases to a value greater than its rest mass, it will require a corresponding greater force to overcome the increased inertia of the body and maintain the same acceleration. Thus more work must be done than would be necessary if the mass did not increase with the speed. Therefore, the K.E. must be represented by a quantity that is greater than the $\frac{1}{2}mv^2$ computed in Chapter 9.

If the ratio v/c is small, we can apply the binomial theorem (see Chapter 2) to the term $(1 - v^2/c^2)^{-1/2}$ and write Eq. (16–20) as

$$m = m_0(1 - v^2/c^2)^{-1/2}$$

$$= m_0\left(1 + \frac{1}{2}\frac{v^2}{c^2} + \text{ higher powers of } \frac{v^2}{c^2}\right).$$

Let us neglect the terms that involve the higher powers of v^2/c^2. Then after multiplying through by c^2 we have

$$mc^2 = m_0c^2 + \tfrac{1}{2}m_0v^2,$$

$$\tfrac{1}{2}m_0v^2 = mc^2 - m_0c^2 = \Delta m \times c^2, \tag{16–21}$$

where $\Delta m = m - m_0$, the increase in apparent mass. Thus if we neglect higher powers of v^2/c^2, the Newtonian K.E. of a body is represented by the gain in mass multiplied by the square of the speed of light.

An exact computation of the work needed to give a body of rest mass m_0 the speed v, where v/c is not necessarily small, requires an integration that is not difficult, if one is familiar with the calculus. The result is:

$$\text{Work done} = \text{gain in K.E.} = mc^2 - m_0c^2. \tag{16–22}$$

Thus the right-hand side of our approximate expression, Eq. (16–21), does represent the K.E. correctly; it is the left-hand side of Eq. (16–21) that is approximate. From Eq. (16–22) and Eq. (16–20) we have

$$\text{K.E.} = m_0c^2(1 - v^2/c^2)^{-1/2} - m_0c^2$$

$$= m_0c^2\left[1 + \frac{1}{2}\frac{v^2}{c^2} + \frac{3}{8}\frac{v^4}{c^4} + \cdots - 1\right]$$

$$= \tfrac{1}{2}m_0v^2 + \frac{3}{8}\frac{m_0v^4}{c^2} + \text{ smaller terms,}$$

which shows that the K.E. is greater than $\frac{1}{2}m_0v^2$.

The kinetic energy of a moving body equals its gain in mass times c^2. We may also say that the apparent mass of a body increases linearly with its kinetic energy, so that an increase in mass is an indication and measure of the gain in kinetic energy. It is also found* that an increase in the potential energy of a system of particles is accompanied by a similar increase in mass equal to the gain in energy divided by c^2. Therefore we may say, in general, that *the gain (or loss) in the energy of a system is equal to the gain (or loss) in its apparent mass multiplied by c^2.*

We may go one step further and interpret the term m_0c^2 in Eq. (16–22) as the *rest energy* of a body whose rest mass is m_0. This rest energy may be regarded as a form of internal energy inherent in the nature of the particles out of which matter is composed. If we solve Eq. (16–22) for mc^2, we then have

$$mc^2 = \text{rest energy} + \text{kinetic energy}$$
$$= \text{total energy}.$$

If here we let E stand for the total energy, we arrive at Einstein's famous principle of the equivalence of mass and energy,

$$E = mc^2. \tag{16–23}$$

The value of any theory is measured by its success in predicting new results. In this respect Einstein's theory has been outstanding. In nuclear physics the equivalence of mass and energy has been put to the test repeatedly and it has always been confirmed. With the ability to measure the masses of atomic particles to a high degree of accuracy, nuclear physicists have been able to predict the energy changes accompanying nuclear and particle transmutations, and they have also been able to verify their predictions experimentally. The whole subject of nuclear energy (popularly called "atomic energy") illustrates the usefulness of the above principle. The energy exchanges involved in chemical reactions must also be accompanied by corresponding mass changes, but in this relatively low-energy field the mass changes are too small to be detected experimentally. (See Chapter 20.)

While chemical reactions and most nuclear ones involve a rearrangement of atomic or subatomic particles, with a consequent change in their potential energy, there are also the interesting pair annihilation reactions referred to in connection with the conservation of charge principle. In these latter reactions a particle of rest mass m_0 and charge e encounters and neutralizes a particle of rest mass m_0 and charge $-e$. One particle is said to be the *antiparticle* of the other; examples are the proton and antiproton, also the positron and the electron. When such particles come together, not only do their charges neutralize each other, but the particles cease to exist as such and in their place electromagnetic radiation is born. In the case where the colliding particles have little K.E. it is found that the energy of the radiation produced just equals $2m_0c^2$. This has been interpreted in different ways. Some physicists say that in this process the mass $2m_0$ is converted into radiant energy. However, we shall see in the next chapter that it is fruitful to con-

---

* See Richtmeyer, Kennard, and Lauritxen, *Introduction to Modern Physics*, 5th ed., pp. 69–70.

sider mass to be associated with radiation as well as with material particles. Radiation is found to possess inertial properties. Pair annihilation must then be interpreted as a process in which mass and energy are transformed together from one form to another. In general, it would seem preferable to regard mass as a property of energy, or energy as a property of mass, the two being inseparable. The basic principle then is the *conservation of mass-energy*.

EXAMPLE. An electron and positron which are practically at rest come together and annihilate each other, producing two photons of equal energy. Find the energy and equivalent mass of the radiant energy created.

Solution. The rest mass m_0 of an electron is 9.1×10^{-31} kg. This is equivalent (in the mks system) to the energy

$$E = m_0 c^2 = 9.1 \times 10^{-31} \times 9 \times 10^{16} \text{ kg-m}^2/\text{sec}^2$$

$$= 81.9 \times 10^{-15} \text{ j}$$

$$= \frac{81.9 \times 10^{-15} \text{ j}}{1.6 \times 10^{-19} \text{ j/electron-volt}}$$

$$= 5.12 \times 10^5 \text{ electron-volts.}$$

The positron has the same rest mass and energy as the electron, hence the total energy radiated is 1.024×10^6 electron-volts and, associated with this radiant energy, there will be an inertial mass of $2m_0 = 1.82 \times 10^{-30}$ kg.

PROBLEMS

1. Referring to the two swimmers in Section 16–4, take the current $v = 3$ ft/sec and the speed c of each swimmer in still water to be 5 ft/sec. Find (a) the times t_1 and t_2 when $\overline{AC} = \overline{AB} = 100$ ft, (b) the distance $\overline{AC}$ for which, with $\overline{AB} = 100$ ft, the swimmers would have the same times.

2. In the Michelson-Morley experiment take $l = 11$ m and $v/c = 10^{-4}$ (the ratio of the earth's orbital velocity to the speed of light). (a) Neglecting terms smaller than v^2/c^2, show that the time difference $t_2 - t_1 = lv^2/c^3$. (b) For light of 5×10^{-7} m wavelength, what should the fringe or phase shift in the interference pattern be, according to the ether theory, when the apparatus is rotated 90°?

3. A certain young lady decides on her twenty-fifth birthday that it is time to slenderize. She weighs 200 lb. She has heard that if she moves fast enough she will appear thinner to her stationary friends. (a) How fast must she move to appear slenderized by a factor of 50%? (b) At this speed what will her mass appear to be (to her stationary friends)? (c) If she maintains her speed until the day she calls her twenty-ninth birthday, how old will her stationary friends claim she is according to their measurements?

4. (a) Define the momentum p of a body, according to relativistic dynamics. (b) Show that $p^2 = m^2c^2 - m_0^2c^2$.

5. For what energy in electron-volts will the ratio m/m_0 for an electron be (a) 1.1, (b) 2, (c) 10, (d) 100?

6. Repeat problem 5 for protons instead of electrons.

7. For what energy in electron-volts will the ratio v/c for an electron be (a) 0.10, (b) 0.50, (c) 0.90, (d) 0.99?

8. A red-hot sphere of iron (specific heat capacity = 0.11 cal*/kg-°C) weighs close to 1 kg. If the sphere cools 1200°C, what is the equivalent loss in mass?

9. An atomic mass unit (amu) is defined as $1/(6.02 \times 10^{26})$ kg. (a) Find the energy equivalence of 1 amu. (b) If a deuteron (H^2) and a triton (H^3) combine in a fusion process to form an alpha particle (He^4) and a neutron (n), find the percent loss in mass if the respective masses are 2.0147, 3.0170, 4.0039, and 1.0090 amu. (c) Compute in kilowatt-hours the energy released per kilogram in (b).

10. Solar radiation reaches the earth, which is 90,000,000 miles or 1.5×10^{11} m away from the sun, at the rate of about 1.4×10^3 watts/m². At what rate is the sun losing mass due to its radiation in all directions?

11. How long would a space traveler think he exists while traveling, relative to the earth, at a speed $v = 0.90c$ to a star that earthmen say is 40 light-years away?

12. At an acceleration equal to g, or 9.8 m/sec², how long would it take a space ship to reach the speed $v = 0.90c$? Compute answer in days.

13. Suppose that in problem 11 the space traveler and his ship (without fuel) have a rest mass of 1000 kg. (a) Compute the equivalent mass of the traveler and ship at a speed $v = 0.9c$. (b) If the fuel itself did not have to be accelerated, what mass of fuel would be needed to furnish the required K.E. if 1% of the mass of the fuel could be passed to the space ship as energy? (At present man has only been able to convert a few tenths of 1% of the mass of nuclear fuel into mass associated with radiant, kinetic, and other forms of energy.) (c) Show that if half of the fuel must, on the average, also be accelerated, then the space ship could not be made to approach a speed at which relativistic effects would be important.

REFERENCES

BARNETT, L., *The Universe and Dr. Einstein*, Harper, 1948.

EDDINGTON, A. S., *The Nature of the Physical World*, Macmillan, 1929.

EINSTEIN, A., *The Meaning of Relativity*, Princeton Univ. Press, 1950.

EINSTEIN, A., and L. INFELD, *The Evolution of Physics*, Simon and Schuster, 1938.

GAMOW, G., *Mr. Tompkins in Wonderland*, Cambridge Univ. Press, 1957.

INFELD, L., *Albert Einstein, His Work and Its Influence on Our World*, Scribner's, 1950.

JEANS, J., *The New Background of Science*, Cambridge Univ. Press, 1953.

---

* This is our large calorie, which equals 4180 joules.

CHAPTER 17

The Quantum Principle

17–1 The need for a new principle

As has been said, the laws of classical physics apply very well to the behavior of objects that we can see with our eyes. However, in modern atomic physics we talk about and experiment with particles too small to be seen even under the highest powered microscope. Physicists have become so familiar with the properties of atoms and electrons that their existence seems just as real as that of a tennis ball. This sense of reality has been enhanced by the invention of models to help us understand the behavior of atoms and subatomic particles. These models, such as Rutherford's planetary model of the atom in which one pictures electrons circling the atomic nucleus just as the planets do the sun, have helped us to assimilate and remember many different experimental facts, and they have led to the discovery of new properties possessed by atoms and particles. However, since such models may also suggest properties that the object in question does not actually possess, one must always guard against taking the model too seriously, as has sometimes been done in atomic physics. Physicists talked so much about the planetary model of the atom that some people, particularly nonphysicists, began to think that given a more powerful microscope, one might actually be able to see the electrons circulating in definite orbits, just as we see the planets move in the sky; it was hard for such people to understand the later developments of atomic theory, according to which there is no sense in talking about an electron occupying a definite position at a given time or being in a sharply defined orbit. We are really on safe ground only when we speak of the *observable* properties of particles that we cannot see and it has become necessary to keep this point more and more in mind. Thus in this chapter we shall discuss measurable energy exchanges on the atomic level, but say little about hypothetical electron orbits.

Let us first list some of the observable facts that cannot be explained just by the fundamental laws of the preceding eleven chapters, but require the introduction of a twelfth law, the quantum principle. In historical sequence the most important of these facts are those relating to (1) the frequency distribution of the radiation emitted by incandescent solids and gases, (2) the photoelectric effect, (3) the Compton effect, in which x-rays are scattered by recoiling electrons, while the frequency of the x-rays decreases, (4) the diffraction properties of corpuscular particles, (5) the "leakage" of particles through a potential barrier, e.g., an alpha particle escaping from an atomic nucleus. Of course there are many other important related facts, but those listed above are outstanding and at the same time so diverse in their nature as to illustrate the wide scope of the quantum principle. That a single unifying principle can "explain" all of these facts is a source of wonder; at the same time, their diversity suggests that it may be difficult to state the quantum principle as easily and concisely as we could our other laws. As a matter of fact, the full meaning of the quantum principle was only realized a little at a time; it was approached from different directions, just as explorers have gone into an unknown territory first from one side and then from another.

It would be nice if one could simply say that the quantum principle states that radiant energy consists of discrete units, just as matter and electricity do. The principle does say that some of the properties of light may be described in this way, but it says a lot more too, such as that all particles (corpuscular and light) have a wave-particle duality, that atomic systems can only exist in certain energy states, and that there is a basic uncertainty related to the simultaneous measurement of the position and momentum of a particle. In order to understand all of this it is necessary to study in more detail the facts listed above and how the quantum principle pertains to them. As we do this the reader will note that the unifying thread that runs through the explanation of all of these facts is the introduction of Planck's constant h, a new universal constant not needed in classical physics.

17–2 Blackbody radiation

When a solid is heated to incandescence it emits radiation of a continuous range of frequencies, such as we find in the solar radiation. Just how the total energy is spread among the different parts of the spectrum is something that depends on the temperature and color of the emitting body. However, for all blackbodies the spectral distribution of the radiation is a function of the temperature only. A black-body is defined as one that does not reflect any of the radiation falling on it. The most practical approach to a perfect blackbody is a *cavity*, like a furnace, with a very tiny hole through which one can see into the interior from outside (Fig. 17–1). Any outside radiation that falls on the hole will go in, be reflected by the inside walls, and eventually be absorbed by them. Thus a cavity with a small hole satisfies the definition of a blackbody. When equilibrium is reached at any given tempera-ture, the walls of a furnace must be emitting and absorbing radiation at equal rates. The radiation contained within a unit volume of the cavity itself will have the same spectral distribution as that emitted and absorbed by the walls, and the energy

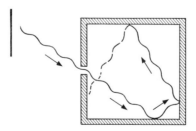

FIG. 17–1.   A cavity with a small opening is equivalent to a blackbody.

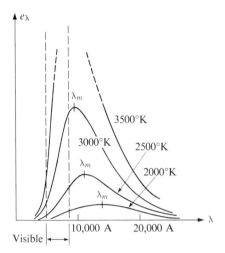

FIG. 17-2. Distribution of the energy radiated by a blackbody at four different temperatures.

density (energy per unit volume) of this radiation will be proportional to the rate of emission of radiation per unit area of the walls.

If one uses a grating, or prism, to form the spectrum of cavity radiation and if one also measures the intensity contained in a given range of wavelengths, say a range of 100 angstroms (10^{-8} m), first in one part of the spectrum and then in another, one will observe the following facts. (1) Very long and very short wavelengths carry very little of the energy. (2) There is a certain wavelength λ_m at which the energy per given range of wavelength is a maximum. (3) As the temperature of the furnace increases, λ_m decreases in such a manner that the product $\lambda_m T$, where T is the Kelvin temperature, is a constant equal to 0.0029 m-°K. (4) As the temperature increases, the total energy emitted at all wavelengths increases with the *fourth power* of the Kelvin temperature. One may summarize all of these facts with the curves shown in Fig. 17-2, where e_λ, the rate at which energy is emitted per unit area per given range of wavelength, is plotted against the wavelength λ for several temperatures. While fact (4) above can be explained in terms of classical thermodynamics, the laws we have discussed so far do not explain the shape of the curves shown in Fig. 17-2, nor do they even account for the presence of the maximum at λ_m.

This was the situation in 1900 when the great German theoretician Max Planck (1858-1947) tackled the problem of finding a theory that would explain the above facts. Planck proceeded to follow a wise plan. First he studied the previous literature on the subject and found that two formulas, based on classical ideas, had been proposed, one describing one part of the energy-wavelength curves of Fig. 17-2, and the other describing another part of the same curves. Neither formula described the complete curves. Second, Planck put these two formulas together in such a manner that he obtained an empirical formula that *did* fit the entire wavelength range. This formula [see Eq. (17-3)] contained only two adjustable constants,

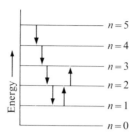

FIG. 17–3.   Energy-level diagram for a Planck oscillator. The energy E corresponding to any level is nhf.

C_1 and C_2, whose values could be chosen so as to make the formula fit the experimental facts.   Third, Planck studied the earlier theories to see in what respect they failed to explain his empirical formula.   Fourth, Planck found that to obtain a successful theory he had to make a radical alteration in one of the previous theories. This alteration was such an arbitrary postulate that even Planck was at first reluctant to make it, but it is one that has successfully withstood the test of time. Let us see what this arbitrary postulate was.

Planck commenced his theory by speculating about how the walls of a furnace emit radiation.   He assumed that these walls contain oscillators, vibrating with all possible frequencies.   Hertz had shown that when electrons move back and forth in an antenna with the frequency f, radiation of this frequency is emitted (see Chapter 15), so Planck assumed that oscillators of the frequency f were responsible for giving out and absorbing this frequency.   When the only force acting on an oscillating particle is a restoring force proportional to its displacement from equilibrium, the oscillator will vibrate with the same frequency regardless of the amplitude of its vibration; the amplitude only determines the total energy of the oscillator.   So for an oscillator to emit energy its amplitude must decrease, while when it absorbs energy its amplitude must increase.

In the case of such familiar oscillators as a pendulum and a vibrating tuning fork, it appears that the energy may decrease *continuously*.   Planck found that he could not assume this for his cavity oscillators if his theory was to lead to the correct empirical radiation law.   Instead, he had to postulate that *an oscillator of frequency f can exist only in states for which the energy E is a whole number multiple n of the product hf*, where h is a constant that is the same for oscillators of all frequencies, i.e.,

$$E = nhf, \qquad n = 0, 1, 2, 3, \ldots . \tag{17–1}$$

Planck found that if he did not restrict n to integral values, but allowed it to vary continuously, then his subsequent theory led to one of the incorrect formulas for e_λ.

If energy is plotted vertically upward, the *energy states* of an oscillator of frequency f that are allowed according to Eq. (17–1) may be represented as a series of equally spaced lines, like the rungs in a ladder, as shown in Fig. 17–3.

To his first postulate Planck had to add another equally arbitrary one, namely that *an oscillator can emit energy only by going from one energy state to the next lower one*, and that it can only absorb energy by going up one step in the energy-state ladder. This implies that a cavity oscillator does *not* emit energy while in a given state. Now Planck's oscillators were presumably electrons moving to and fro, and we have seen that such accelerated charges should, according to the laws of electromagnetism, continually radiate energy in the form of electromagnetic waves. Planck simply assumed that his cavity oscillators did not radiate as do free electrons in a wire.

With the above assumptions Planck derived the following formula for e_λ:

$$e_\lambda = \frac{2\pi hc^2}{\lambda^5(e^{hc/\lambda kT} - 1)}, \tag{17-2}$$

where h is Planck's new constant, c is the speed of light, λ is the wavelength in the neighborhood of which the emission is e_λ per unit wavelength range, e is the base of natural logarithms, namely 2.718 . . . , and k is Boltzmann's constant. This formula agrees with all of the facts listed earlier in this section; furthermore, it is of the same form as the empirical law Planck found to describe the curves in Fig. 17–2, namely

$$e_\lambda = \frac{C_1}{\lambda^5(e^{C_2/\lambda T} - 1)}, \tag{17-3}$$

where C_1 and C_2 are constants whose values he had already computed from experimental data.

The agreement in form of Eq. (17–2) and Eq. (17–3) assured Planck's theory of qualitative success. More surprising was its quantitative agreement with the facts. By comparing the two equations we see that $2\pi hc^2$ should equal C_1. Since h is a new constant, Planck could choose its value so as to make $2\pi hc^2 = C_1$. The required value of h came out to be

$$h = 6.6 \times 10^{-34} \text{ j-sec.} \tag{17-4}$$

Further comparison of the two equations for e_λ shows that hc/k should equal C_2. Since Planck had already chosen a value for h, and since the values of c and k had also been determined, he could test his theory by computing hc/k and comparing its value with the experimental value of C_2, namely

$$C_2 = 0.014 \text{ m-°K.}$$

If we apply the above test, we find that

$$\frac{hc}{k} = \frac{(6.6 \times 10^{-34} \text{ j-sec}) \times (3 \times 10^8 \text{ m/sec})}{1.38 \times 10^{-23} \text{ j/°K}} = 0.0143 \text{ m-°K.}$$

This equality of hc/k and C_2 furnishes strong experimental support to Planck's theory.

In spite of its qualitative and quantitative success, Planck's theory was not universally accepted at first because its postulates were so radically new. Wise scientists must, on the one hand, keep their minds open to new ideas, while on the other hand they must use judgment in accepting them. The latter usually involves applying the tests of a good theory, which have been listed elsewhere in this book (see Chapter 5 and the end of Chapter 15). For example, some said that Planck's theory was built to explain cavity radiation and so of course it did explain cavity radiation, but nothing more. Time has shown the incorrectness of this argument. Instead we may now say that very little in atomic physics can be explained without the introduction of a constant whose magnitude and units are the same as those of h in Eq. (17–4). Some people still find it difficult to accept a point of view at odds with that of everyday life, even though this new way of thinking is *not* applied to the events of everyday life, but to ones of an entirely different order of magnitude. However, to a person whose mind dwells among the atoms or the stars, these unorthodox views may seem the most natural ones.

EXAMPLE. A pendulum has a period of 2 sec. The bob, whose mass is 50 gm, is pulled out sufficiently far to raise it 10 cm above its equilibrium position. (a) Compute the initial energy of the bob. (b) If the bob loses the energy hf, what fraction of its original energy will be lost?

Solution. (a) Here $T = 2 \sec, f = 1/T = 0.5/\sec$. The bob's initial energy E is potential, therefore

$$E = mg \times \text{height lifted}$$
$$= (5 \times 10^{-2} \text{ kg}) \times (9.8 \text{ m/sec}^2) \times (0.1 \text{ m})$$
$$= 4.9 \times 10^{-2} \text{ j}.$$

(b) Here $hf = (6.6 \times 10^{-34} \text{ j-sec}) \times (0.5/\sec)$
$$= 3.3 \times 10^{-34} \text{ j}.$$

$$\frac{hf}{E} = \frac{3.3 \times 10^{-34}}{4.9 \times 10^{-2}} = 6.7 \times 10^{-33}.$$

Thus in this case hf represents a change in the energy that is far, far too small to measure. This shows that the postulate of discrete, or individually separated, energy states is not in conflict with the observation that in everyday life we do not observe such a limitation on the energy of a mechanical system.

17–3 The photoelectric effect

While Hertz was experimenting on the production of electromagnetic waves by means of a spark discharge between two neighboring spheres, he observed that ultraviolet radiation produced in the discharge caused negative electric charges to be emitted from the negative sphere. These negative charges were later identified as electrons and it was also found that they could be ejected from the cold surface of an alkali metal, such as sodium, by visible light. This phenomenon is called the *photoelectric effect.* We are all familiar with its application to light meters in photography and to "magic eye" devices for opening doors, etc.

Further study of the photoelectric effect disclosed the following facts.

(a) If the incident light is monochromatic (of one frequency only), then the number of photoelectrons emitted is proportional to the *intensity* of the light.

(b) Increasing the *intensity* of the light in (a) does not affect the K.E. with which the individual electrons are emitted.

(c) If a certain light causes photoelectrons to be emitted, then, when the light is turned on, emission commences immediately, with no apparent delay, even when the light is very weak.

(d) For a given metal the K.E. of the individual photoelectrons increases with the *frequency* of the light used. There is a certain threshold frequency f_0 below which no emission occurs. For frequencies above f_0, the K.E. of the photoelectrons is proportional to $(f - f_0)$, where f is the frequency of the light used.

Here, then, are four sets of facts that a photoelectric theory must explain. Let us take the theory that light consists of waves and test it by seeing how well it accounts for these facts. The wave theory explains fact (a) satisfactorily, since with light of greater intensity more energy must be absorbed by the metal and more electrons could thus be emitted; but, according to this reasoning, we would also expect some of the electrons to come out with greater individual K.E. when the light is more intense, and this prediction is contrary to fact (b). Fact (c) is also hard to explain. Some work must be required (call it W) to get an electron out through the surface of a metal or else electrons would "evaporate" from the metal all the time. How can an electron gather this energy to itself from a succession of broad waves in which the energy per electron cross section is very small? Calculations show that if an electron could only absorb the energy falling on it directly, it would in some instances have to wait many seconds in order to accumulate sufficient energy to escape. The wave theory fails completely to explain fact (d) above, so altogether its score of success is very low.

In 1905 Einstein proposed another theory, one suggested by Planck's work on blackbody radiation. If, argued Einstein, radiation of frequency f is emitted in units of energy equal to hf and if it is absorbed by the oscillators of the cavity walls in units of the same energy, then why should we not regard the energy of an electromagnetic wave of frequency f as being concentrated in small bundles, each of energy hf? These bundles of energy are called *photons*, or *light quanta*. According to this theory, an increase in the intensity of a beam of light implies an increase in the *number* of photons passing through unit cross-sectional area of the beam in unit time, while an increase in the *frequency* of the light corresponds to an increase in the amount of energy carried per photon. As an analogy, consider two machine guns, A and B, and let B fire bullets of higher calibre than A. The bullets correspond to the photons in a beam of light. If either gun is caused to fire more bullets per second, the total energy output, or intensity of the firing, will increase, but since the energy of each bullet depends only on the powder in its case, the energy of the individual bullets will not be affected by the rate of firing. On the other hand, the bullets from gun B will possess more energy than those from gun A. Shifting from gun A to gun B corresponds in the case of light to increasing the frequency of the light.

Applying the photon theory to the photoelectric effect, Einstein reasoned as follows: If light of frequency f falls on the surface of a metal, then concentrated bundles of energy, each of magnitude hf, must strike the metal and penetrate to where they are stopped by the electrons in the metal. Thus a photon of energy hf may give all of its energy to one electron and the latter may use this energy to escape through the surface of the metal. The work function W represents the portion of the energy given to the electron that must be used in getting the electron out of the metal. What is left over should, according to the conservation of energy principle, be the K.E. of the emitted electron. The above reasoning may be expressed mathematically by the equation

$$hf - W = \text{K.E. of photoelectron}, \qquad (17\text{--}5)$$

called *Einstein's photoelectric equation;* W varies with the metal used, but not with the frequency of the light. The threshold frequency f_0 is determined by

$$hf_0 = W, \qquad (17\text{--}6)$$

so that we may write

$$h(f - f_0) = \text{K.E. of photoelectron}. \qquad (17\text{--}7)$$

The reader should now subject Einstein's theory to the test of seeing whether or not it explains the facts (a), (b), (c), and (d) of the photoelectric effect. He should be able to satisfy himself that the photon theory is completely successful in this respect. However, as he makes this test of the photon theory he should note an important point, namely that the theory does not enable one to make an exact prediction as to which electron in the metal will be ejected in a given interval of time. All that the theory does in this regard is to give us a *statistical* prediction as to the most probable number of electrons that will be emitted per unit area in a given time interval by light of a known wavelength and intensity.

A good analogy to the photoelectric effect is that of a group of prisoners in jail, each under a bond W. A friend arrives, goes at random to one of the group, and offers to loan him x dollars. If x is less than W, the loan is declined; accepting the money will not enable the prisoner to get out of jail and he cannot spend money in jail. However, if x is greater than the bond W, the prisoner eagerly accepts the x dollars, pays his bond and leaves the jail with $(x - W)$ dollars in his pocket, which he may spend at the tavern of his choice!

EXAMPLE 1. Light of wavelength $\lambda = 6200$ angstroms (A) falls on a metal and photoelectrons are ejected, each with a K.E. $= 0.3$ electron-volt (ev). Find (a) the energy in ev of each photon of the light, and (b) the work function of the metal in ev and joules.

Solution. The energy per photon is hf. Since $\lambda f = c$, the speed of light, we have

$$hf = \frac{hc}{\lambda} = \frac{(6.6 \times 10^{-34} \text{ j-sec}) \times (3 \times 10^8 \text{ m/sec})}{6200 \times 10^{-10} \text{ m}}$$

$$= 3.2 \times 10^{-19} \text{ j}.$$

Recall that 1 ev $= 1.6 \times 10^{-19}$ coul $\times 1$ volt $= 1.6 \times 10^{-19}$ coul $\times 1$ j/coul $= 1.6 \times 10^{-19}$ j, so that

$$hf = \frac{3.2 \times 10^{-19} \text{ j}}{1.6 \times 10^{-19} \text{ j/ev}} = 2 \text{ ev}.$$

Substitution in Eq. (17–5) gives us

$$2 \text{ ev} - W = 0.3 \text{ ev}, \qquad W = 1.7 \text{ ev} = 2.72 \times 10^{-19} \text{ j}.$$

EXAMPLE 2. (a) Suppose that light of 3100 A strikes the same metal as in the previous example. With what K.E. will the photoelectrons now escape from the metal? (b) What is the threshold frequency for the metal?

Solution. (a) Halving the wavelength of the light from 6200 A to 3100 A is equivalent to doubling the frequency to $f' = 2f$, which in turn means doubling the energy per photon. Hence we now have photons of energy $hf' = 4$ ev. Since W is unchanged in value, $W = 1.7$ ev. The photoelectric equation now tells us that

$$4 \text{ ev} - 1.7 \text{ ev} = 2.3 \text{ ev} = \text{K.E. of photoelectrons}.$$

(b) We have $hf_0 = W = 1.7$ ev, while $hf' = 4$ ev, so that $f_0/f' = 1.7/4$. The frequency f', corresponding to light of 3100 A, is

$$f' = \frac{c}{\lambda'} = \frac{3 \times 10^8 \text{ m/sec}}{3100 \times 10^{-10} \text{ m}} = 9.7 \times 10^{14}/\text{sec}.$$

Hence

$$f_0 = \frac{1.7}{4} \times 9.7 \times 10^{14} = 4.12 \times 10^{14}/\text{sec}.$$

The wavelength of light of this frequency f_0, for which $hf_0 = 1.7$ ev, is

$$\lambda_0 = \frac{c}{f_0} = \frac{3 \times 10^8 \text{ m/sec}}{4.12 \times 10^{14}/\text{sec}} = 7.3 \times 10^{-7} \text{ m} = 7300 \text{ A}.$$

The photoelectric effect furnishes one of the best methods for measuring Planck's constant h. Light of wavelength λ is allowed to fall on a photocell, as in Fig. 17–4; λ may be measured with a diffraction grating and the corresponding frequency f computed. The K.E. of the photoelectrons is determined by finding the potential difference necessary to stop the electrons. If a charge e moves against the force of an electric field and through a given p.d., the work that it must expend is e times this p.d. If the electron expends all of its K.E. in this way, then

$$\text{K.E. of photoelectron} = eV,$$

where V is the *stopping potential*, or potential of the collector C, relative to the emitting surface, for which electrons will just fail to reach the collector. The

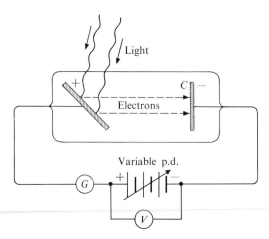

FIG. 17–4.   Use of the photoelectric effect to measure Planck's constant h.

potential of C is slowly increased from zero until the galvanometer G records no current, then the potential V of C is read with a voltmeter.   We have

$$hf = W + eV. \tag{17–8}$$

Next, light of different frequencies is used and the corresponding stopping potentials measured.   According to Eq. (17–8), V plotted against h should give a straight line and the slope of this line will be h/e.

The charge e on an electron was first determined by Millikan, who balanced charged oil drops of determinable mass m in a known electric field $\mathbf{E}$.   His experiment is described in Section 12–6.   Thus knowing e one may compute h from the value of h/e.   (See Experiment 23 at end of chapter.)

The value of h found from the photoelectric effect agrees, within the limits of experimental error, with the value it must be given to fit the blackbody radiation curve.   This agreement constitutes further support for the postulates, made by Planck and Einstein, involving the new constant h.

17–4 Atomic spectra and energy states

For about 200 years it has been known that an incandescent gas emits light whose spectrum consists of a series of bright lines.   This *line emission spectrum* may also be obtained by passing an electric discharge through a tube containing the gas at low pressure.   When the gas consists of a single chemical element, such as hydrogen, helium, or sodium, the pattern of lines or wavelengths is characteristic of the element.   These patterns have been classified and used to identify the elements present in some unknown substance heated to incandescence.

In the case of the sun, the very hot interior emits a continuous spectrum of all wavelengths.   As this white light passes through the cooler outer atmosphere certain wavelengths are absorbed from the continuous spectrum, leaving a continuous spectrum with dark lines superimposed upon it.   Generally speaking, the dark *line absorption spectra* obtained in this manner and in simulated laboratory experiments are pretty much the same as the line emission spectra of the absorbing elements. Thus line absorption spectra are useful in determining stellar compositions and the relative abundance of the chemical elements throughout the universe. Furthermore, the fact that the line spectra of distant stars show the same line patterns of certain elements as do the nearer stars, but with every line displaced to a lower frequency, is taken as an indication that the distant stars are moving away from us. The decrease in frequency is assumed to be of the same nature as the drop in pitch of an automobile horn or a train whistle when the vehicle is moving away from the observer, a phenomenon in wave motion called the *Doppler effect.*

Let us now consider the question of how atoms of a given element produce line spectra. This problem was first successfully solved for the case of hydrogen atoms by the great Danish physicist Niels Bohr (1885–1962). Bohr tried to explain the spectrum of hydrogen because its atoms are the simplest of all. He adopted Rutherford's planetary model of the atom, which in the case of hydrogen reduces to one electron orbiting around a nucleus containing just one proton. As a start Bohr postulated that Coulomb's law and Newton's law of motion hold for such an atomic system. This was a pure guess, for these laws had never been tested on the atomic scale and so it was quite possible that they would be found not to hold inside atoms. Bohr's second postulate was equivalent to that which Planck made in regard to the emission of radiation by the oscillators in the walls of a cavity. Bohr assumed that *atoms may exist in states of definite energies without radiating, but transitions between these states may occur, and when an atom passes from an initial allowed state of energy E_i to a final one of lower energy E_f, a photon of energy hf is radiated such that*

$$hf = E_i - E_f. \tag{17–9}$$

Note that Eq. (17–9) combines Einstein's definition of the photon, or quantum, with the principle of the conservation of energy; the energy lost by an atom is radiated as a single quantum. Continuous radiation results from the successive emission in a short time of billions of quanta by billions of atoms each undergoing similar transitions.

The essentially new feature in Bohr's theory was the fact that he had to postulate that *a nonradiating atom can exist in only one of a discrete set of energy states* and that these states are *not* equally spaced. Bohr found an arbitrary rule for determining the allowed states for a hydrogen atom. This rule will not be stated, since it has been superseded by a more general one, applicable to all atomic systems, which will be given later. However, we shall see that Bohr's theory, like Planck's, met with both qualitative and quantitative success.

The spectrum of hydrogen in the visible and nearby ultraviolet region consists of a series of lines that are closer and closer together (and also less intense) at the high-frequency end of the series, as shown in Fig. 17–5. Such a series suggests some sort of regularity, which implies that there must be an empirical formula, with a limited number of constants, that describes the above series. This formula had indeed been discovered long before Bohr's work by a Swiss school teacher

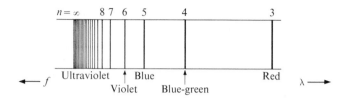

FIG. 17–5.   The Balmer series in the emission spectrum of hydrogen.

named J. J. Balmer (1825–1898). Balmer's formula may be written as

$$\frac{1}{\lambda} = R_H \left(\frac{1}{2^2} - \frac{1}{n^2} \right), \qquad n = 3, 4, 5, \ldots, \qquad (17\text{--}10)$$

where λ is the wavelength of one of the lines of the series corresponding to an integral value of n greater than 2, and R_H is a constant whose experimental value is 10,967,758/m. (The high accuracy implied here is characteristic of wavelength measurements in modern optics.)

Bohr's theory led him to a formula for the energy E_n of a hydrogen atom when it is in one of the allowed nonradiating states; he deduced that

$$E_n = C - \frac{2\pi^2 k_e^2 m e^4}{n^2 h^2}, \qquad (17\text{--}11)$$

where C is a constant representing the energy of the ionized atom, i.e., one whose electron has been completely removed from the field of its nucleus, k_e is the constant in Coulomb's law, m is the mass of the electron, e its charge, and $n = 1$, $2, 3, \ldots$. When this formula was combined with Eq. (17–9), Bohr obtained for the frequency of the emission lines of hydrogen the expression

$$f = \frac{2\pi^2 k_e^2 m e^4}{h^3} \left(\frac{1}{n_f^2} - \frac{1}{n_i^2} \right), \qquad (17\text{--}12)$$

where n_f is the value of n for the final state of a transition and n_i its value for the initial state. In atomic physics a quantity, such as n, which is limited to integral or half-integral values, is called a *quantum number*.

To obtain a formula similar to Balmer's, Bohr put $n_f = 2$ and $f = c/\lambda$; he then got

$$\frac{1}{\lambda} = \frac{2\pi^2 k_e^2 m e^4}{h^3 c} \left(\frac{1}{2^2} - \frac{1}{n_i^2} \right), \qquad (17\text{--}13)$$

where, since n_i must exceed n_f, $n_i = 3, 4, 5, \ldots$.

Equations (17–10) and (17–13) agree in form, but do they agree quantitatively? The final test of Bohr's theory was the comparison of his factor $2\pi^2 k_e^2 m e^4 / h^3 c$, which involves only previously measured constants, with the experimental value of Balmer's constant R_H. It turns out (see problem 8) that

$$\frac{2\pi^2 k_e^2 m e^4}{h^3 c} = 1.097 \times 10^7 /\text{m}$$

within experimental errors, so that the agreement is most striking.

Bohr's theory of the hydrogen atom scored many other notable successes. For instance, if the value of n_f is put equal to 1 and $n_i = 2, 3, 4, \ldots$, one obtains a formula giving the correct wavelengths of another series of lines in the hydrogen spectrum, a series found in the far ultraviolet called the Lyman series. With $n_f = 3, n_i = 4, 5, 6, \ldots$, one obtains an infrared series, and so on. The energy-level diagram for hydrogen is shown in Fig. 17–6; it furnishes a good method of illustrating and summarizing the known facts about the energy states and emission lines of hydrogen. The directed lines represent the transitions between states which give the

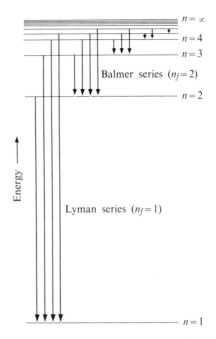

Fig. 17–6. Energy-level diagram for hydrogen, with transitions that give rise to its line emission spectrum.

various lines in the spectrum. Absorption of radiation by an atom corresponds to the reverse of emission and would be represented by lines directed upward from one energy state to a higher one.

Let us now consider the atoms of some other element. The line spectrum of an element indicates the existence of discrete energy states. The lowest of these states must be that of greatest stability and the one usually occupied; hence it is called the *normal state*. Above this state are the *excited* states of the neutral atom; an atom may be raised to one of these states by giving it energy, say through intense thermal agitation at high temperatures, through electron bombardment, or by the absorption of a photon of exactly the right amount of energy. Additional energy states may have to be postulated in order to account for all the lines of the emission spectrum. An energy-level diagram may then be drawn and possible transitions indicated. For all transitions

$$hf = E_i - E_f.$$

EXAMPLE 1. Suppose that atoms of a certain element are found by electron bombardment to have an excited state 1.7 ev above the normal state. The line spectrum of the element contains the following three wavelengths: 7300 A, 5400 A, and 3100 A. Find the energy-level diagram with the fewest energy levels that will account for the facts.

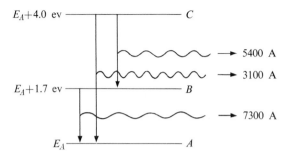

FIG. 17–7. Atom with normal state A and excited states B and C.

Solution. In Fig. 17–7 the normal state is represented by the line A. There must be an excited state B at 1.7 ev above A. The transition from B to A accounts for the 7300-A line in the spectrum (see Example 2 of Section 17–3).

To account for the 3100–A line we must introduce a second excited state C that is 4 ev above A (see Example 2 of Section 17–3).

For the transition from C to B we have

$$hf = hc/\lambda = E_i - E_f,$$

$$\lambda = \frac{hc}{E_i - E_f} = \frac{(6.6 \times 10^{-34}\ \text{j-sec}) \times (3 \times 10^8\ \text{m/sec})}{(2.3\ \text{ev}) \times (1.6 \times 10^{-19}\ \text{j/ev})}$$

$$= 5.4 \times 10^{-7}\ \text{m, or 5400A.}$$

This transition thus accounts for the third line of the spectrum and no additional energy levels need be assumed.

EXAMPLE 2. *Optical pumping.* Suppose that the atoms of a given material have three allowed states A, B, and C, as in Fig. 17–7. Normally most of the atoms will be in state A, but if the material is exposed to radiation of frequency f such that $hf = E_C - E_A$, then photons of this frequency will be absorbed by atoms in state A and these atoms will be raised to state C. Some of the atoms in state C will return to state A and some will drop back to state B, where, after some delay, they may eventually return to state A. If the rate at which atoms are "pumped" up to state C and fall back to B is made to exceed the rate at which they fall from level B to level A, one will succeed in increasing the population of level B. This is made easier by the fact that impurities present may slow down the "leakage" from B to A.

Several interesting applications have resulted from optical pumping. For one thing, the transition A to C may, with regard to energy, be a large one requiring ordinary visible light, while that from B to A may be much smaller and result in the emission at a slow rate of low-frequency radiation in the microwave region. Microwaves of fixed frequency, suitable for measuring time in a satellite, may thus be produced without employing electronic circuits to produce them. Such a device is referred to as an *atomic clock*. On the other hand, if state B is close to C, the overpopulation of state B may result in the almost simultaneous transition of many atoms from B to A, in which case radiation of an individual atom is affected by that of its neighbors in such a way that a coherent beam of light of large intensity is emitted in a certain direction, that is, the photons seem to combine to produce a single electromagnetic wave of large amplitude. This is the principle of the *laser*, i.e., *light amplification by stimulated emission of radiation*.

17–5 The dual nature of light

In discussing light, we may say that the three basic processes are *emission*, *propagation*, and *absorption*. In emission and absorption we are concerned with how light *energy* is produced at the expense of some other form of energy, and vice versa. Actually, we do not detect the presence of light until it falls on some absorbing object such as the human eye, a strip of film, or a photocell, in which cases the light energy is transformed into an electric nerve pulse, chemical energy, and the energy of photoelectrons, respectively.

We have seen that photoelectric and other measurements indicate that light energy is emitted and absorbed in quantum units, rather than continuously. Remember that the emission and absorption processes have nothing to do with determining what *path* the light will follow as it travels from its source to its sink. However, suppose that we use a system of slits to limit the path of the light and that we observe to where on a screen the greatest amount of energy travels. Then we can explain or predict our results correctly by means of the wave theory. In wave theory, we must introduce the concept of wavelength λ and velocity of propagation c, both of which may be determined experimentally. The frequency f associated with light of wavelength λ is found from the wave relation $f = c/\lambda$.

We see, then, that the photon theory is used to describe emission and absorption, and the wave theory to describe the propagation of light. These theories complement each other, since they apply to different phenomena and describe different aspects of light; by using each at the appropriate occasion our description of nature is more complete. On the other hand, we must not use both theories at the *same* time because they lead to contradictory conclusions. Evidently neither theory by itself is a completely right or wrong description of nature.

It is tempting to think of photons as maintaining their identity along the path between where we observe them to be emitted and where we see them absorbed, but such a postulate has no experimental basis. A photon cannot be both a particle and a wave at the same time, and since it is not just one of these alternatives alone, we are forced to conclude that it is really neither. Both the wave model and the particle model are helpful if we use them selectively to describe and predict the behavior of light, but we must not believe that either model offers us the real picture. Perhaps the trouble is that man, conditioned by the events of his everyday life, just does not have the mental capacity to picture the strange realm of atomic particles and photons any more than he can that of an infinite universe. At least the quantum theory and pictorial models do not seem to be compatible.

To remain on firm ground we must return to the discussion of what we measure. In the photoelectric effect we measure the stopping potential V for the electrons emitted by light of known frequency f. Equation (17–7) holds for the electrons escaping with the maximum energy and the photon theory "explains" this well. In diffraction experiments we measure the intensity, or energy per unit area per unit time, reaching various points on a screen. The wave theory "explains" these results, but we may also say that what we measure is the fraction of a large number of emitted photons received by a given area per unit time, or *the probability that one photon will reach this area.* The wave theory enables us to compute the correct probability. The completely causal relationship between past and future events which is assumed in classical theory is replaced, because of insufficient information, by a statistical relationship giving the probability that a certain future event will occur. An analogous situation occurs in the throwing of dice.

17-6 The Compton effect

The photon theory has been further developed in order to explain other experimental results involving the interaction of light with matter. If a photon possesses energy, we may, if we wish, speak of the mass associated with, or equivalent to, that energy. We shall call this "associated mass" of the photon m. Note, however, that a photon does not have a rest mass, since there is no such thing as a photon at rest. A photon either moves with the speed of light, or it has been absorbed and no longer exists.

Let us combine Einstein's expression $E = hf$ for the energy of a photon with the one $E = mc^2$, which he derived from the relativity principle. We see that the "associated mass" of a photon must be

$$m = \frac{E}{c^2} = \frac{hf}{c^2}.$$ (17–14)

Since a photon travels with the speed of light, it must possess a momentum μ equal to the product of its mass and velocity, or of magnitude

$$\mu = mc = \frac{hf}{c} = \frac{h}{\lambda}.$$ (17–15)

We shall see that this relationship for the momentum of a photon is experimentally supported.

When high-frequency radiation, such as a beam of x-rays, strikes matter the radiation is scattered in different directions. It was observed that some of the scattered x-rays were less penetrating and presumably had a longer wavelength than the incident radiation. In the early 1920's the American physicist Arthur H. Compton thoroughly investigated this effect and showed that his results could be interpreted only in terms of the above theory, in which a momentum as well as energy are ascribed to photons. Compton used x-rays of a single frequency f so that all of the incident photons would have the same energy hf and momentum hf/c. He measured the wavelength λ of the incident radiation and that of the scattered radiation, using the planes of atoms in a crystal for his grating. It was found that radiation scattered at a given angle ϕ contained a single new wavelength λ' that was longer than λ by a definite amount, independent of the incident wavelength used. Compton's explanation was based on the theory that a photon of the incident radiation may collide with an electron in the scattering material, causing the electron to recoil with some K.E. and thus leaving the quantum with less energy than it started with. The recoil electrons were soon observed and their energies were also measured as a function of the angle θ between the direction of recoil and the direction of the incident beam.

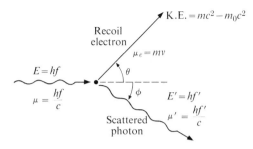

FIG. 17–8.   Compton collision between photon and electron.

Let us assume that the collision between a photon and an electron is like an elastic one in mechanics, that is, one in which K.E. is conserved. Momentum must be conserved in any collision (see Chapter 7). It is unlikely that the photon and electron will have the same effective mass. If the energy E of a photon is expressed in electron-volts (ev), its "associated mass" is

$$m = \frac{E}{c^2} = \frac{E(\text{ev}) \times 1.6 \times 10^{-19}\,\text{j/ev}}{(3 \times 10^8\,\text{m/sec})^2}$$

$$= 1.78 \times 10^{-36} E\,\text{kg}.$$

This equals the rest mass of an electron ($m_0 = 9.1 \times 10^{-31}$ kg) when E is about 512,000 ev, so that for x-ray photons of about 100,000 ev, m is less than one-fifth of m_0. It is shown in mechanics that in an elastic impact between a moving and a stationary particle very little K.E. is transferred, even in a head-on collision, unless the two masses are of the same order of magnitude. Accordingly, we might expect that the Compton effect would be of little practical significance in the case of low-energy photons corresponding to the visible and ultraviolet regions; this also is verified experimentally.

As in Fig. 17–8, consider a photon of energy hf to strike an electron of low kinetic energy. Let the electron recoil at the angle θ with the speed v and let the photon be scattered at the angle ϕ with the reduced energy hf'. From the principle of conservation of energy, we have

$$hf = \text{K.E. of electron} + \text{energy of scattered photon}$$

$$= m_0 c^2 \left[\frac{1}{\sqrt{1 - v^2/c^2}} - 1 \right] + hf'. \tag{17–16}$$

The relativistic expression for kinetic energy must be used, because, for the recoil electrons, v may be an appreciable fraction of c.

Let us apply the conservation of momentum principle to the collision. Since momentum is a vector, we write two equations, expressing the conservation of momentum for both the x- and y-directions. Using Eq. (17–15) for the momentum of the electron, we have

$$\frac{hf}{c} = \frac{m_0 v}{\sqrt{1 - v^2/c^2}} \cos \theta + \frac{hf'}{c} \cos \phi, \qquad (17\text{--}17)$$

$$0 = \frac{m_0 v}{\sqrt{1 - v^2/c^2}} \sin \theta - \frac{hf'}{c} \sin \phi. \qquad (17\text{--}18)$$

Between these last three equations we may eliminate θ and v, solving for f' in terms of f and ϕ. We now introduce the wavelengths $\lambda = c/f$ and $\lambda' = c/f'$, since these are what are measured, and find (see problem 12) that

$$\lambda' - \lambda = \frac{h}{m_0 c} (1 - \cos \phi). \qquad (17\text{--}19)$$

The factor $h/m_0 c$, called the *Compton wavelength*, has a numerical value of about 0.024 A, where $1 \text{ A} = 10^{-10}$ m. For monochromatic x-rays scattered through 90°, it is found that part of the beam undergoes just this change in wavelength.

The kinetic energy of the recoil electrons is given by

$$\text{K.E.} = hf - hf'.$$

EXAMPLE. Suppose that $\lambda = 0.124$ A. Then

$$hf = \frac{hc}{\lambda} = \frac{(6.6 \times 10^{-34} \text{ j-sec}) \times (3 \times 10^8 \text{ m/sec})}{0.124 \times 10^{-10} \text{ m}}$$

$$= 1.6 \times 10^{-14} \text{ j} = 10^5 \text{ ev}.$$

Such x-rays are obtained from a tube operating at over 100,000 volts (see problem 11). If $\lambda' - \lambda = 0.024$ A, λ' will be 0.148 A, or about $\frac{6}{5}$ of λ. Then hf' will be about $\frac{5}{6}$ of hf, or about 83,000 ev, so that the K.E. of the recoil electron will be about 17,000 ev. The coincident production of a scattered photon and recoil electron has been observed by means of devices that count simultaneous events.

17–7 The dual nature of atomic particles

We must now face the problem of why atomic systems can exist in certain discrete energy states and not in any state for which the energy lies between the values allowed. In other words, why do quantum numbers, such as n in Bohr's theory, which are limited to integral values (half-integral in some cases) appear in expressions relating to atomic systems? This question was answered by extending to material particles the properties of waves discussed in Chapter 11; it was then postulated that such wave properties based on Huygens' principle, rather than the properties of a particle moving according to Newtonian mechanics, should be used to describe the behavior of atomic systems. This new theory is called *wave mechanics*.

Prince Louis de Broglie first proposed in 1924, in his thesis for the doctorate, that a material particle such as an electron might have a dual nature, just as light does. In the study of light the wave properties, involving λ, f, and c, are the more familiar ones. In terms of these properties we have defined the mechanical properties of the light corpuscles as follows:

$$E = hf, \qquad \mu = \frac{h}{\lambda}. \qquad\qquad (17\text{–}20)$$

For a material particle it is the other way around; we are used to speaking of its mass m, momentum μ, and energy E. These are measurable quantities. Therefore when de Broglie postulated that such a particle may also have wave properties, he defined the associated wavelength λ and frequency f in terms of m, μ, and E. In doing so, de Broglie was guided by the relations for light [Eqs. (17–20], and so he postulated that associated with a particle are waves of wavelength λ and frequency f, given by

$$\lambda = \frac{h}{\mu}, \qquad f = \frac{E}{h}. \qquad\qquad (17\text{–}21)$$

The waves associated with a particle are not to be regarded as being mechanical or electromagnetic, but rather "probability waves." By this we mean that the intensity of the waves at any point will be taken as giving the fraction of a large number of similar particles, emitted with the same initial velocity, that will reach a given area in unit time, or the probability of one particle reaching that area. The waves are thus a device for computing the probability that a particle will behave in a certain way. De Broglie argued that in the case of light one cannot think of a photon without associating with it a wavelength and frequency, and that therefore material particles, like protons, must be accompanied by waves of some sort, be they only probability waves.

The behavior of a material particle is usually computed from the laws of mechanics. Is there, then, any need for a new method? If so, what are its advantages? De Broglie suggested that wave mechanics might stand in relation to particle mechanics as wave optics does to geometrical optics. In geometrical optics light is assumed to travel through a homogeneous medium in straight lines or rays. To explain the details of the diffraction pattern caused by an obstacle, one must resort to wave optics and be concerned with distances of the order of magnitude of one wavelength. When we compute the wavelength h/mv associated with an ordinary object, it turns out to be insignificantly small, but for an electron the mass m is very much less than for ordinary objects and h/mv is found (see example below) to be comparable to x-ray wavelengths. Since x-rays are diffracted by crystals, why should not such electrons be, too? This question was answered by Davisson and Germer who, while studying the scattering of electrons from metals, found that electrons are indeed diffracted by crystals just as x-rays are, and in accordance with the relation $\lambda = h/mv$.

De Broglie also realized that in dealing with atomic systems, where the dimensions are also comparable to x-ray wavelengths, wave mechanics might be able to explain things that ordinary mechanics could not. For example, according to the

Bohr theory of the hydrogen atom, only those electron orbits are allowed for which

$$mvr = n\frac{h}{2\pi}, \qquad n = 1, 2, 3, \ldots, \qquad (17\text{–}22)$$

where mv is the momentum μ of the electron and r is the radius of its orbit about the nucleus of a hydrogen atom. This whole number rule was empirical when it was first proposed, the argument in its favor being that it worked. De Broglie suggested, by way of explanation, that if waves accompany an electron around its orbit, then a sort of resonance might occur when the circumference of the orbit equals an integral multiple of the electron's wavelength. This idea, which was later refined by Schroedinger, amounted to saying that the allowed quantum orbits correspond to the various possible modes of vibration, or standing waves, in a string. For such a string, waves are reflected back and forth with constructive interference only when the wavelength λ is such that the complete distance down the string and back is an integral number n of wavelengths. Here the restriction that n must be a whole number has a physical basis, hence it was appealing to carry the idea over to the case of the atomic orbit and its electron waves.

Consider a circular orbit of radius r. Taking $\lambda = h/\mu$, where μ is linear momentum, de Broglie put the orbital circumference $2\pi r$ equal to $n\lambda$, or

$$2\pi r = n\lambda = n\frac{h}{\mu} = n\frac{h}{mv},$$

$$mvr = n\frac{h}{2\pi},$$

which is the same as Eq. (17–22).

Bohr viewed the transition of a hydrogen atom from one state to another as being equivalent to the jump of its electron from one allowed orbit to another such orbit. According to wave mechanics such an atomic transition corresponds to the fading out of the waves accompanying one mode of vibration and the appearance of a second set of waves that accompany another such mode; at the same time the probability of finding the electron at any given distance from the nucleus must change because the intensity of the waves at that point has been altered. Thus there is a correspondence between the old particle picture and the newer viewpoint of wave mechanics.

ILLUSTRATION.   Find the de Broglie wavelength of an electron whose kinetic energy equals V electron-volts (eV joules), using the nonrelativistic expression for kinetic energy.

We have

$$\tfrac{1}{2}mv^2 = eV,$$

$$mv = \sqrt{2me V},$$

$$\lambda = \frac{h}{mv} = \frac{h}{\sqrt{2me V}}.$$

Taking $h = 6.6 \times 10^{-34}$ j-sec, $m = 9.1 \times 10^{-31}$ kg, and $e = 1.6 \times 10^{-19}$ coul, we get

$$\lambda = \frac{1.23 \times 10^{-9}}{\sqrt{V}} \text{ m.}$$

Thus for 1600-volt electrons, $\lambda = 0.3 \times 10^{-10}$ m $= 0.3$ A, which is of the order of the separation of the planes in a crystal lattice.

17–8 The uncertainty principle

We have seen that in wave mechanics all predictions are statistical, whereas in classical mechanics it was assumed that, given sufficient data, future events could be forecast with certainty, as in celestial mechanics. Of course, in atomic physics we do not have the "sufficient data." Attempts to simultaneously measure the position and the velocity of a particle always meet with frustration.

Suppose, for example, that we decide to observe the position of an electron. To do so, we must let at least one photon of light be scattered by the particle. We know that an electron is too small to "see" in a microscope using visible light because no matter how large we may be able to make the magnification, we are limited by the resolving power, which in turn depends on the diffraction of the light. Since the resolving power is inversely proportional to the wavelength of the light, we may increase the practicable magnification by using radiation of shorter wavelengths, such as x-rays, but then the trouble is that one photon of such radiation strikes our electron with greater momentum and energy than does one photon of radiation of longer wavelength. We have seen in the Compton effect that when a photon is scattered by an electron, the latter recoils in some forward direction. The energy imparted to the electron increases with the energy of the incident photon. When we use radiation of shorter wavelength we improve our resolving power and thus may locate an object more accurately in *position*, but at the same time we increase the disturbance of the particle and make our knowledge of its *momentum* more uncertain.

We have seen that Planck's constant h has a finite value and in the mks system its units are joule-seconds. The product of energy and time is called *action*, so that Planck's constant is known as "the quantum of action." The quantum theory tells us that h is the smallest amount of action that has physical meaning. Now the product of length and momentum has the same units as energy times time. In the mks system the units of length times momentum are m $\times$ (kg-m/sec) = kg-m^2/sec = (kg-m^2/sec^2) $\times$ sec = j-sec, or the units of action. Thus suppose that we measure at the same time the position of a particle to within the uncertainty Δs and its momentum to within the uncertainty $\Delta \mu$, and then compute the product $\Delta s \cdot \Delta \mu$. The quantum theory then informs us that it is meaningless to talk about a $\Delta s \cdot \Delta \mu$ less than h, so that in general we must have

$$\Delta s \cdot \Delta \mu > h. \tag{17–23}$$

This is *Heisenberg's uncertainty principle*. The uncertainties referred to are inherent in the nature of light and matter, according to quantum mechanics; the usual errors due to imperfect equipment and measurement are additional to these. Since errors must be treated statistically, the numerical degree of inequality in Eq. (17–23) depends on whether we are referring to possible errors, probable errors, standard deviations, etc.

It is in the nature of things that, since Planck's constant has a finite value, infinitely detailed experience and sharp predictions are physically impossible. As a result of this inherent uncertainty, an event considered "certain" in classical physics becomes only "highly probable" in wave mechanics, and an event termed "impossible" in Newtonian theory is now classed as one having a "very low probability."

EXAMPLE 1.   The position of a 100-gm weight is measured with an uncertainty of ±0.1 mm. The weight is to be allowed to fall from "a state of rest." According to quantum mechanics it is meaningless to specify the initial velocity more specifically than to say that it may be Δv in any direction (up, down, or sideways), where

$$m \, \Delta v = \Delta \mu > \frac{h}{\Delta s}.$$

How large is Δv?

Solution. Here $m = 0.1$ kg, $\Delta s = 10^{-4}$ m, so that

$$\Delta v > \frac{h}{mv} = \frac{6.6 \times 10^{-34} \text{ j-sec}}{0.1 \text{ kg} \times 10^{-4} \text{ m}}$$

$$= 6.6 \times 10^{-29} \text{ m/sec.}$$

This is an uncertainty far below that which we could detect experimentally. In this case instrumental and personal errors would far outweigh the uncertainties of quantum mechanics.

EXAMPLE 2.   *The tunnel effect.* An alpha particle of mass $m = 6.4 \times 10^{-27}$ kg is moving with a speed v which is known to be $(1.0 \pm 0.1) \times 10^7$ m/sec. (a) Find the uncertainty Δs in the position of the particle. (b) Compute the uncertainty ΔE in the energy and discuss what sort of a barrier the particle might "leak" through.

Solution. (a) Since $\Delta v = 10^6$ m/sec, we have

$$\Delta s > \frac{h}{m \, \Delta v} = \frac{6.6 \times 10^{-34} \text{ j-sec}}{(6.4 \times 10^{-27} \text{ kg}) \times (10^6 \text{ m/sec})}$$

$$= 10^{-13} \text{ m, or } 10^{-11} \text{ cm,}$$

which is a distance over ten times greater than the diameter of an atomic nucleus.

(b) If $v = 10^7$ m/sec,

$$E = \tfrac{1}{2}mv^2 = 3.2 \times 10^{-27} \text{ kg} \times 10^{14} \text{ m}^2/\text{sec}^2$$

$$= 3.2 \times 10^{-13} \text{ j} = \frac{3.2 \times 10^{-13} \text{ j}}{1.6 \times 10^{-19} \text{ j/ev}} = 2 \times 10^6 \text{ ev.}$$

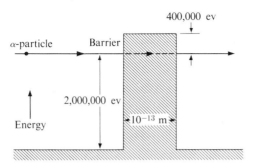

FIG. 17–9. Leakage of an alpha particle through a potential barrier.

If v is increased by 10%, E will increase by about 20%, or $0.2 \times 2 \times 10^6$ ev $= 4 \times 10^5$ ev. Thus $\Delta E > 400,000$ ev. The particle possesses an energy that may lie anywhere in the range between 1,600,000 ev and 2,400,000 ev.

Suppose that this particle approaches a barrier (see Fig. 17–9) which is 10^{-13} m wide and requires the conversion of 2,400,000 ev of energy into work if the particle is just to clear the top of the barrier (which is due to some sort of opposing field.) We see that within the uncertainty ΔE there is a possibility that our particle may have the required energy. Since Δs equals or exceeds the width of the barrier, we cannot say with certainty whether the particle is on one side or the other, so again it may be found to have "leaked" or "tunneled" through! Should the barrier be made higher and wider, the probability of leakage through the barrier would rapidly decrease as the product of the height and the width of the barrier increased.

This example illustrates the process that is believed to occur when a sample of a radio-active element such as radium decays through the loss of alpha particles by its nuclei.

17–9 The quantum principle. Fundamental Law XII

How shall we summarize all of the topics discussed in this chapter? The fact that each involves the same constant h implies that they are related through a common principle. The quantum theory embraces an area comparable with that of all classical physics, and it is for this reason that it cannot be summed up in a single sentence or equation.

Perhaps for the purpose of summarizing the facts discussed in this chapter the following statement may be taken as our *Fundamental Law XII* relating to quantum phenomena.

Every particle, corpuscular or radiant, behaves as though it possesses both particle properties and wave properties, related as follows:

XII. $$\lambda = \frac{h}{\mu} \quad \text{and} \quad f = \frac{E}{h},\tag{17–24}$$

where h is a universal constant. It is further assumed that the particle properties are governed by the classical laws of Newton, Coulomb, etc., while the wave properties are those (such as diffraction and interference) described by Huygens' principle.

The statements just made must be put in conjunction with what was said in Section 17-5. The particle model and the wave model, alone or together, do not give us the true and complete picture, but they may be of considerable help when it comes to describing or predicting the results of experiments in atomic physics.

If one abandons pictorial models and turns to the mathematical and logical development of quantum mechanics one will find that it is a complete theory undisturbed by any wave-particle dilemma. It presents mathematical difficulties, but if these are overcome the results obtained are correct. The formalized method of presenting quantum mechanics is herewith summarized for those who may be interested.

By an *observable* will be meant a familiar mechanical quantity q such as the position, momentum, or energy of a particle, which we are accustomed to measuring. For each observable an *operator* is defined. (In general an operator is something that changes whatever it operates on. Thus 6, the square root, and the sine are operators.) In quantum mechanics the operator signifies that a measurement is made on the observable q, resulting in a *measured value* q_m. These quantities are then related through the equation

$$\text{(Operator)}\,\psi = q_m\psi, \tag{17–25}$$

where ψ is a function of the coordinates of the particle concerned. It is postulated that solutions of this equation for ψ must be such that ψ is finite everywhere and has only one value at any given point. Finally it is postulated that the expected mean of a series of measurements on an observable q is proportional to the average throughout space of q weighted by the factor $|\psi|^2$. This last postulate may be interpreted as saying that $|\psi|^2$ measures the probability of finding the particle in a given locality. Planck's constant h is introduced into the theory through the way in which the various operators are defined. The definitions of some of the operators involve the calculus and so will not be given here.*

PROBLEMS

1. How many photons of light of wavelength equal to 2000 A have the same total energy as (a) six photons of light of 6000 A? (b) a photon of light of 3000 A plus a photon of light of 6000 A?

2. Show that according to Eq. (17–2) the function e_λ approaches zero for very small and for very large values of λ and that therefore there is a value λ_m for which e_λ is a maximum.

3. When the solar spectrum was measured by instruments carried by rocket above the earth's atmosphere, it was found that λ_m for solar radiation is about 4700 A (at the earth's surface the peak intensity is in the green region). Compute the temperature of the sun's surface, assuming that it radiates as would a blackbody.

---

* See, for example, Constant, *Theoretical Physics—Electromagnetism*, Section 15–10.

4. (a) Find the ratio of the energy emitted by a blackbody at 3000°K to that emitted at 2000°K. (b) Find the ratio of the emission of a black steam radiator at 100°C to its emission at 27°C (about room temperature).

5. Light of wavelength λ strikes a photocell and photoelectrons of energy E are emitted. (a) What is the work function W of the metal in terms of λ, E, h, and c (the speed of light)? (b) Find, in terms of the same quantities, the energy E' of the photoelectrons emitted from the same metal by light whose wavelength is λ/2.

6. Show that Einstein's theory of the photoelectric effect can account for all of the experimental facts listed in Section 17–3.

7. In this problem you are not to assume the value of h but are to calculate it from the following data. Light from a sodium lamp falling on a photocell causes the emission of electrons for which the stopping potential is $V = 0.4$ ev, while when violet light from a mercury arc is used, $V = 1.3$ ev.   Take λ $= 5.89 \times 10^{-7}$ m for sodium light and 4.05×10^{-7} m for the violet light used. (a) Compute h/e. (b) Assume $e = 1.60 \times 10^{-19}$ coul and find h. (e) Compute the work function W of the metal used.

8. Compute $2\pi^2 k_e^2 m e^4 / h^3 c$, using the values of k_e, m, etc., given eleswhere; show that the units of your answer are m^{-1}.

9. Compute λ in angstroms for the first line of the Lyman series and the first three lines of the Balmer series.

10. Compute in electron-volts the energy required to ionize a hydrogen atom that is initially in its normal state.

11. In an x-ray tube electrons are accelerated through a p.d. of V volts and then strike a metal target, Most of the electrons contribute their K.E. to the internal energy of the target, but some electrons that are stopped radiate photons of various wavelengths. In terms of e, V, h, and c, what is the *shortest* wavelength that this tube could emit?

12. Derive Eq. (17–19) for the shift in wavelength in the Compton effect, starting with the three preceding equations.

13. Suppose that a photon whose "associated mass" equals that of an electron at rest, strikes such an electron head-on in a Compton collision. Find what fraction of the photon's energy will be transferred to the electron. $(\theta = 180°, \cos \theta = -1.)$

14. Determine the wavelength λ associated with (a) a 10-gm golf ball traveling at 1m/sec, (b) an electron whose speed is 10^7 m/sec.

15. Show that if Δt is the time taken by a particle in traversing the distance Δs and $E = \frac{1}{2} mv^2$, then Eq. (17–23) becomes $\Delta E \Delta t > h$.

16 Refer to Example 2 of Section 17–8 in which an alpha particle with an energy of 2.0×10^6 ev approaches a barrier 10^{-13} m wide and 2.4×10^6 ev high. (a) Show that if the uncertainty in the energy of the particle is less than 0.4×10^6 ev, then there still is a possiblity that the particle will penetrate the barrier. (b) What would the situation be if we limited the uncertainty in the particle's position at a given moment to $\pm 0.5 \times 10^{-13}$m?

EXPERIMENT 23

THE PHOTOELECTRIC EFFECT
(Determination of Planck's Constant *h*)

Object: To verify the quantum principle as applied to the photoelectric effect and to measure Planck's constant *h*.

Problem: In order to explain blackbody radiation, Planck in 1900 made a radical (he scarcely believed it himself!) postulate which became the keystone of the quantum theory. This theory forms the theoretical basis for all atomic physics. The first great success of the theory, aside from explaining blackbody radiation, was in connection with the experiment you are about to do.

The photoelectric effect was discovered by Hertz, explained in terms of quantum theory by Einstein, and an experimental verification of Einstein's theory was made by Millikan.

Suppose that light of frequency f strikes a metal such as sodium. According to the quantum hypothesis, the light energy is received by the metal surface in bundles called *photons*, or *quanta*. The energy E of one photon is postulated to be proportional to the frequency f of the light. The constant of proportionality is called h, or *Planck's constant*. Then

$$E = hf, \tag{1}$$

where h is a universal constant.

Suppose that a photon gives its energy to an electron just inside the metal. This electron may use the energy to escape from the metal, but in so doing it must, so to speak, pay to get out. The work that must be done to escape is called the work function, W. The energy left after escape $(hf - W)$ must be the kinetic energy of the electron; rather than measuring this K.E. directly, we shall let the electron turn its K.E. into potential energy as it moves through a potential drop of V volts. The gain in P.E., or loss in K.E., will be eV joules, so if V is just sufficient to stop the electrons,

$$hf - W = eV. \tag{2}$$

The stopping potential V can be measured directly.

We want to use Eq. (2) to determine f. We shall eliminate W by using successively two or more values of f and measuring the value of V for each. The best procedure is to plot V against f; f is computed from the relation $f = c/\lambda$, where c is the speed of light and λ the wavelength, in meters, of light of a known wavelength (see Experiments 14 and 15). Equation (2) predicts a straight line graph with a slope $\Delta V/\Delta f$ equal to h/e and an intercept on the V-axis at $-W/e$. Since e has been previously measured, h and W may be calculated.

Procedure:

Step 1. Let light from a known monochromatic source strike the plate of your photocell. The electrons flow to a collector and from it through the external circuit and back to the plate. The external circuit contains a galvanometer to measure the electron current and a variable voltage source (+2 to −2 volts) with a voltmeter to measure V. Make the collector slightly negative and increase V until the galvanometer shows no current. Read V.

Step 2. Repeat 1 for two other wavelengths. Suggested light sources are: sodium light (λ = 5.89 $\times$ 10^{-7} m), the green light filtered from a mercury arc (λ = 5.46 $\times$ 10^{-7} m), and the violet light from a mercury arc (λ = 4.05 $\times$ 10^{-7} m).

Step 3. Compute each frequency used. Plot V versus f and determine the slope and intercept of the line that best fits your experimental data.

Step 4. Calculate h and compare your value with the accepted value of 6.63 $\times$ 10^{-34} j-sec. Can you justify your error?

Step 5. Calculate W in joules and in electron-volts (1 ev = 1.6 $\times$ 10^{-19} j).

CHAPTER 18

Pauli's Exclusion Principle

18–1 Introduction

Motorists are advised to remember that "two bodies cannot occupy the same place at the same time." What is implied in this statement is that the space, say at an intersection, occupied by car A at a given instant must be vacated by car A before car B can move into any portion of said space, provided the cars are to remain intact. Of course solid objects may be jammed and telescoped together, or they may be compressed into smaller volumes, until two or more such objects occupy no more space than one alone did originally, but even in such cases we would still say that it is impossible for a piece of each object to pass through the same mathematical point at the same time.

Next consider liquids and gases. When a substance A is dissolved in a liquid B, the volume of the solution is less than the sum of the original volumes of A and B. Does this mean that some of A and some of B occupy the same space at the same time? They do in the macroscopic sense, but not from the microscopic point of view. We postulate that in a liquid the molecules are loosely packed and do not themselves occupy all of the available space, so that additional molecules may be fitted in between those of the liquid. In the case of a gas the molecules behave as though they occupy an even smaller fraction of the available space than in the case of a liquid, for it is easy to compress a given amount of gas into a greatly reduced volume, or to add more gas molecules to a given volume. On the molecular level we may raise the question: can two *molecules* occupy the same space at the same time? If molecules behave as do hard elastic spheres, the answer must be "no." On the other hand, molecules may combine chemically, and when they do so the new compound molecule may result from the partial merging of the original molecules. The molecules fit together as though they also contain within themselves some empty space. When hydrogen and oxygen combine to form water, two molecules of hydrogen (H_2) join with one of oxygen (O_2) to form two molecules of H_2O. The equation describing the reaction is

$$2H_2 + O_2 \rightarrow 2H_2O. \tag{18–1}$$

The two moles ($2N_0$ molecules) of H_2O occupy, at a given temperature and pressure, the same volume as do two moles of H_2 plus one mole of O_2, ($3N_0$ molecules in all).

Lord Rutherford (1871–1937) performed, around 1910, some crucial experiments which indicated that individual atoms behave as though they have a plane-

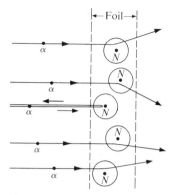

Fɪɢ. 18–1.   Scattering of alpha particles by atomic nuclei (N) in a thin foil.

tary structure. The mass of the atom seemed to be concentrated in a central positive nucleus (the atom's "sun"), around which negative electrons of much smaller mass (the atom's "planets") circulated in orbits.   The diameter of the nucleus appeared to be about 10^{-15} m. Rutherford determined this by firing alpha particles (fast-moving nuclei of helium) through a foil that was so thin that one alpha particle passed close to only one atomic nucleus in the foil (see Fig. 18–1). He could estimate the distance of closest approach, and he found that if this distance exceeded a few times 10^{-15} m, the nuclei behaved as though they had not penetrated one another; for smaller distances penetration was evident.

The diameter of an atom may be estimated from the average volume per atom of a solid. The apparent diameters of atoms are thus computed to be of the order of magnitude of 10^{-10} m, or some hundred thousand times that of their nuclei. Evidently atoms themselves are largely empty space. Thus when atoms combine to form a molecule there is ample opportunity for the atoms to share some of their unoccupied space.

EXAMPLE. The density of aluminum (Al) is 2700 kg/m³ and its atomic weight is 27. Compute the size of the cube whose volume is the volume of a given mass of aluminum divided by the number of atoms in that mass.

Solution. A kg-mole of Al is 27 kg, for which the volume V is

$$V = \frac{27 \text{ kg}}{2700 \text{ kg/m}^3} = 10^{-2} \text{ m}^3.$$

Since a kg-mole contains $N_0 = 6 \times 10^{26}$ atoms of an element, we have for the volume per atom

$$\frac{V}{N_0} = \frac{10^{-2} \text{ m}^3}{6 \times 10^{26} \text{ atoms}} = 16.7 \times 10^{-30} \text{ m}^3/\text{atom}.$$

For a cube of this volume the length of one edge would be $(16.7 \times 10^{-30})^{1/3}$, or about 2.5×10^{-10} m. If the atoms of Al were of cubical shape and completely occupied a given volume of the metal, 2.5×10^{-10} m (2.5 A) would represent the length of one edge of such a cubic atom. If the atoms are not cubical or tightly packed, they may be somewhat different in size, but the fact that metals are nearly incompressible indicates that their atoms fill almost all of the available volume. The diameter of an atom is thus of the order of 10^{-10} m.

Do particles exist that truly behave like hard, incompressible spheres, two of which cannot occupy the same place at the same time? Perhaps the so-called "elementary particles" are of this type. The electron is classed as an elementary particle. Can two electrons occupy the same place at the same time? Because of Heisenberg's uncertainty principle this last question is meaningless; the mass of the electron is so small that it is pointless to think of an electron as occupying an exact position in space at a given time. Nevertheless, there is definite evidence that there is a limit to how closely electrons may be crowded together, and the postulate that accounts for this evidence forms the fundamental principle of this chapter. The facts supporting this postulate will be discussed in Sections 18–4 through 18–7; to grasp the significance of these facts one must first understand what is meant by a "quantum state" and how the energy of an electron depends on the quantum state in which it is situated.

18–2 Quantum numbers

We saw in the last chapter that the quantum number n, whose value could be 1, 2, 3, . . . , played an important role in both the Bohr theory and the wave-mechanical theory of the hydrogen atom. The normal state of lowest energy corresponded to $n = 1$, the next higher state corresponded to $n = 2$, etc., as shown in Fig. 17–6. It was explained that each value of n corresponds to a resonance of the waves associated with the electron in its orbit, just as there are various possible modes of vibration, or standing waves, in a string.

Further study of atomic spectra has revealed the necessity of introducing other quantum numbers to define quantum states. This is because atoms are three-dimensional systems and their allowed energy states correspond not so much to the possible standing waves in a one-dimensional string as they do to the possible resonance conditions in a small closed room. The allowable resonance states of such a room are determined by *three* sets of integers, rather than just one such set. So for atomic systems we must introduce at least three quantum numbers. Finally, when it was postulated that every electron has a spin in one of two opposite senses (see below) it became necessary to add a fourth quantum number, one limited to just two possible values. Thus it is found that the state of an electron in an atom may be described in terms of the following quantum numbers.

(1) The *total quantum number*, n, whose value may be 1, 2, 3, ... The energy of a state depends primarily on the value of n.

(2) The *orbital quantum number*, l, whose value may be 0, 1, 2, . . . , $(n - 1)$. Thus if $n = 3$, l may be 0, 1, or 2. The energy of a state depends to a lesser extent on l. If one wishes to adopt the planetary model of the atom one may consider l to be related to the eccentricity, or shape, of an electron orbit.

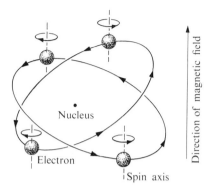

FIG. 18-2. Electron may spin in one of two opposite senses about its spin axis.

(3) The *magnetic quantum* number, m_l, whose value may be $l, l-1, l-2, \ldots,$ $-l$. Thus if $l = 2$, m_l may be 2, 1, 0, -1, or -2. This quantum number is associated with the orientation (inclination) of the electron's orbit relative to the direction of the magnetic field of the nucleus. This magnetic field is explained by attributing a spin to the positively charged nucleus, somewhat analogous to the spin of the sun in our planetary system; such a rotating nucleus must have a magnetic field. Just as a magnetic compass needle has less energy when it swings around to its equilibrium position, in which it points north, than when it points east or south, so the energy of an orbiting electron (which magnetically is equivalent to a small magnet) depends to some extent on the orientation of its orbit in the magnetic field within the atom.

(4) The *spin quantum number*, m_s, whose value may be either $+\frac{1}{2}$ or $-\frac{1}{2}$. It is postulated that every electron has a spin of constant magnitude about an axis parallel to the magnetic field present and that the sense of the rotation about this axis may be one way (say clockwise to a certain viewer) or the opposite (counterclockwise), as in Fig. 18-2. The spin of the electron corresponds to that of a planet about its polar axis, with the difference that the planets are not alike and do not have the same spin, while electrons are alike and do have spins of identical magnitude and (in a given atom) the same or opposite direction.

18-3 Quantum states

A set of allowed values of the quantum numbers determines the so-called *quantum state* of a *bound electron* in an atom. The energy associated with a given quantum state varies with the values of n, l, m_l, and m_s, and it also depends on what other states are occupied in the same atom.

The *free electrons* in a metal are not restricted to motion around a particular nucleus, yet these electrons are not completely free because they cannot normally escape from the metal. These electrons are confined to the interior of the metal and in this respect resemble molecules in a box. Due to this restriction, only certain modes of vibration are possible for the waves associated with the free electrons, just as there are only certain resonant acoustical frequencies associated with a small enclosed room. As a result, the energy of each electron is restricted to a discrete set of values which, on an energy-level diagram, lie one above another like the rungs of a ladder. Since Heisenberg's uncertainty principle is equivalent to the postulate of wave-particle duality, one may arrive at the same conclusion of discrete energy states for the free electrons in a metal on the basis of the argument that the simultaneous uncertainty in position and momentum makes it meaningless to pinpoint the state of an electron too closely. The reasoning is that if the difference in the states of two electrons is less than one can measure, then one might as well say that the two electrons are in the same state. Thus we may speak of an electron, bound or free, as being in a certain *state*.

18–4 Evidence that electrons cannot be crowded into the quantum state of lowest energy

We saw in Chapter 10 that our universe seems to be "running down." If a group of fast (hot) molecules is mixed with a group of slow (cold) molecules, the more energetic molecules share, through collisions, their excess energy with the less energetic ones until the two groups are indistinguishable as far as their energy distribution is concerned. We did not go into the study of what the energy distribution is for gas molecules in thermal equilibrium, but only found that the mean K.E. of translation per molecule is $\frac{3}{2} kT$. Actually some molecules have more and some less than this average energy; a large percentage have practically no energy, while a few have many times the average amount. For gas molecules there seems to be no restriction other than the temperature as to how many of them may be in the quantum state of lowest energy, but for electrons the situation appears to be quite different.

We shall consider three important lines of evidence which suggest that electrons cannot be crowded into the state of lowest energy regardless of how low the temperature may be. These three topics are: (1) the heat capacities of metals, (2) atomic diameters, and (3) the periodic table of the elements.

18–5 The heat capacities of metals

We picture a metal as a latticelike arrangement of atoms, or ions (atoms that have lost one or more of their electrons), between which circulate free electrons. At room temperature the atoms are considered to be oscillating about their respective lattice points. To raise the temperature of a metal, one must add energy, usually by giving heat to the metal, so as to increase the thermal agitation of the atoms about the lattice points. One would expect that if the free electrons behave like gas molecules, their K.E. would also have to be increased as the temperature is raised, but it is found experimentally that this is not the case!

The average K.E. of translation of a gas molecule is $\frac{3}{2} kT$, regardless of its mass, so that when T is raised by one degree the mean K.E. of translation per molecule is raised by $\frac{3}{2} k$, and the mean K.E. per kg-mole by $\frac{3}{2} kN_0 = \frac{3}{2} R$. The oscillating atoms or ions of a crystal lattice possess this same mean K.E., and in addition an equal average potential energy, so that altogether they must be given the energy $3R$ per kg-mole to raise their temperature one degree. Since $3R$ ($=24,930$ joules per kg-mole per degree) is about the measured value of the heat capacity of most metals at ordniary temperatures, one must conclude that the free electrons do not appear to take any of the energy that must be given to a metal when its temperature is raised. To see how this might be possible, consider the following analogy.

Ski Club A sends a group of men to a resort where there is a large hotel. This hotel has available one dormitory room with a dozen bunks that rent for $1.00 a night, another large room with cots at $2.00 a night, and better rooms with beds at $3.00 per person, $4.00 per person, and up. There are twelve men in the group and they have $16.00 between them to spend per night. They might decide to put eight men in bunks and four on cots, or to put eleven men in bunks and then give their leader a $5.00 bedroom. (Can you think of other possible arrangements that total $16.00?) Now suppose that unexpectedly the group meets a wealthy friend of the club and that this person offers each of the twelve members in turn one dollar to improve the respective member's sleeping accommodations. Each person gratefully accepts the dollar and moves up to the next higher-priced accommodation. The friend thus contributes $12.00 in all.

Ski Club B sends twelve men to another resort where the hotel has a similar bunkroom and cot-room plus *one* two-bed room at $3.00 per person per night, *one* at $4.00, and so on up. This group of skiers is peculiar in that no two of them will share a room. The cheapest arrangement possible is to put one man in the bunkroom, one in the cot-room, one in the $3.00 bedroom, one in the $4.00 bedroom, etc., with the leader taking a bed in the $12.00 room. This totals $78.00 in all, so Club B allots this amount to its group per night. This group also meets a gentleman who approaches each of them privately and makes the same offer of one dollar to improve the member's accommodations. The man in the bunkroom refuses to move up to the cot-room where he knows another member is lodged. When the would-be benefactor speaks to the man in, say, the $4.00 room, this man explains that he would prefer not to move up into the $5.00 room as he would then have to share it with the member assigned to it. The cheapest unoccupied room costs $13.00 and the benefactor is not willing to contribute the $9.00 needed to move the skier in the $4.00 room into this expensive room. So the benefactor only succeeds in helping the leader move from his $12.00 room to the $13.00 room. Unfortunately the men do not all get together in time to realize that with $12.00 extra they could have moved simultaneously, each going up one notch on the room scale. Thus the group actually gains little from the benefactor.

In this analogy, dollars per bed correspond to the energy associated with a particle in a given state. The members of Club A, who will gladly share a bedroom, correspond to the atoms of a metal and the members of Club B, who must sleep in separate rooms, correspond to the free electrons. The contribution of the wealthy friend is analogous to giving the metal sufficient energy to raise its temperature, say by one degree. In other words, suppose that only one electron can occupy each possible energy state; then the distribution leading to the lowest total energy (such as one would expect near absolute zero) is that where the states of lowest energy

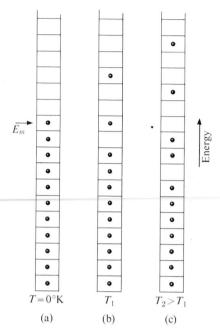

FIG. 18–3. Distribution of electrons among possible energy states at three different temperatures.

are all solidly filled, each with one electron. Enough of these states from zero energy up to, say, E_m must be occupied to accommodate all of the electrons, as shown in Fig. 18–3(a). States of energy above E_m will be empty.

Picture a metal near absolute zero being given enough energy to raise its temperature one degree. Very little of this energy will be transferred to the electrons in the metal, for the average thermal energy of the atoms ($3kT$) is not enough to disturb those electrons which are not near the top of the filled states. Such electrons would have to jump all the way up to the unfilled states above E_m. However, a little energy might be absorbed by electrons in those states just below the highest one filled, raising them to nearby unfilled states, as in Fig. 18–3(b) and (c). The fraction of the free electrons moving to higher energy states is small at ordinary temperatures, and thus the free electrons contribute little to the heat capacity.

18–6 Atomic diameters

In the Example of Section 18–1, the diameter of an Al atom was calculated from the density of the metal to be no greater than 2.5×10^{-10} m, or 2.5 A. By the same method one finds the maximum possible diameter of a uranium (U) atom to be 2.8 A. There are more exact methods for computing the sizes of atoms, but they all indicate that atoms of large atomic weight are of approximately the same size as those of small atomic weight. If one compares elements of similar chemical properties, such as the alkalis, one finds a steady *increase* in diameter with atomic weight, as follows: 1.56 A for lithium (Li), 1.86 A for sodium (Na), 2.23 A for potassium (K), 2.36 A for rubidium (Rb), and 2.55 A for cesium (Cs). (These values are based on the best methods of computation.) This increase in diameter is not what one would expect if all of the orbital electrons of an atom are in the quantum state of lowest energy.

From his work on the scattering of alpha particles by nuclei Rutherford deduced among other things that the positive charge on the nucleus of an atom increases steadily from $+e$ for hydrogen to $+92\,e$ for uranium. Thus the nucleus of a heavy atom must be surrounded by a more intense electric field than that around the nucleus of a light atom. A stronger field should pull an electron that is orbiting in the quantum state of lowest energy (the one for which $n = 1$) in closer to the nucleus. Hence, if all of the orbital electrons of an atom could exist in the quantum state of lowest energy, the atoms of large atomic weight and nuclear charge, such as those of uranium, should be the smallest in diameter. Since this is not the case, we must conclude that all of the electrons in an atom cannot be in the lowest quantum state, but must occupy states of different energies. Again we see evidence for the existence of a principle that forbids the crowding of electrons into the same quantum state.

18–7 The periodic table of the elements

We have noted that certain groups of elements of widely different atomic weights, such as the alkalis, have similar chemical properties. The alkalis form one such group, the alkaline earths (Be, Mg, Ca, Sr, Ba, Ra) another, and the halogens (F, Cl, Br, I) still another. This recurrence of similar chemical properties as one goes from the lighter to the heavier elements was the subject of much speculation. Finally in 1869 the great Russian chemist Dmitri Mendeléeff (1834–1907) hit upon a fruitful scheme for classifying and arranging the then known elements. His method consisted of writing down the symbols of the elements in such an order that the atomic weights of the respective elements steadily increased throughout the series; as he did this, Mendeléeff placed elements with similar chemical properties in the same vertical column. He then found that if gaps were left for presumably "missing" elements, a regular periodicity occurred. Each even series of his table, which is reproduced in Table 18–1, commences with an alkali element, followed by an alkaline earth; the third elements in each column resemble one another, as do the ones in the fourth column, the fifth column, etc.

The chemical properties of an element are determined by the ability of its atoms to combine with those of other elements. A halogen atom has the capacity to *combine with one atom of hydrogen* to form molecules such as HCl, HBr, etc., while the elements of the sixth column, or group, consist of atoms that may combine with two atoms of hydrogen to form molecules such as H_2O, H_2S, etc. An alkali atom may *replace one hydrogen atom* in a molecule, thus forming molecules like LiCl, NaCl, KBr, etc. An alkaline earth atom may replace two hydrogen atoms in a molecule, and so on. The term *valence* has been introduced to summarize what has just been said. Valence measures the capacity of atoms to react with

TABLE 18-1

PERIODIC CLASSIFICATION OF THE ELEMENTS (MENDELÉEFF, 1872)

Group →		I	II	III	IV	V	VI	VII	VIII
Series	1	H							
	2	Li	Be	B	C	N	O	F	
	3	Na	Mg	Al	Si	P	S	Cl	
	4	K	Ca	—	Ti	V	Cr	Mn	Fe, Co, Ni, Cu
	5	[Cu]	Zn	—	—	As	Se	Br	
	6	Rb	Sr	Yt?	Zr	Nb	Mo	—	Ru, Rh, Pd, Ag
	7	[Ag]	Cd	In	Sn	Sb	Te	I	
	8	Cs	Ba	Di?	Ce?	—	—	—	
	9	—	—	—	—	—	—	—	
	10	—	—	Er?	La?	Ta	W	—	Os, Ir, Pt, Au
	11	[Au]	Hg	Tl	Pb	Bi	—	—	
	12	—	—	—	Th	—	U		

one another. *Positive valence* is the number of hydrogen atoms which an atom of the element may replace, and *negative valence* is the number of hydrogen atoms with which an atom of the element may combine. Some elements have more than one valence, such as a positive valence of v and a negative valence of $(8 - v)$. The valences of some common elements are listed in Table 18–2. We see that as one passes from the first group to the seventh in Mendeléeff's table, the positive valence increases from 1 on up, while the negative valence becomes less negative and reaches -1 for the seventh group, the halogens.

Mendeléeff's table was an empirical accomplishment; it summarized many facts, and this alone made it important. It serves as a table to which one may refer when one wishes to recall the general chemical properties of any element. However, the importance of Mendeléeff's achievement is enhanced by the fact that it (1) made successful predictions and (2) stimulated work on a theory to "explain" the periodicity of the table. Recall that in a similar manner Kepler's empirical laws summarized planetary motion and led to Newtonian theory, the Bode-Titus law for the radii of planetary orbits helped lead to the discovery of new planets, the laws of blackbody radiation led to Planck's quantum theory, and Balmer's formula for the wavelengths of the lines in the hydrogen spectrum resulted in Bohr's important work.

TABLE 18–2

VALENCES OF SOME COMMON ELEMENTS

Element	Symbol	Valence
Hydrogen	H	$+1$
Lithium	Li	$+1$
Sodium	Na	$+1$
Potassium	K	$+1$
Beryllium	Be	$+2$
Magnesium	Mg	$+2$
Calcium	Ca	$+2$
Zinc	Zn	$+2$
Boron	B	$+3$
Aluminum	Al	$+3$
Carbon	C	$(+4),\ -4$
Silicon	Si	$(+4),\ -4$
Nitrogen	N	$(+5),\ -3$
Oxygen	O	-2
Sulphur	S	$(+6),\ -2$
Chlorine	Cl	$(+7),\ -1$
Bromine	Br	$(+7),\ -1$
Copper	Cu	$+1,\ +2$

Mendeléeff wisely left spaces in his table for "missing" elements. He predicted the chemical and physical properties of each missing element, which helped lead to the eventual discovery of these elements. Now all of the gaps in the table have been filled, either by elements found to occur naturally in the earth, or by elements made artificially through nuclear transmutation, the latter including ten elements beyond uranium (the transuranic elements). The original table has been greatly modified, such as by the addition of Group O, which contains the inert gases (He, Ne, A, Kr, Xe, Rn) whose valence is zero. These inert elements were not known in Mendeléeff's time. Another change is the addition of the lanthanide rare earth elements between Ba and Hf, and a similar series following radium. It has also been found necessary in certain cases to disregard the rule that elements are to be arranged in order of increasing atomic weight; thus argon (A), an inert gas, obviously belongs under helium (He) and neon (Ne), while potassium (K) belongs under lithium (Li) and sodium (Na), which puts A ahead of K in spite of the fact that A has the greater atomic weight of the two.

A modern version of the periodic table is shown in Table 18–3. The elements are numbered in order and this position number is called the *atomic number Z*. One of the most important features of this modern table is that the periods are not of equal length. A *period* may be defined as any consecutive group of elements starting with hydrogen or an alkali and ending with an inert gas. The successive periods contain 2, 8, 18, 18, and 32 elements, respectively. Note that $2 = 2(1)^2, 8 = 2(2)^2, 18 = 2(3)^2, 32 = 2(4)^2$.

TABLE 18-3

MODERN VERSION OF THE PERIODIC TABLE

Outer electrons are in the	I	II	III	IV	V	VI	VII	VIII			O	Electrons per shell
First or K-shell	1 H 1.0080										2 He 4.003	2
Second or L-shell	3 Li 6.940	4 Be 9.013	5 B 10.82	6 C 12.011	7 N 14.008	8 O 16.000	9 F 19.00				10 Ne 20.183	2, 8
Third or M-shell	11 Na 22.991	12 Mg 24.32	13 Al 26.98	14 Si 28.09	15 P 30.975	16 S 32.066	17 Cl 35.457				18 Ar 39.944	2, 8, 8
Fourth or N-shell	19 K 39.100	20 Ca 40.08	21 Sc 44.96	22 Ti 47.90	23 V 50.95	24 Cr 52.01	25 Mn 54.94	26 Fe 55.85	27 Co 58.94	28 Ni 58.71		
	29 Cu 63.54	30 Zn 65.38	31 Ga 69.72	32 Ge 72.60	33 As 74.91	34 Se 78.96	35 Br 79.916				36 Kr 83.80	2, 8, 18, 8
Fifth or O-shell	37 Rb 85.48	38 Sr 87.63	39 Y 88.92	40 Zr 91.22	41 Nb 92.91	42 Mo 95.95	43 Tc (98)	44 Ru 101.10	45 Rh 102.91	46 Pd 106.4		
	47 Ag 107.880	48 Cd 112.41	49 In 114.82	50 Sn 118.70	51 Sb 121.76	52 Te 127.61	53 I 126.91				54 Xe 131.30	2, 8, 18, 18, 8
Sixth or P-shell	55 Cs 132.91	56 Ba 137.36	57-71 La series*	72 Hf 178.50	73 Ta 180.95	74 W 183.86	75 Re 186.22	76 Os 190.2	77 Ir 192.2	78 Pt 195.09		
	79 Au 197.0	80 Hg 200.61	81 Tl 204.39	82 Pb 207.21	83 Bi 209.00	84 Po (209)	85 At (210)				86 Em (222)	2, 8, 18, 32, 18, 8
Seventh or Q-shell	87 Fr (223)	88 Ra 226.05	89 — Ac series**									

*Lanthanide series:	57 La 138.92	58 Ce 140.13	59 Pr 140.92	60 Nd 144.27	61 Pm (145)	62 Sm 150.35	63 Eu 152.0	64 Gd 157.26	65 Tb 158.93	66 Dy 162.51	67 Ho 164.94	68 Er 167.27	69 Tm 168.94	70 Yb 173.04	71 Lu 174.99	2, 8, 18, 32, 9, 2
**Actinide series:	89 Ac (227)	90 Th 232.05	91 Pa (231)	92 U 238.07	93 Np (237)	94 Pu (242)	95 Am (243)	96 Cm (247)	97 Bk (247)	98 Cf (251)	99 Es (254)	100 Fm (253)	101 Md (256)	102 No (253)	103 Lw (253)	2, 8, 18, 32, 32?, 9, 2

We now come to the important question of what is the significance of all this. Why does this periodicity of the elements occur, and why do we encounter the "magic numbers" 2, 8, 18, and 32? Is there some fundamental principle? Physicists are generally inclined to believe that in such a situation a fundamental law of nature must be involved. In this case the principle was first stated by the Austrian-born physicist Wofgang Pauli in 1925. Pauli's postulate "explains" the periodic table and also the energy distribution of the free electrons in a metal and the variations in atomic diameters that we discussed earlier.

18–8 Pauli's exclusion principle. Fundamental Law XIII

Pauli's important postulate was simply the following.

No two electrons in a given system can be in the same quantum state.

The word *system* is here taken to mean either an atom or a certain volume of a metal. Since the quantum state of an electron in an atom is determined by the values of the four quantum numbers n, l, m_l, and m_s, Pauli's principle asserts that *no two electrons in an atom can have the same set of quantum numbers.*

Pauli's postulate immediately predicts that the free electrons in a metal must be distributed among the quantum states of various energies as shown in Fig. 18–3. If only one electron can occupy each state, the behavior of the free electrons will be analogous to that of the skiers in Club B who refused to share the same room. It was explained that this sort of behavior would result in the free electrons making almost no contribution to the heat capacity of a metal. In other words, if a metal is given heat to raise its temperature, only a slight amount of this heat goes into increasing the energy of the free electrons and almost all of it goes into raising the internal energy of the atoms or ions of the metal.

The nucleus of any of the heavier atoms is surrounded by many electrons. Pauli's principle states that these electrons cannot all be in the state of lowest energy, i.e., the state for which the total quantum number n equals one. If the possible energy states are filled, each with one electron, in order of increasing energy, just as they are in the case of a metal, then electrons must be located in states for which $n = 2, 3$, or more. Higher values of n correspond to greater distances from the nucleus. On the other hand, the stronger electric field of a heavy nucleus pulls all of the orbiting electrons in closer. The result of these two phenomena, which have opposing effects in regard to the size of an atom, is that light and heavy atoms of elements in the same group differ little in size. The diameter of an atom of a given element depends more on the group in the periodic table to which the element belongs than it does on the period in which the element is found (see Fig. 18–4).

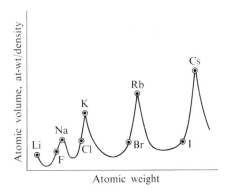

FIG. 18–4.   Relative atomic volumes.

TABLE 18-4

POSSIBLE DIFFERENT QUANTUM STATES FOR $n = 1$ AND $n = 2$

n	l	m_l	m_s	Number of possibilities
1	0	0	$\frac{1}{2}$	$\left.\begin{array}{c}\\\\\end{array}\right\}$ 2
1	0	0	$-\frac{1}{2}$	
2	0	0	$\frac{1}{2}$	$\left.\begin{array}{c}\\\\\\\\\\\\\\\\\end{array}\right\}$ 8
2	0	0	$-\frac{1}{2}$	
2	1	1	$\frac{1}{2}$	
2	1	1	$-\frac{1}{2}$	
2	1	0	$\frac{1}{2}$	
2	1	0	$-\frac{1}{2}$	
2	1	-1	$\frac{1}{2}$	
2	1	-1	$-\frac{1}{2}$	

Finally we come to the explanation of the "magic numbers" 2, 8, 18, and 32. In order to count the number of possible atomic states associated with $n = 1$, $n = 2$, $n = 3$, etc., it is best to list all of the different combinations of the four quantum numbers, as in Table 18-4.

Remember that l can be any integer from 0 up to $n - 1$, m_l can be any positive or negative integer from 0 to $\pm l$, and m_s can only be $+\frac{1}{2}$ or $-\frac{1}{2}$. Thus for $n = 1$ there are only *two* possibilities, while for $n = 2$ there are *eight*. The reader should satisfy himself that for $n = 3$, there are 18 states and for $n = 4$, there are 32 states. Thus the magic numbers come out of the theory in this way.

For the first two elements, H and He, the electrons may be in $n = 1$ states (Fig. 18-5). In the case of He, which normally has two electrons, the $n = 1$ states are filled. When we come to Li, which has a third electron, we see that it must be located in an $n = 2$ state, a state of considerably higher energy. A state of higher energy is one of lower stability, therefore Li should be more prone to enter into chemical combination than is He; this is the case. Thus as we progress through the periodic table, we think of He as marking the end of the first period of elements, since with it the $n = 1$ states are filled and closed to further electrons. The $n = 1$ electrons are said to form a closed "shell" of two electrons, but the term "shell" should not be taken too literally.

With the tenth element, Ne (neon), the $n = 2$, or second, shell of electrons is filled. The eight electrons in this shell are divided as follows: two in $l = 0$ states and six in $l = 1$ states. From the inert chemical property of Ne we deduce that this arrangement is also a particularly stable one.

With the eighteenth element, A (argon), the $n = 3$, or third, shell of electrons also is found to contain two electrons in $l = 0$ states and six in $l = 1$ states. Since the electrons in the outermost shell are the ones that are most readily available for chemical combination, we may reason that because of the similar 2 and 6 ar-

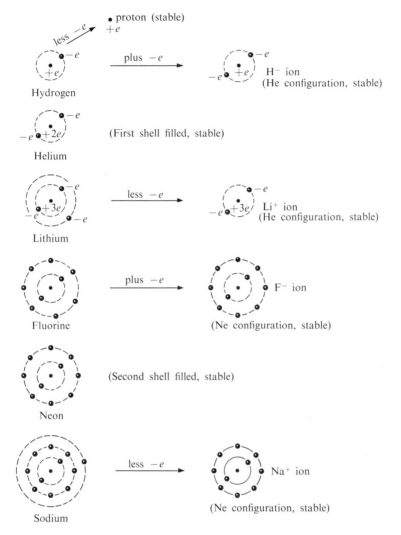

FIG. 18–5.   Representative electron structures.

rangements of electrons in their outermost shells, A and Ne should have similar chemical properties, which they do. Argon is also an inert gas. Thus the third period of the periodic table of the elements also contains 10 (and not 18) elements.

It is found that in the elements beyond A (argon), the additional electrons are added according to the same principle, according to which the allowed states are filled, with one electron each, in order of increasing energy per state. However, it turns out that states of higher n and lower l values may thus be favored over those of lower n and higher l values. With the 36th element, Kr, also an inert gas, the $n = 3$ shell is filled and the $n = 4$ shell contains two electrons in $l = 0$ states and six in $l = 1$ states. The period from K (the element after A) to Kr contains

18 elements and is represented by the addition of 10 electrons in $n = 3$, $l = 2$ states, 2 electrons in $n = 4$, $l = 0$ states, and 6 electrons in $n = 4$, $l = 1$ states. The next period also contains 18 elements and is accounted for by the addition of 10 electrons in $n = 4$, $l = 2$ states, 2 in $n = 5$, $l = 0$ states, and 6 in $n = 5$, $l = 1$ states.

The long period of 32 elements following Xe and ending with Rn is represented by the addition of 14 electrons in $n = 4$, $l = 3$ states, 10 in $n = 5$, $l = 2$ states, 2 in $n = 6$, $l = 0$ states, and 6 in $n = 6$, $l = 1$ states. A similar period of 32 elements should end with element number 118, but such an element is far beyond the range of stable elements and even beyond those unstable ones that have been produced artificially.

We see that with the aid of Pauli's principle a complete explanation of the periodic table is possible.

18–9 Chemical bonds. Valence

The key to the chemical behavior of an element is its valence, which, in turn, is determined by the arrangement of electrons in its outermost shell or shells. When two atoms combine to form a molecule they usually do so because the resulting combination is more stable, which means that to break up such a combination an agent must supply energy to it. Thus when atoms freely combine they do so with the release of energy to the outside world. Since the resulting molecule is more stable than are the two atoms separately, it is convenient to think of the atoms in molecules as being held together by *bonds*. This is a concept that is introduced for convenience; it helps us to picture the situation.

Chemical bonds are of different types. We shall recognize three such types, namely (a) the *ionic bond*, (b) the *covalent bond*, and (c) a combination of (1) and (2) that is referred to as the *coordinate covalent bond*.

(a) *Electrovalence, or ionic valence.* The alkali elements (Li, Na, K, Rb, Cs, and Fr) in the first column of the periodic table have an important characteristic in common, namely, that their atoms each contain one more electron than does an atom of the preceding inert-gas element. A lithium atom possesses one more electron than does a helium atom, a sodium atom possesses one more electron than does a neon atom, and so on, as shown in Fig. 18–5. This additional electron of the alkali atom is always in a state for which n is greater than for any of the other electrons; this electron may be pictured as being by itself and pretty much outside the other electrons and the nucleus. To this outermost electron the electrostatic attraction of the nucleus is small because of the distance of this electron from the nucleus and because the positve charge on the nucleus is almost neutralized by the intervening negative electrons. This outermost electron may, therefore, be detached more easily than any other electron. When it is removed, the resulting positive ion has the same outer electronic structure as does an atom of the neighboring inert-gas element, a structure which we know is chemically inert and hence very stable. Thus the process

$$Na \rightarrow Na^+ + e^-, \tag{18–2}$$

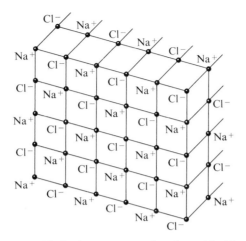

FIG. 18–6.   Cubic lattice structure of sodium chloride crystal.

where e⁻ represents the electron, may be made to occur by giving the sodium atom a relatively small amount of energy.

All of the neutral atoms of the halogen elements (F, Cl, Br, I, and At) also have similar outer electronic structures; their common characteristic is that they have seven electrons in the outermost shell, so that the addition of one more electron to such an atom will give this atom the octet structure of a stable inert-gas atom, as shown in Fig. 18–5. The tendency of a halogen atom to gain this octet structure means that the atom is actually more stable after it has gained an extra electron and become a negative ion. Thus the process

$$Cl + e^- \rightarrow Cl^- \tag{18–3}$$

involves the release of energy.

Common table salt is composed of sodium chloride, for which the chemical symbol is NaCl. It is a crystalline solid at ordinary temperatures and its crystal structure is represented by a cubic lattice in which sodium and chlorine ions alternate, as shown in Fig. 18–6. Evidently when a sodium and a chlorine atom are close to one another, the sodium atom in effect loses its outermost electron to the chlorine atom because the resulting configuration represents a state of lower energy and greater stability. The energy released in the process of Eq. (18–3) plus the work done by the electrostatic forces of attraction (see Coulomb's law) as the positive sodium and negative chlorine ions are drawn together more than compensates for the energy needed to remove the electron from the sodium atom. Thus the process

$$Na + Cl \rightarrow Na^+ + e^- + Cl \rightarrow Na^+ + Cl^- \tag{18–4}$$

can proceed with the release of energy. In the crystalline state shown in Fig. 18–6, we find that a large number of oppositely charged ions have been pulled together to form a "supermolecule." Thus sodium chloride is a very stable substance. When dissolved in water the electrostatic attractions between the Na^+ and Cl^- ions are weakened and the two kinds of ions may break away from one another and move separately through the water; these ions may serve as conductors of electric current, so that salt solutions are good conductors of electricity. If sodium chloride dissociated in solution into neutral atoms, a salt solution would not be a good conductor.

The process of Eq. (18–4) may be expressed as follows:

$$\text{Na} \cdot + \cdot \overset{\displaystyle \cdot\cdot}{\underset{\displaystyle \cdot\cdot}{\text{Cl}}} : \rightarrow \text{Na}^+ + \overset{\displaystyle \cdot\cdot}{\underset{\displaystyle \cdot\cdot}{:\text{Cl}}} :^{-} \tag{18–5}$$

Here the dots represent electrons in the outermost shell of an atom or ion. If the number of such electrons is eight, the stable inert-gas configuration has been attained, as in the case of Cl^-. If the number of dots is zero, as for the Na^+, the valence electron(s) has (have) been removed, leaving the stable octet structure of the next inner shell. The dots around Cl^- have been arranged symmetrically in pairs, because in each pair the states of the two electrons differ only in the values of the spin quantum number m_s, which is $+\frac{1}{2}$ for one and $-\frac{1}{2}$ for the other electron.

The stability of sodium chloride is attributed to a process in which a metallic atom such as sodium donates an electron to an atom of negative valence such as chlorine and the resulting ions are held together by electrostatic forces. We therefore say that sodium chloride is held together by an *ionic bond*, or, as it is called by some people, an *electrostatic bond*.

A barium atom has two outer electrons to donate to atoms of negative valence; hence we find that barium chloride is another stable salt and is represented by the symbol $BaCl_2$. Each barium atom donates electrons to two chlorine atoms. The process may be represented as follows:

$$: \overset{\displaystyle \cdot\cdot}{\underset{\displaystyle \cdot\cdot}{\text{Cl}}} \cdot + \cdot \text{Ba} \cdot + \cdot \overset{\displaystyle \cdot\cdot}{\underset{\displaystyle \cdot\cdot}{\text{Cl}}} : \rightarrow \overset{\displaystyle \cdot\cdot}{\underset{\displaystyle \cdot\cdot}{:\text{Cl}}} :^{-} \; \text{Ba}^{++} \; \overset{\displaystyle \cdot\cdot}{\underset{\displaystyle \cdot\cdot}{:\text{Cl}}} :^{-} \tag{18–6}$$

In general, stable salts of relatively high melting point may be formed out of combinations of positive and negative ions, the positive ions being atoms of an element of positive valence minus one or more electrons and the negative ions being atoms of an element of negative valence plus one or more electrons. Examples other than the above are LiF, LiCl, KCl, KBr, KI, $MgCl_2$, $AlCl_3$, etc.

(b) *Covalence.* Electrovalence accounts for the tendency of atoms of elements on opposite sides of the periodic table to combine, but it does not explain why molecules such as N_2, O_2, H_2, and CO_2 are stable. Atoms of elements in the middle of the periodic table and atoms of the same element may combine through a process that involves the *sharing* of electrons in pairs. One pair of shared electrons constitutes one *covalent bond* and is indicated symbolically by a horizontal line.

Consider two oxygen atoms. Each O atom contains six electrons in its outermost shell. Suppose that two such atoms are brought close together and share two pairs of electrons in common; then each atom will have eight electrons in its outermost shell, which is the stable inert-gas configuration. Thus we have the reaction

$$: \overset{..}{\underset{..}{O}} + \overset{..}{\underset{..}{O}} : \rightarrow \quad \overset{..}{O} : : \overset{..}{\underset{..}{O}}, \quad \text{or} \quad O{=}O. \qquad (18\text{–}7)$$

One must think of the shared electrons as belonging to both atoms.

In a similar manner an N_2 molecule may be formed through the sharing of three pairs of electrons by two N atoms:

$$: \overset{.}{\underset{..}{N}} + \overset{.}{\underset{..}{N}} : \rightarrow : N \overset{..}{::} N :, \quad \text{or} \quad N{\equiv}N. \qquad (18\text{–}8)$$

The formation of the CO_2 molecule may be pictured as follows:

$$\overset{..}{\underset{..}{O}} : + \overset{..}{\underset{..}{C}} + : \overset{..}{\underset{..}{O}} \rightarrow \overset{..}{O} : : \overset{..}{\underset{..}{C}} : : \overset{..}{\underset{..}{O}}, \quad \text{or} \quad O{=}C{=}O. \qquad (18\text{–}9)$$

Note that in these last three equations the total number of dots remains constant during each reaction; the electrons are only rearranged.

The stability of the H_2 molecule is attributed to the completion of the $n = 1$ shell of two electrons for each of the two H atoms when they share a pair of electrons, that is,

$$H \cdot + \cdot H \rightarrow H : H, \quad \text{or} \quad H{-}H. \qquad (18\text{–}10)$$

Each atom thus acquires an electronic structure similar to that of the stable He atom.

The covalent bond is the most common one in chemistry and it plays a fundamental role in all of organic chemistry, the chemistry of molecules found in living matter. Further examples of covalent-bonded compounds are shown in Fig. 18–7.

(c) *Coordinate covalence.* There appear to be stable molecular configurations in which two atoms are held together by a bond in which a pair of electrons is shared by the two atoms, but *one* of the atoms contributes *both* of the shared electrons and the other none. This is referred to as *coordinate covalence.*

The two gases, hydrogen chloride (HCl) and ammonia (NH_3), combine to

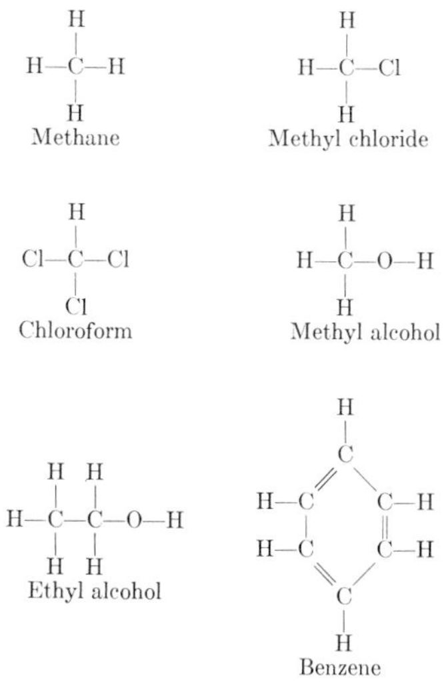

FIG. 18–7.   Covalent molecules.

form a stable salt called ammonium chloride (NH_4Cl). Chemist write the reaction as follows:

$$NH_3 + HCl \rightarrow NH_4Cl. \tag{18–11}$$

In water solution the ammonium chloride molecules split apart into stable NH_4^+ and Cl^- ions. Why is NH_4^+ stable?

Let us imagine that we combine an ammonia molecule (NH_3) and a hydrogen ion, or proton (H^+). The NH_3 molecule is already stable because it is held together by three covalent bonds, but the nitrogen atom still has one pair of electrons which, under favorable circumstances, it might share with another atom. The H^+ ion needs two electrons to complete the stable electronic structure of helium; hence we might postulate the following:

$$
\begin{array}{c}
\text{H} \\
.. \\
\text{H : N :} + \text{H}^+ \rightarrow \\
.. \\
\text{H}
\end{array}
\left[
\begin{array}{c}
\text{H} \\
.. \\
\text{H : N : H} \\
.. \\
\text{H}
\end{array}
\right]^+ .
$$

Once formed, the complex would become symmetrical, with each hydrogen attached to the nitrogen by a similar covalent bond. We may now picture the reaction of Eq. (18–11) as follows:

$$
\begin{array}{c}
\text{H} \\
.. \\
\text{H : N :} \\
.. \\
\text{H}
\end{array}
+
\begin{array}{c}
.. \\
\text{H : Cl :} \\
..
\end{array}
\rightarrow
\left[
\begin{array}{c}
\text{H} \\
.. \\
\text{H : N : H} \\
.. \\
\text{H}
\end{array}
\right]^+
+
\left[
\begin{array}{c}
.. \\
\text{: Cl :} \\
..
\end{array}
\right]^- . \tag{18–12}
$$

When the H moves from the chlorine atom to the ammonia molecule it leaves behind its electron (which the Cl atom needs) and shares the uncommitted pair of electrons of the nitrogen, forming what is called a *coordinate covalent bond* with the nitrogen. The resulting molecule, NH_4Cl, is held together in the crystal form by the usual electrostatic force. Thus NH_4Cl illustrates a combination of covalent and ionic bonding.

As another example consider carbon monoxide (CO). If the oxygen atom donates an electron to the carbon atom, each ion will have the electron configuration of nitrogen and CO will have the bond structure of N_2, as follows:

$$
\text{: C :} + \text{: O :} \rightarrow
\left[\text{: C :} \right]^-
+
\left[\text{: O :} \right]^+
\rightarrow \text{: C}^- \text{:: O}^+ \text{: ,}
$$

or $C^- \!\equiv\! O^+$.

Situations have been encountered in which more than one stable electronic configuration exists for a given molecule. In this case the molecule may exist alternately in, or *resonate* between, one form and the other; according to wave mechanics, greater stability results from such resonance.

Summarizing, we may say that chemical bonding, which is the heart of chemistry, may be explained in terms of fundamental physical laws, particularly in terms of Pauli's exclusion principle, the quantum principle, and Coulomb's and Ampere's laws. Of these principles that of Pauli plays the most significant role, since it forms the basis for the concept of the stable octet configuration to which all chemical bonding is related.

PROBLEMS

1. Take the diameter of the hydrogen molecule to be 1.4×10^{-10} m. A kg-mole $(6 \times 10^{26}$ molecules) of hydrogen (molecular weight = 2) at 0°C and 1 atmosphere occupies 22.4 m^3. What fraction of the occupied space is taken up by the molecules themselves?

2. (a) Prove that if two molecules collide as hard elastic spheres of radii R, the center of one molecule is excluded by the other from a volume equal to eight times the volume of either molecule. (b) Oxygen gas behaves in a way that indicates that this excluded volume is 0.032 m^3 for 3×10^{26} *pairs* of molecules. Find the radius of the oxygen molecule.

3. Compute the volume and approximate size of a uranium atom from the density $(18.6 \times 10^3$ kg/m^3) and atomic weight (238) of uranium.

4. List the values of l, m_l, and m_s for all the quantum states of an atom for which $n = 3$ and $n = 4$.

5. The 14 elements following La are called the "rare earths"; they are similar chemically because they differ only in the number of inner electrons that each possesses. What are the quantum numbers for the states filled by these inner electrons? Why are there 14 of these rare earth elements?

6. Why does copper, an element in Group I of the periodic table, differ chemically from the alkalis, Li, Na, K, etc.?

7. Indicate what ions are formed when each of the following salts is dissociated: (a) KI, (b) CuCl, (c) CuCl$_2$, (d) MgO, (e) AlCl$_3$, (f) Al$_2$O$_3$.

8. Using the dot notation, indicate the outer electronic structure of each atom and the pairs of electrons shared by two atoms in the following: (a) Cl$_2$, (b) CH$_4$ (methane), (c) CHCl$_3$ (chloroform), (d) C$_2$H$_5$OH (ethyl alcohol), (f) C$_6$H$_6$ (benzene). Refer to Fig. 18–7.

9. In the molecule N=N=O, which bond involves coordinate covalency and what are the net charges on the outer N atom and on the middle N atom, respectively?

10. Describe the bonds found in NaOH (sodium hydroxide).

11. Common salt is formed in the reaction

$$HCl + NaOH \rightarrow NaCl + H_2O.$$

What is the physical explanation of this reaction? In a salt solution, which ionizes more readily, the salt or the water?

EXPERIMENT 24

MONOMOLECULAR LAYERS
(Size of an Atom and Avogadro's Number)

Object: (1) To form a film one molecule thick and then to determine its thickness. (2) To determine, from the size of an atom, also approximate values of Avogadro's number N_0 and Boltzmann's constant k.

Problem: Atomic physics provides much indirect evidence that atoms and molecules have dimensions of around 10 angstrom units, or 10^{-9} m. In this experiment we shall measure the length of a molecule directly.

Because of their polar properties, the class of organic compounds known as fatty acids lend themselves quite effectively to monomolecular layer studies. As early as 1917 Langmuir pointed out that such molecules must line up vertically in a monomolecular layer, that is, with their longest dimension perpendicular to the surface of the layer. Then the length of such a molecule is determined if the thickness of the layer is known. In this experiment we shall try to form a monomolecular layer with a circular periphery, then we shall compute its volume V and area A. The thickness t will be given by

$$t = V/A. \tag{1}$$

Having found the length of the molecule of fatty acid we may consult the chemists for information regarding its molecular weight and shape. From the latter we may estimate the volume of one molecule, while from the former and the density of the substance we may compute the volume per kg-mole, i.e., the volume of N_0 molecules. Then

$$N_0 = \frac{\text{volume per kg-mole}}{\text{volume per molecule}}. \tag{2}$$

Of course this is not an accurate method for determining N_0, but it is direct. More reliable methods all involve the use of sophisticated and expensive apparatus such as an x-ray spectrometer, Millikan's oil-drop apparatus, a mass spectrometer, or a radioactivity laboratory. Avogadro's number is not easy to measure!

Boltzmann's constant k may be found from Avogadro's number and the gas constant R, using the relation

$$k = R/N_0. \tag{3}$$

To find R one must measure the mass of a gas at a known temperature T and pressure p in a container of known volume V. The container must be weighed both with the gas in it and evacuated. The number of kg-moles of gas equals its mass divided by its molecular weight. Call this n. Then the equation

$$pV = nRT \tag{4}$$

may be used to determine R and hence k. Boltzmann's constant is a measure of the average kinetic energy acquired by a gas molecule per degree rise in temperature. Actually

$$\overline{\text{K.E.}} \text{ (translation)} = \tfrac{3}{2}kT. \tag{5}$$

Procedure:

Step 1. Clean a large tray-shaped vessel thoroughly and fill it with distilled water. Cover the surface with powder or chalk dust.

Step 2. Calibrate a medicine dropper, that is, measure the volume of one of its drops by measuring the volume of 20 or more drops.

Step 3. Compute roughly the volume of fatty acid one drop should contain in order that it will form a circular area one molecule thick and around 10 cm in diameter. (Assume the thickness to be approximately 2×10^{-9} m.) Now compute how much the fatty acid should be diluted. Prepare a solution of this strength. Oleic or stearic acid diluted with benzene or alcohol (which evaporates quickly when spread on water) should work well. Let one drop of the dilute solution fall on and spread across your powdered water surface, then measure its diameter. Compute the thickness t of the monomolecular layer.

Step 4. To estimate the volume per molecule we must use the information, based on various studies, that the fatty acid molecules are shaped like cylinders whose lengths are four times their distances across. For oleic acid the molecular weight is 282 and the density is 900 kg/m³, from which you can compute the volume per kg-mole. Now use Eq. (2) to find N_0.

If desired, the experiment may be continued, as outlined above in the "Problem," to find k.

CHAPTER 19

The Conservation of Matter Principle

The assumption that matter is indestructible is a postulate of long standing. When processes that might be viewed as exceptions to this principle have been encountered, scientists have "saved" the principle by defining other forms of matter. (In a similar manner, the conservation of energy principle has been maintained by inventing different forms of energy.) The evolution in our thinking about matter has led to the realization that what is conserved in regard to matter is not its volume or its mass, but its constituent particles. Yet with the discovery of pair production and annihilation and our recent knowledge about the reactions between elementary particles, even the concept of particle conservation has required modification. Let us follow step by step this evolutionary development of the conservation of matter principle.

19–1 The conservation of matter in physical processes

If a child is playing with marbles and one gets lost, he soon learns to assume that the missing marble still exists somewhere, even though he cannot find it. Time and again lost objects do eventually turn up. The idea that objects such as marbles really vanish into, or materialize from, nowhere is regarded as superstitious.

Should an object like a marble break, we assume that the sum of the parts equals the original whole. This postulate is often substantiated experimentally. We believe that the fragments contain all of the molecules that the object possessed when whole.

When water boils it disappears from sight, but we postulate that the water molecules still exist in the form of an invisible gas which is called water vapor. This postulate is supported by the further fact that if water is boiled in an enclosed container, so that the water vapor cannot escape out into the atmosphere, then the visible water may be recovered by cooling and condensing the vapor. We have seen how pressure is attributed to molecular impacts; water vapor also exerts a pressure on the walls of its container, just as air and other gases do, and so the H_2O molecules must still exist in the vapor.

When sugar and salt are dissolved in water they too seem to disappear, but again we postulate that their molecules are not destroyed but exist in a dissolved state, as witnessed by the change in taste. This assumption also serves to explain why dissolved salt may be recovered in the original solid state by evaporating or boiling away the water.

In processes such as the above, in which molecules are neither gained nor lost, mass also appears to be conserved. Thus when 1 kg of water is boiled away, 1 kg of water vapor is produced. Actually the mass of the water vapor should, according to the relativity principle, be a *little* greater than that of the water from which it came. This follows from Einstein's relationship $E = mc^2$, according to which one must associate the mass E/c^2 with the energy E. Let us write

$$\text{1 kg-mole of water (liquid)} + Q = \text{1 kg-mole of water vapor,} \quad (19\text{--}1)$$

where Q is the heat of vaporization per kg-mole, i.e., the heat energy that must be transferred to one kg-mole of water to vaporize it. The value of Q varies somewhat with temperature, but at 100°C it is close to 4×10^7 j/kg-mole. One kg-mole of water is 18 kg of water. The mass equivalence of Q is

$$m = \frac{Q}{c^2} = \frac{4 \times 10^7 \text{ j}}{9 \times 10^{16} \text{ m}^2/\text{sec}^2}$$

$$= 4.4 \times 10^{-10} \frac{\text{kg-m}^2/\text{sec}^2}{\text{m}^2/\text{sec}^2}$$

$$= 4.4 \times 10^{-10} \text{ kg.}$$

This is obviously far too small a fraction of the mass to be observable.

19–2 The conservation of matter in chemical processes

We have seen in the last chapter that in chemical reactions atoms and electrons are rearranged, but not destroyed. For example, when sodium hydroxide, a base, is neutralized with hydrochloric acid, the reaction is as follows:

$$\text{NaOH} + \text{HCl} \rightarrow \text{NaCl} + \text{H}_2\text{O} + Q. \quad (19\text{--}2)$$

We conclude that in chemical reactions the number of *molecules* of a given kind does change, but not the number of *atoms*. So we must modify our previous conservation of molecules principle and convert it into a conservation of atoms principle.

The Q in Eq. (19–2) represents the *heat of reaction*, or the chemical energy released as a result of the rearrangement of the valence electrons so as to form new and stronger bonds. When Q is on the right-hand side of the equation the reaction is termed *exothermal* if Q is positive, for in this case chemical energy is released; if Q is negative, the reaction is said to be *endothermal* and energy must be supplied from outside to make the process proceed as indicated.

Our modern atomistic view of chemical reactions dates back to the beginning of the 19th century. Before that time it was difficult for people to believe that the conservation of matter principle applied to chemical processes. People saw that when a candle burned its substance and mass obviously decreased, while when a metal was allowed to rust its mass increased. Then the discovery of oxygen threw new light on the process of combustion. In 1804 an English school teacher named Dalton postulated that every elementary substance is composed of indestructible atoms and that the atoms of a given element are all alike and hence possesses the same mass. The atomic weights, or the relative atomic masses, of the known elements were determined. The atomic weight of carbon is 12 and that of oxygen is 16. When a candle burns we say that its carbon atoms combine with the oxygen molecules (two atoms each) in the air to form carbon dioxide, an invisible gas. The reaction is

$$C + O_2 \rightarrow CO_2 + Q. \tag{19-3}$$

We find that 12 kg of C combine with 2×16 kg of O_2 to form 44 kg of CO_2 and that Q is about 4×10^8 j. The 12 kg of C contain the same number of atoms as there are molecules in 32 kg of O_2 and in 44 kg of CO_2; this common number is Avogadro's number $N_0 = 6 \times 10^{26}$. Here N_0 atoms of carbon combine with $2N_0$ atoms of oxygen to form N_0 molecules of CO_2, each molecule of which contains three atoms, (one of C and two of O). Thus the conservation of atoms principle holds for the reaction. Since the mass equivalence of Q is again negligibly small, the conservation of mass principle is also valid.

When iron rusts, oxygen atoms are added to those of the metal, and thus the increase in mass of a rusty metal is explained.

Due to the small mass equivalence of Q in chemical reactions, the conservation of atoms principle and the conservation of mass principle hold together, as though they were a single law.

19-3 Nuclear chemistry

In 1919 Lord Rutherford performed and explained the first experiment in which *man* changed atoms of one kind of element into those of another. This was the beginning of our current nuclear era. The medieval alchemists had sought to turn base metals into precious ones, and some pretended to have done so, but they never really succeeded. We shall see in Section 19-5 that radioactivity is a *natural* process involving transmutation of one kind of atom, such as radium, into another, such as lead.

Rutherford had observed that radium and associated radioactive materials emitted various radiations among which were high-speed positively charged particles called *alpha particles*. He collected these in an evacuated vessel and proved by spectral analysis of the gas that accumulated that he was collecting *helium*. Thus the alpha particle is a helium nucleus, or a helium atom with its electrons stripped off. These particles served as the bullets in Rutherford's transmutation experiment in 1919. He observed that when alpha particles from a given source passed through air they usually traveled just so far and stopped, that is, they had a definite range in air. Sometimes, however, particles seemed to travel at least four times farther. These long-range particles were identified as protons, or hydrogen nuclei, by (1) the way in which they ionized air and so produced vapor tracks in cloud chambers*

---

* In cloud chambers we view the tracks of charged particles just as we do the vapor trails of fast airplanes and missiles in the sky. The particles ionize the air and the ions in turn serve as centers of moisture condensation. The water drops formed are large enough to be visible.

FIG. 19–1. Photograph of α-particle tracks in a cloud chamber filled with nitrogen gas.

(see Fig. 19–1), (2) their long range, and (3) the manner in which they could be deflected by magnetic fields. These protons did not appear when pure oxygen was substituted for air, and they appeared in greater numbers when pure nitrogen was used. In this systematic and scientific manner Rutherford found that when his alpha particles struck nitrogen nuclei some of the latter were transmuted into oxygen nuclei, while protons of high energy and long range were emitted. The reaction may be expressed as follows:

$$_2\text{He}^4 + {}_7\text{N}^{14} \rightarrow {}_8\text{O}^{17} + {}_1\text{H}^1 + Q. \tag{19–4}$$

This is the standard form for expressing nuclear reactions, so it will be explained in detail.

Note that each chemical symbol in Eq. (19–4) has both a subscript and a superscript. The subscript is the *atomic number Z* of the element, or its position number in the periodic table. Helium is the second element, nitrogen the seventh, oxygen the eighth, and the proton is the nucleus of hydrogen, element number one. Rutherford's work on the scattering of alpha particles by nuclei showed that the charge on a nucleus is Ze, where $e = 1.6 \times 10^{-19}$ coul, the magnitude of the electronic charge. Therefore, according to the conservation of charge principle, the subscripts should add up to the same value on each side of a nuclear equation. Thus $2 + 7 = 8 + 1$. Since the subscript and the chemical symbol both identify an element, the fact that element number eight must appear on the right-hand side in order to balance subscripts leads us to conclude that the nitrogen nucleus has been changed into one of oxygen.

TABLE 19–1

ABUNDANCE OF STABLE ISOTOPES OF THE TEN LIGHTEST ELEMENTS

Element	Isotope	Relative abundance
Hydrogen	H^1	99.985%
	H^2	0.015%
Helium	He^3	10^{-4}%
	He^4	~100%
Lithium	Li^6	7.5%
	Li^7	92.5%
Beryllium	Be^9	100%
Boron	B^{10}	18.7%
	B^{11}	81.3%
Carbon	C^{12}	98.9%
	C^{13}	1.1%
Nitrogen	N^{14}	99.6%
	N^{15}	0.4%
Oxygen	O^{16}	99.76%
	O^{17}	0.04%
	O^{18}	0.20%
Fluorine	F^{19}	100%
Neon	Ne^{20}	90.92%
	Ne^{21}	0.26%
	Ne^{22}	8.82%

The superscript is used to represent the *mass number A*, which is defined as the integer nearest the actual mass of the atom when the mass is expressed on the scale O^{16} equals exactly 16 atomic mass units ($O^{16} = 16$ amu).* For most of the chemical elements it has been found that atoms of two or more different mass numbers exist. Thus ordinary oxygen is a mixture of 99.76% O^{16}, 0.04% O^{17}, and 0.20% O^{18}. These three kinds of oxygen atoms are called the stable *isotopes* of oxygen. The stable isotopes of hydrogen are H^1 (99.985%) and H^2 (0.015%); the latter is called "heavy hydrogen" or *deuterium*. The stable isotopes of the ten lightest elements are listed in Table 19–1. The superscripts on each side of a nuclear equation must balance since otherwise the conservation of mass principle would be grossly violated. The fact that many types of nuclear transmutation have been performed since Rutherford's original experiment and that in every case the nuclear equation is one in which subscripts and superscripts balance may be taken as strong proof of the conservation of charge and mass principles.

Let us now look at the question of mass conservation more closely. Masses of isotopes have been measured very accurately by electromagnetic deflection experi-

---

* A slightly different scale that has recently found some favor takes C^{12} to have a mass of exactly 12 units ($C^{12} = 12$ u).

TABLE 19–2

SOME ISOTOPIC MASSES

Name	Symbol	Mass, amu
Neutron	N^1	1.00898
Hydrogen	H^1	1.00814
Deuterium	H^2	2.01474
Tritium	H^3	3.01700
Helium	He^4	4.00388
Lithium	Li^7	7.01822
Beryllium	Be^9	9.01504
Boron	B^{11}	11.01287
Carbon	C^{12}	12.00380
Nitrogen	N^{14}	14.00756
Oxygen	O^{16}	16.00000
Oxygen	O^{17}	17.00453
Uranium	U^{235}	235.1170

ments. Some typical values are listed in Table 19–2. We see that the masses are *not exactly* integers. If we add the masses for the isotopes on each side of Eq. (19–4), respectively, we find:

$$He^4 = 4.00388 \qquad O^{17} = 17.00453$$
$$N^{14} = 14.00756 \qquad H^1 = 1.00814$$
$$\text{Sum} = 18.01144 \qquad \text{Sum} = 18.01267$$

Thus the atomic masses on the two sides of the equation fail to balance by

$$18.01267 - 18.01144 = 0.00123 \text{ amu},$$

where amu stands for *atomic mass units*. While this gain in mass is small percentagewise, it is much greater than the possible errors involved in the determination of isotopic masses and so must be accepted as real. Its explanation is based on Einstein's principle of the equivalence of mass and energy, $E = mc^2$, of Section 16–11. In the reaction of Eq. (19–4) the K.E. (kinetic energy) of the alpha particle (He^4) exceeds that of the O^{17} and H^1 together, so that the reaction is endothermal and Q is negative. We shall see that the mass equivalence of Q turns out experimentally to be equal to minus the gain in mass calculated above. Hence if we count the mass equivalence of the Q term in Eq. (19–4), mass is exactly conserved. The conservation of mass principle is now to be regarded as identical with the conservation of energy principle, or, as we now say, the conservation of mass-energy principle.

EXAMPLE. Find the energy whose mass equivalence is 1 amu so that we may compute Q in Eq. (19–4).

Solution. Since an atomic mass unit and a chemical mass unit are very nearly the same (most oxygen atoms are of the O^{16} variety), we may say that 6×10^{26} atoms of O^{16} have a mass of 16 kg. The mass of one atom of O^{16}, which we call 16 amu, must also be $16 \text{ kg}/(6 \times 10^{26})$, so that

$$1 \text{ amu} = \frac{1 \text{ kg}}{6 \times 10^{26}} = 1.66 \times 10^{-27} \text{ kg}.$$

The energy E whose equivalent mass is 1.66×10^{-27} kg is

$$E = mc^2 = (1.66 \times 10^{-27} \text{ kg}) \times (3 \times 10^8 \text{ m/sec})^2$$
$$= 1.5 \times 10^{-10} \text{ j}.$$

It is customary to express atomic energies in terms of the small energy unit called the *electron-volt*, or *ev*, defined as the energy gained by an electron when accelerated through a potential difference of 1 volt. Thus

$$1 \text{ ev} = 1.6 \times 10^{-19} \text{ coul} \times 1 \text{ j/coul} = 1.6 \times 10^{-19} \text{ j},$$

and the energy equivalent to 1 amu is

$$E = \frac{1.5 \times 10^{-10} \text{ j}}{1.6 \times 10^{-19} \text{ j/ev}} = 930 \times 10^6 \text{ ev}$$
$$= 930 \text{ Mev},$$

where Mev stands for *million electron-volts*.

We now have for Q in Eq. (19–4)

$$Q = -0.00123 \text{ amu} \times 930 \text{ Mev/amu} = -1.14 \text{ Mev}.$$

When Rutherford used alpha particles with a K.E. of 7.7 Mev he found that the K.E. of the H^1 was 6.2 Mev and that of the O^{17} was 0.4 Mev, giving an experimental value for $Q = 6.6 - 7.7 = -1.1$ Mev, which agrees with the value computed according to the conservation of mass-energy principle. Since Q is negative, the initial K.E. must exceed 1.14 Mev if the reaction is to proceed; actually the alpha particle must have a much greater energy in order to penetrate into the positively charged nitrogen nucleus and trigger the reaction.

19–4 Particle conservation in artificial nuclear transmutations

We have seen that in nuclear reactions the conservation of mass is regarded as part of the conservation of energy principle rather than the conservation of matter principle. As for the latter it is evident that we must again modify our views. The theory of chemical reactions required us to substitute the conservation of atoms principle for the conservation of molecules principle. Now we see that in nuclear reactions not even atoms are conserved!   Charge, energy, and *mass number* are conserved; what does the latter represent?

Physicists currently postulate that all nuclei are composed of protons and neutrons.   While the proton is positively charged and the neutron is uncharged, these two particles have about the same mass, namely one that is approximately 1840 times that of the electron, or 1 amu.   These two particles are thus relatively "heavy" particles; they are also classified together as *nucleons*, or nuclear constituents.   Since only the protons contribute to the nuclear charge, each proton having a charge of $+e$, a nucleus of atomic number Z, with a charge of $+Ze$, must contain Z protons.   Each proton and neutron adds about 1 amu to the nuclear mass, hence a nucleus whose mass is close to A amu must contain A nucleons in all.   Hence,

$$Z = \text{number of protons in a nucleus,}$$

$$A - Z = \text{number of neutrons in a nucleus.}$$

We have seen that in a nuclear reaction such as that of Eq. (19–4) the subscripts add up to the same value on each side of the equation and so do the superscripts. In each term the subscript is Z and the superscript is A.   Hence we see that the current theory of nuclear structure postulates that in an artificial transmutation *the number of protons remains constant and the number of neutrons remains constant.* This is the third form in which we have stated the conservation of matter principle.

ILLUSTRATION 1.   *Discovery of the neutron.*   In 1932 James Chadwick, who had worked with Rutherford, discovered the neutron by bombarding beryllium with alpha particles.   This experiment had already been tried by M. and Mme. Curie-Joliot in France, who observed that beryllium bombarded with alpha particles yielded a penetrating radiation which, in turn, could knock protons out of matter containing hydrogen.   What was the nature of this penetrating radiation?   The first guess was that it was similar to the most penetrating x-rays, i.e., electromagnetic radiation of very high frequency.   Chadwick proceeded to show experimentally that this radiation did not interact with matter the way such radiation should. However, if he assumed that the new radiation consisted of a stream of neutral particles ("neutrons") with a mass near that of the proton, then all of his results could be explained.   For example, a head-on collision of a neutron with a proton of the same mass should result, according to Newton's laws, in the complete transfer of K.E. from neutron to proton, just as in the head-on collision of two billiard balls of equal mass.   The impact of a neutron with a nitrogen nucleus of fourteen times its mass should result in little transfer of K.E., just as when a pea strikes a tennis ball.   As predicted by the neutron hypothesis, Chadwick found that the penetrating radiation transferred much more energy to protons than to nitrogen nuclei; he computed the neutron's mass to be about 1 amu.

The alpha particle-beryllium reaction thus is the following:

$$_2\text{He}^4 + {}_4\text{Be}^9 \rightarrow {}_6\text{C}^{12} + {}_0\text{n}^1 + Q, \tag{19–5}$$

where n is the symbol for the neutron.   Here we see that the alpha particle adds

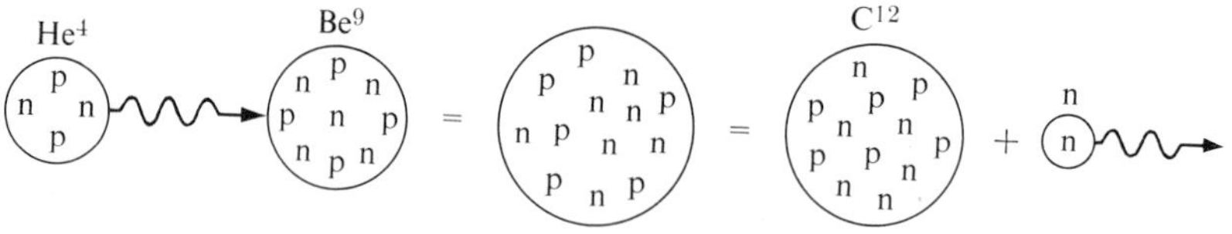

FIG. 19–2. Conservation of neutrons and protons in a nuclear transmutation.

2 protons and 2 neutrons to a Be nucleus that is composed of 4 protons and 5 neutrons (the only stable isotope of Be). The resulting compound nucleus of 6 protons and 7 neutrons is unstable and a neutron is ejected, leaving a C^{12} nucleus. Figure 19–2 shows the reaction pictorially.

ILLUSTRATION 2. *First transmutation with accelerated particles.* In the reaction

$$_1H^1 + {_3}Li^7 \rightarrow {_2}He^4 + {_2}He^4 + Q, \tag{19–6}$$

the product nuclei are both alpha particles. Since $Q = +17.2$ Mev, Sir John Cockroft of the Cavendish Laboratory in Cambridge, England, was able to obtain this reaction by accelerating protons to rather modest energies (about 0.3 Mev) and firing them at a lithium target; he and his colleague Walton showed that pairs of oppositely directed, high-energy alpha particles were produced, as shown in Fig. 19–3. In this reaction the constant number of protons is 4 and the constant number of neutrons is also 4. The combination of 2 protons plus 2 neutrons, i.e., the alpha particle, is evidently very stable.

19–5 Particle conservation in radioactive transformations

Radioactivity was first discovered in 1896 by Henri Becquerel. Here again is an example of how an experiment undertaken to explore one phenomenon may lead an alert and trained observer to the discovery of something quite new and different.

Becquerel was initially interested in the radiation emitted by certain substances after they have been exposed to light. We say that such substances are *phosphorescent*; after exposure to light they will glow in the dark. Becquerel wondered whether there was any connection between phosphorescent radiations and the x-rays that the German physicist Roentgen had discovered only a few weeks previously. By chance Becquerel left a phosphorescent uranium compound that he had *not yet* exposed to light next to a photographic plate that was wrapped in heavy black paper, and by chance he later developed the plate and found it blackened as though it had been greatly exposed to radiation of some kind. Becquerel was quick to trace the radiation to its source, namely the uranium compound.

The most active ingredient in uranium ore was painstakingly tracked down by Mme. Curie, who in 1898 isolated the element radium and showed that it was a much more intense source of radiation than uranium.

We now know that nuclei of uranium, radium, and other heavy elements may undergo spontaneous transmutation with the emission of three kinds of rays, α, β, and γ (alpha, beta, and gamma). We have seen that the α-particle is a helium

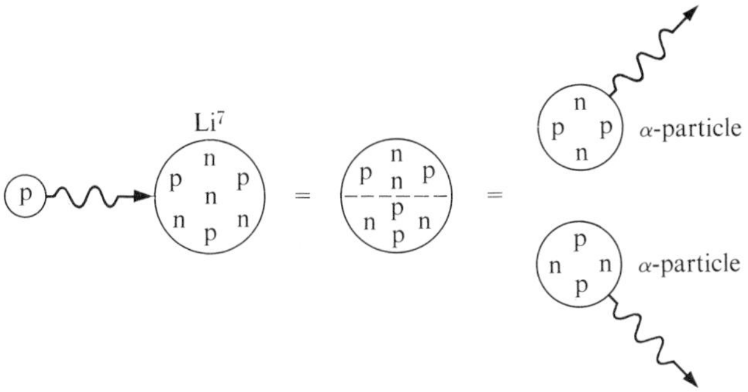

FIG. 19-3. Cockroft and Walton's disintegration of Li^7 into two α-particles.

nucleus, the β-particle is an electron, and γ-rays ("gamma rays") are very penetrating electromagnetic radiation. A γ-ray photon may possess an energy of several
Mev; this makes it destructive to living tissue and capable of inducing gene muta-
tions in cell chromosomes.*

Since 1934 it has been found possible to produce artificially radioactive isotopes
of the common lighter elements. This may be accomplished through various
nuclear transmutations, but the most effective methods are (1) to bombard an
element with neutrons or (2) to induce nuclei of a heavy element to *fission*, i.e., to
split in two. Typical reactions leading to a radioactive product are the following:

$$_{13}Al^{27} + {}_0n^1 \rightarrow {}_{13}Al^{28} + Q, \tag{19-7}$$

$$_7N^{14} + {}_0n^1 \rightarrow {}_6C^{14} + {}_1H^1 + Q, \tag{19-8}$$

$$_{92}U^{235} + {}_0n^1 \rightarrow {}_{38}Sr^{90} + {}_{54}Xe^{136} + 10\,{}_0n^1 + Q. \tag{19-9}$$

In (19-7), Al^{27}, the only stable isotope of aluminum, is changed into Al^{28}, which is
radioactive. In (19-8) radioactive C^{14} is formed. The stable isotopes of carbon
are C^{12} and C^{13}; C^{10}, C^{11}, and C^{14} are radioactive (semistable) and all other
possible carbon nuclei are completely unstable. Equation (19-9) represents the
fission process in which radioactive strontium and xenon are formed. There are
other possible ways in which U^{235} may fission (see Section 20-1), but (19-9) is a
fairly likely one. Since "A-bombs" explode through the fission process, and since
"H-bombs" employ A-bombs to build up the high temperature required to explode
an H-bomb, both types of bombs release radioactive "fallout" containing such
products as Sr^{90} and Xe^{136}.

An important property of radioactivity is that the rate of decay of a given
isotope is characteristic of that isotope and is unaffected by the physical environment (temperature, pressure, state, etc.) or by chemical combination. The decay

---

* While there is no threshold of intensity below which γ-rays are completely harmless,
the risk of danger from weak doses is small. Although a dose of 400 roentgens (4 j of
radiant energy absorbed per kg of body) in a short period of time is regarded as lethal,
the normal background radiation is only 0.1 or 0.2 roentgens per year.

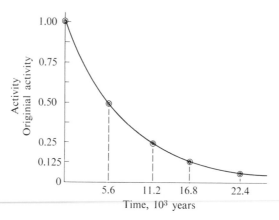

FIG. 19–4.   Radioactive decay of C^{14}.

of a pure sample of some radioactive isotope is exponential, which means that if half decays in 5600 years, as happens with C^{14}, then half of what is left after 5600 years will decay in another 5600 years, and so on. We say that C^{14} has a *half-life* of 5600 years. Its activity as a function of time is shown in Fig. 19–4 and the fraction remaining at various times is indicated in Table 19–3. The fact that the ratio of C^{14} to stable carbon is fairly constant in living matter, but in dead matter decays with the half-life of 5600 years, has made C^{14} a useful tool in dating archeological remains of matter that was once living.

Let us now examine the process, known as *beta decay*, by which nuclei such as C^{14} and C^{11} change into stable nuclei. For isotopes such as C^{14}, in which the number of neutrons is apparently too great for stability (remember that C^{12} and C^{13} are stable), decay occurs by a process in which a neutron near the edge of the nucleus is, in effect, changed into a proton plus an electron plus a neutrino; the proton remains in the nucleus and the electron is emitted as a β-ray, accompanied by the neutrino. The latter is a particle with no charge and no appreciable rest mass, but it carries away energy and momentum. The neutrino was proposed by

TABLE 19–3

DECAY OF C^{14}

Time, years	Fraction of C^{14} left
0	1
*3960	$\frac{3}{4}$
5600	$\frac{1}{2}$
11,200	$\frac{1}{4}$
16,800	$\frac{1}{8}$
22,400	$\frac{1}{16}$

* $3960 = 5600/\sqrt{2}$. Why?

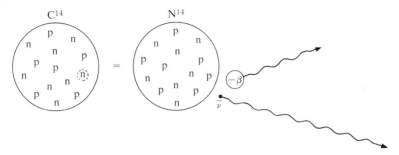

FIG. 19-5. In β-decay of a heavy isotope a neutron is changed into a proton plus an electron plus a (anti) neutrino.

Enrico Fermi (1901–1954), the great Italian-American physicist who first made a nuclear chain reaction work. Recall that in Chapter 9 we saw that new forms of energy have been postulated whenever new discoveries seem at first to suggest a violation of the conservation of energy principle. Thus in β-decay one finds an apparent loss of energy in the usual forms, so we say that the neutrino carries away the unaccounted-for energy The neutrino and its energy can rarely be recaptured, since the neutrino is chargeless (not subject to electromagnetic forces), massless (not subject to gravitational or inertial reactions), and not a photon of electromagnetic radiation. Fermi worked out a self-consistent theory which has "grown gracefully"; the neutrino's existence is now firmly supported by direct as well as by indirect evidence.

Letting $_{-1}\beta^0$ represent the electron and $_0\bar{\nu}^0$ the neutrino, we have for the decay of C^{14}

$$_6C^{14} \rightarrow {}_7N^{14} + {}_{-1}\beta^0 + {}_0\bar{\nu}^0 + Q, \tag{19–10}$$

where the product nucleus, N^{14}, is the common stable isotope of nitrogen. Note that the mass number of the electron is zero, since its actual mass is only 0.00055 amu, for which the nearest integer is zero. The conservation of subscripts and of superscripts holds in Eq. (19–10), but the pictorial representation of the transmutation shown in Fig. 19–5 makes it obvious that neither the number of protons nor the number of neutrons remains constant. There are 6 protons and 8 neutrons at the start, and there are 7 protons and 7 neutrons at the end. Hence we must once again modify our conservation of matter principle and state that *in β-decay the number of nucleons, or protons plus neutrons, remains constant.*

The C^{11} nucleus is unstable, presumably because it contains too *few* neutrons. It undergoes a decay process in which a proton is changed into a neutron, a positron, and a neutrino. The *positron* is the positive counterpart of the ordinary negative electron. Both particles have the same mass. The positron was first discovered in the cosmic radiation in 1932. It is a rare particle, whereas the electron is a constitutent of all matter. We may represent the positron by the symbol $_{+1}\beta^0$. The decay of C^{11} is then given by the equation

$$_6C^{11} \rightarrow {}_5B^{11} + {}_{+1}\beta^0 + {}_0\nu^0 + Q, \tag{19–11}$$

where $_0\nu^0$ is the neutrino. (The difference between $\bar{\nu}$ and ν will be explained shortly.) The boron isotope B^{11} is stable.

In β-decay charge is conserved and (with the postulate of the neutrino) mass-energy is conserved, but the conservation of matter seems to apply only with respect to the number of heavy particles, or nucleons. Electrons, positrons, and neutrinos appear to be created. We investigate this further in the next section.

19–6 Pair annihilation and pair production

In the example at the end of Section 16–11, reference was made to the fact that when a positron meets an electron the two particles annihilate one another. Their charges of course neutralize each other ($+e - e = 0$) and so in a sense does their matter. The combined mass of the two particles is 18.2×10^{-31} kg, or 0.0011 amu, and the equivalent energy is

$$0.0011 \text{ amu} \times 930 \text{ Mev/amu} = 1.02 \text{ Mev}.$$

It has been observed that when positrons from a source such as C^{11} are absorbed by matter, pairs of γ-ray photons, each bearing the energy 0.51 Mev, are emitted in opposite directions. This is strong evidence for postulating that the reaction is that shown in Fig. 19–6, namely

$$_{-1}\beta^0 + {}_{+1}\beta^0 \rightarrow 2 \text{ γ-ray photons,} \tag{19–12}$$

and that in this process the conservation of mass-energy as well as of charge hold true. However, electrons, positrons, and photons are not individually conserved.

The reverse process, pair production, may occur when a γ-ray photon bearing an energy in excess of 1.02 Mev encounters matter. The mass associated with the photon materializes as that of the created electron and positron. The conservation of momentum principle (a corollary of Newton's laws) requires that pair production occur in the presence of some particle of matter that may absorb momentum (see Fig. 19–7).

It was predicted that just as the positron is the positively charged counterpart of the electron, there should be the negative counterpart of the positive proton.

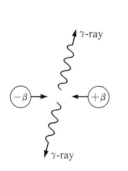

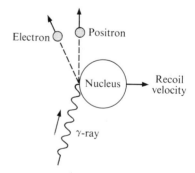

FIG. 19–6.   Annihilation of electron and positron.

FIG. 19–7.   Pair production occurs only in the presence of matter.

This predicted particle, called the *antiproton*, should be capable of annihilating a proton and it should make its appearance, along with a proton, through a process of pair production. Since the process

$$Q \text{ (energy)} \rightarrow \text{proton} + \text{antiproton} \tag{19-13}$$

involves the materialization of about 2 amu (3.3×10^{-27} kg) of mass, Q must exceed 1860 Mev = 1.86×10^9 ev. This high energy of around 2 Bev (billion electron-volts) has been given to particles in the largest atomic accelerators, and antiprotons have been created by such machines since 1955.

Pair production of heavy particles results in altering the total number of protons plus neutrons in our world. Once again we must modify our conservation of matter principle! This time we shall see that it may be "saved" by introducing the new concept of *antimatter*. The "anti-P particle" is defined as that particle which (1) can annihilate a "P-particle" and (2) is created in pair production along with a "P-particle." Thus the positron is the electron's antiparticle, the antiproton is the proton's, and so on. The $\bar{\nu}$ of Eq. (19-10) is the antiparticle of the ν in Eq. (19-11); $\bar{\nu}$ is often called the *antineutrino*, but ν and $\bar{\nu}$ are alike in charge (they are both uncharged). The neutrino that appears in the β-decay of a heavy isotope like C^{14} is always the antineutrino, whereas the neutrino that appears in the β-decay of a light isotope such as C^{11} is the neutrino.

Let us start to count the particles in a closed system and as we do so let us count "plus one" for every proton, electron, and neutrino and "minus one" for every antiproton, positron, and antineutrino. This is the sort of thing we would do when counting up positive and negative charges to find the total net charge in a region. When we count an antiparticle as minus a particle we do not mean that it is negative with respect to charge or mass; we only imply that it is negative in our counting system. If we apply this system of counting to pair production and annihilation, then we may state that in pair annihilation and pair production, as well as in radio-activity and other processes, *the net number of particles in our world remains constant*, provided that photons are not counted as particles. This is still another modification of the conservation of matter principle.

EXAMPLE 1. Consider the process of pair production, as given by Eq. (19-13). The system starts with a particle count of zero and ends with a count of $1 - 1 = 0$.

EXAMPLE 2. In pair annihilation, Eq. (19-12), the system starts with a particle count of $1 - 1 = 0$ and, since we do not count γ-ray photons, the count at the end is zero.

EXAMPLE 3. In the β-decay of C^{11}, Eq. (19-11), the system starts with a count of 11 and ends with one of $11 - 1 + 1 = 11$. Here the positron counts -1 and neutrino $+1$.

Example 4. In the β-decay of C^{14}, Eq. (19-10), the count remains at 14 because the electron counts $+1$ and the antineutrino -1.

EXAMPLE 5. In artificial transmutation processes antiparticles are not involved; hence the number of ordinary particles is conserved.

19-7 Conservation of elementary particles. Fundamental Law XIV

The reader may have read from time to time about the various new particles of matter that physicists have been discovering. For example, an article in a New York newspaper dated September 1, 1961 described the discovery of the *omega meson* at the Lawrence Radiation Laboratory of the University of California. Mention has been made in this chapter of the discovery of the neutron, the positron, the antiproton, the neutrino, and the antineutrino, while earlier in the book the electron and proton were introduced. These are all called *elementary particles* to indicate that they are not, as far as we now know, compounded out of more fundamental particles. This may eventually prove to be a poor assumption; remember that the atom was once regarded as indivisable and now we postulate a very complex structure for an atom of a heavy element! Be that as it may, we find that at present physicists have classified the various elementary particles as follows.

(a) *Photons*. Photons, or light quanta, are the bundles of energy in which electromagnetic waves are emitted and absorbed. A photon travels with the speed of light and it ceases to exist when stopped. It has mass associated with its energy, but no rest mass. Its energy is related to the frequency f of the waves through the postulate of Planck, $E = hf$. We have seen that the photon is not counted as a particle of matter.

(b) *Leptons*. These light-weight particles include the following:

$$\left. \begin{matrix} \nu \\ \bar{\nu} \end{matrix} \right\} \text{neutrinos*} \qquad\qquad \text{mass} \sim 0,$$

$$\left. \begin{matrix} e^- = -\beta = \text{electron} \\ e^+ = +\beta = \text{positron} \end{matrix} \right\} \quad \text{mass} = m_0 = 9.1 \times 10^{-31} \text{ kg},$$

$$\left. \begin{matrix} \mu^- \\ \mu^+ \end{matrix} \right\} \text{muons} \qquad\qquad \text{mass} = 207\, m_0.$$

The muons form a particle-antiparticle pair.

(c) *Mesons*. These intermediate-weight particles include

$$\left. \begin{matrix} \pi^- \\ \pi^+ \\ \pi^0 \end{matrix} \right\} \text{pions} \qquad\qquad \text{mass} \sim 270\, m_0,$$

$$K\text{-particles, or heavy mesons} \qquad \text{mass} \sim 1000\, m_0.$$

The name *meson* refers to the fact that a meson particle has a mass whose value lies *between* that of a lepton and that of the proton or neutron.

(d) *Baryons*. These heavy particles include

$$\left. \begin{matrix} p^+ = \text{proton} \\ p^- = \text{antiproton} \\ n \;\; = \text{neutron} \\ \bar{n} \;\; = \text{antineutron} \end{matrix} \right\} \quad \text{mass} \sim 1840\, m_0,$$

$$\text{hyperons} \qquad\qquad \text{mass} \sim 2200\, m_0 \text{ to } 2600\, m_0.$$

---

* Recent evidence indicates that there may be more than one kind of ν and $\bar{\nu}$.

An important characteristic of all the above particles, except the photon, the neutrinos, the electron and positron, and the proton and antiproton, is their *instability*. Mesons and hyperons decay with very short half-lives into lighter particles. Even the neutron decays with a half-life of 12.5 minutes when it is free, although within a nucleus it appears to be stable. The various modes of decay are most complex and not yet completely understood, but we shall study a few in order to see in what manner the conservation of matter principle must be stated for elementary particle transformations.

The muons decay as follows:

$$\mu^- \rightarrow e^- + \bar{\nu} + \nu + Q,$$
$$\mu^+ \rightarrow e^+ + \nu + \bar{\nu} + Q. \tag{19-14}$$

To ensure particle conservation in these two processes we count "minus one" for the μ^+ as well as for the e^+, and "plus one" for the μ^- and the e^-. In other words, the negative muon, the electron, and the proton are all particles of the same kind of matter, the kind that predominates in our own world. The μ^+ and e^+ are both particles of antimatter.

The pions decay as follows:

$$\pi^- \rightarrow \mu^- + \bar{\nu} + Q,$$
$$\pi^+ \rightarrow \mu^+ + \nu + Q, \tag{19-15}$$
$$\pi^0 \rightarrow \gamma + \gamma + Q.$$

[Here the ν and $\bar{\nu}$ react differently with matter than do the ν and $\bar{\nu}$ in Eqs. (19-14).] We have ruled that the μ^+ and $\bar{\nu}$ are particles of antimatter and the μ^- and ν are particles of matter. The γ-ray photon is not counted. Then the count for the right-hand side of each of these equations is 0. In order to maintain the particle count constant we must say that *we will not count the pion!* The decay of K-mesons indicates that they must not be counted either. Hence we see that *the conservation of particles does not apply to mesons or photons.*

The decay of the neutron is given by

$$_0n^1 \rightarrow {}_1p^1 + {}_{-1}e^0 + \bar{\nu} + Q, \tag{19-16}$$

where $_1p^1$ stands for the proton and $_{-1}e^0$ for the electron. Here the particle count remains constant and equal to 1.

The subject of hyperon transformations is a most complex one. The following is a typical decay process:

$$\text{hyperon} \rightarrow \text{proton} + \text{pion}. \tag{19-17}$$

Here again we must apply the rule above, namely not to count pions.

The present status of the conservation of the number of particles in our world may be summarized as follows.

The number of heavy particles (baryons) remains constant and the number of light particles (leptons) also remains constant in any transformation process.

Here we have the latest version of the *conservation of matter principle*, our *Fundamental Law XIV*. The evolution of this principle is a good illustration of the way in which physicists modify their views, introduce new concepts such as that of antimatter and the neutrino, and yet hold firm to a basic postulate that has stood them in good stead through the years. One also tends to acquire an intuitive belief in what seems to be a general rule; why abandon this belief because of an apparent exception in some esoteric field, especially when modification of the principle is the most fruitful procedure?

PROBLEMS

1. Ten grams of salt are dissolved in 100 grams of water in an open bowl. The next day the mass of the solution is found to be 95 grams. Explain, stating any postulate assumed.

2. How many kilograms of oxygen are chemically bound up in 10 kg of quartz sand (SiO_2)? (The atomic weight of silicon is 28.)

3. If 100 grams of Fe (iron, atomic weight $= 55.85$) are oxidized into Fe_2O_3, what will the change in mass be?

4. Compute the energy in electron-volts released when one carbon atom is oxidized as in Eq. (19–3). How much is this energy per nucleon of carbon? Per nucleon of CO_2?

5. Complete the following equations and identify the missing term by name.

(a) $Li^6 + n^1 \rightarrow H^3 + ?$
(b) $H^2 \rightarrow H^1 + ?$
(c) $Li^6 + H^2 \rightarrow Li^7 + ?$
(d) $H^2 + H^2 \rightarrow H^3 + ?$
(e) $H^2 + H^2 \rightarrow He^3 + ?$
(f) $H^2 + H^3 \rightarrow He^4 + ?$

6. Compute Q for the process

$$He^4 \rightarrow 2H^1 + 2n^0 + Q,$$

using Table 19–2. Why is $-Q$ called the "binding energy"? What is this binding energy per nucleon of He^4?

7. Compute the binding energy per nucleon for (a) C^{12}, (b) O^{16}.

8. Compute Q for process (f) of problem 5.

9. Compute the Q in Eq. (19–6) from the masses given in Table 19–2 and compare your value with the measured value.

10. Compute the energy released when a free neutron decays.

11. The stable isotopes of nitrogen are N^{14} and N^{15}. Write the equations for the decay of N^{13}, N^{16}, and N^{17}.

12. The half-life of I^{131} is 8 days. In what time will the activity decrease to (a) 25%, (b) about 1%, (c) about 0.1% of its initial value?

13. If a radioactive sample loses 20% of its activity in 10 hours, what percent will it lose in (a) 20 hours, (b) 40 hours?

14. Is the π^+ a particle of matter, or one of antimatter? Explain.

15. (a) If a neutral hyperon decays into a proton and a pion, should the neutral hyperon be regarded as a particle of matter, or as a particle of antimatter? (b) If the pion decays into a muon and the muon into an electron, list all of the final particles obtained from the decay of the neutral hyperon. (c) If these final particles are counted according to the rules given, what is the net particle count?

REFERENCES

GAMOW, GEORGE, *Mr. Tompkins Explores the Atom*, Cambridge Univ. Press, 1958.
—,*The Atom and Its Nucleus*, Prentice-Hall, 1961.

EXPERIMENT 25

STATISTICAL FLUCTUATIONS IN THE BACKGROUND RADIATION

Object: To observe and measure the background radiation, a quantity that does not have a constant value, but varies in a random manner.

Problem: In some experiments we measure quantities that are believed to have a definite value, such as G, c, e/m for electrons, etc. For such quantities repeated experiments lead to what we call their "accepted values." If our measurement of G differs from the accepted value, we can justify our "error" by saying that the method used was not sufficiently sensitive nor the instruments sufficiently accurate.

Suppose, however, that one tosses a coin 10 times and counts the number of times heads are observed. The observations can certainly be made accurately, but you may get 6 heads, another student 5, another 4, etc. Is 5 the "accepted" value? If you got 6, was your result in error? The new element in this sort of experiment is the presence of random fluctuations that can only be handled statistically. The theory of probability enables us to compute the chances of getting 10, 9, 8, . . . , 0 heads when a coin is tossed 10 times, but in 100 such trials even these computed chances may not be borne out experimentally. Evidently nothing is certain in this sort of experiment! There are fluctuations about the most probable value (5), and fluctuations in the fluctuations.

There are such random fluctuations in the cosmic and other background radiation reaching us. A Geiger counter recording this radiation may register 0, 1, 2, 3, . . . counts in a given time interval. It is interesting to observe the counts for many successive 10-second intervals and to see how many times the count is 0, 1, 2, 3, . . . , respectively. The results may then be compared with those predicted statistically.

Procedure:

Step 1. Find the cosmic ray counts in successive 10-second intervals for 20 or 30 minutes. The best procedure is for one man to watch the clock and call out "Read" at the end of each 10 seconds. Another man reads the glow tubes, and a third records data, etc.

Step 2. After the data has been taken, subtract each reading from the following one. Next prepare a chart with headings "0, 1, 2, 3, ..." Now if during the first 10 seconds you got 6 counts, put a mark under "6" on your chart. Continue for all the 10-second intervals in your data.

Step 3. Count the number of times (N) you got 0, 1, 2, 3, . . . counts, and plot these numbers (N), versus the respective count numbers (n), that is, against 0, 1, 2, 3, ... Connect your points on the graph with a smooth curve. What count number n occurred most often?

Step 4. Compute the average number of counts per 10 seconds. How does this number compare with the most probable count number?

Step 5. If we let $\bar{n}$ equal the average number of counts per interval and $A =$ the total number of intervals during the 20 or 30 minutes of the run, then probability theory tells us that the most likely distribution is the one for which

$$N = \frac{A}{e^{\bar{n}}} \cdot \frac{(\bar{n})^n}{n!}. \tag{1}$$

Here $n!$ means $1 \cdot 2 \cdot 3 \cdot 4 \cdot 5 \cdots n$ and e is the base of natural logarithms (2.718). Those mathematically inclined may use Eq. (1) to compute N for $n = 0, 1, 2, 3 \ldots$; they may then compare their experimental values of N with those values which statistical theory says are most likely to be observed. Does the difference seem reasonable? Under what circumstances would you expect better agreement?

EXPERIMENT 26

EXPONENTIAL DECAY
(Relaxation Phenomena)

Object: To study the physical conditions leading to exponential decay and the mathematical properties of a decay curve.

Problem: As physical systems approach a final state of equilibrium they "relax," as it were. Let some parameter (variable) y represent the departure of a system from equilibrium at the time t; the rate at which y is decreasing at that instant is $-\Delta y/\Delta t$, where Δy represents the *increase* in y during the change Δt in t. Now it is a matter of experimental observation that in many relaxation phenomena the final state is approached more and more slowly the nearer the system gets to this state and that the quantitative relationship is

$$-\frac{\Delta y}{\Delta t} = ky, \tag{1}$$

where k is independent of t and y and is called the *decay constant*. Under these circumstances the decay is always exponential, that is, it is given by the relationship

$$y = y_0 e^{-kt}, \tag{2}$$

in which y_0 is the original value of y (for which $t = 0$). If y is plotted against t, the curve will resemble that in Fig. 19–4.

Let us see what distinguishes the exponential curve represented by Eq. (2) from other curves and what part k plays in determining the steepness of the curve, or how rapidly the system relaxes.

We define the *half-life* of the decay as a time $t = T$ for which $y = y_0/2$, or

$$\frac{y_0}{2} = y_0 e^{-kT}.$$

This leads to $e^{kT} = 2$, $T = (\ln 2)/k = 0.693/k$. The half-life is inversely proportional to k.

Note that when $y = y_0/4$, $t = (\ln 4)/k = (2 \ln 2)/k = 2T$, and when $y = y_0/8$, $t = 3T$, etc. So y goes on being halved for every additional half-life increase in the time. In general we may say that equal increases in time result in the same *fractional* change in y. The converse is also true. This provides us with one way of testing to see if a curve is exponential; if it meets this test it is, otherwise not.

In Eq. (2) let $t = 1/k$. Then $y = y_0/e$, or $1/k$ is the time it takes y to decay to one eth of its initial value; this is the same as $y_0/2.718$ or 37% of y_0. When $t = 1/k$ the system has progressed 63% of the way to the final state.

Suppose that we plot ln y against t; what sort of a curve will we obtain? Your answer to this question should suggest another sensitive test of whether or not y depends exponentially on t. What is this test?

Procedure: There are many experimental examples of exponential decay; the choice must depend on the equipment available. It is recommended that you choose one of the following experiments and for it plot the decay curve, find the half-life and value of k, and apply the exponential tests.

Experiment 1. Measure with a Geiger counter the initial activity y_0 of a sample of radioactive iodine-131. Remeasure the activity at 1-day intervals for 2 or 3 weeks.

Experiment 2. Charge a 0.5-microfarad *mica* capacitor from a low-voltage battery. Disconnect battery and discharge the capacitor through a galvanometer, measuring the deflection (y_0). Connect a very high (say 150 million ohms) leakage resistance across the capacitor, recharge, disconnect the battery, and wait t seconds before discharging. The deflection (y) after waiting t seconds will be less than y_0 because charge leaks through the high resistance at a rate proportional to the charge left. Find y for various values of t, plot a graph, etc.

Experiment 3. Heat a thimble of water to about 50°C and place it in a large bath of water at room temperature. Here y is the temperature difference between the warm water and the bath. Measure y at 1-minute intervals, starting with $y_0 = 20$°C and continuing until $y = 5$°C or less. Exponential decay would mean that the rate of cooling of a warm body is proportional to the difference in temperature between the body and its surroundings. Newton first propounded this as an empirical law; see how closely you agree with Newton.

Experiment 4. Observe the absorption of beta rays by successive layers of cardboard. Here the thickness of absorbing material plays the role of t.

Experiment 5. Observe the decreasing amplitude of an underdamped oscillating system, say a galvanometer coil.

CHAPTER 20

Nuclear Forces and the Search for Additional Principles

Near the close of the 19th century it was felt by a number of physicists that all of the fundamental laws of nature had been discovered and that further work would consist mainly of measuring some quantity to another decimal place. The course of events turned out to be quite different from this prediction. The decade 1895–1905 saw the discovery of x-rays, radioactivity, the electron, the quantum principle, and the relativity principle. This was indeed a fruitful period and the explanation is that in this decade physicists first began to explore a new realm of the physical world, namely inside the atom. When research is carried on in completely new areas the chances of discovering new fundamental principles are greatly improved.

At the present time the frontiers of investigation in physics have been pushed far out beyond the realm of our everyday life. Current fundamental research generally requires increasingly advanced training on the part of the physicist and more sophisticated and expensive equipment with which to work. The trend is toward extremes, such as investigation at very low or very high temperatures, in the very small realm of the atomic nucleus or the huge one we call the universe.

There is a feeling (which could be wrong) that experiments at very low temperatures will probably not reveal any new fundamental principles. Discoveries in solid state research also seem likely to be mostly of technological value. High temperatures, such as ten million degrees or more, involve high energies, and with particles of high energy one may explore the atomic nucleus. Nuclear physics in turn is closely related to the elementary particles and the interactions between these particles. Here in nuclear-particle physics we feel sure that principles are involved that are not yet completely understood, such as (1) the law(s) of nuclear forces and (2) the principle that explains why elementary particles of certain masses, and not other masses, have been discovered in nature.

Considerable thought of a philosophical nature is also being given to the behavior of our physical world and here some further fundamental principles have been formulated. We shall touch upon these after first reviewing our current knowledge of nuclear forces.

20–1 Nuclear energy

We saw in the last chapter that when nuclear particles are rearranged the energy change is usually great enough to involve a measurable change in mass. This amounts to saying that nuclear energy changes are much greater than those re-

370

sulting from the rearrangement of atoms and their orbital electrons in chemical transformations. Let us compare the energy released per kilogram and per nucleon in a typical chemical combustion process with that emitted per kilogram and per nucleon in the nuclear processes of fission and fusion.

(a) *Combustion.* The burning of wood and coal chiefly involves the process

$$C + O_2 \rightarrow CO_2 + Q, \tag{20-1}$$

where $Q = 4 \times 10^8$ j/kg-mole of C, O_2, and CO_2. The atomic weight of C is 12 and that of O is 16. Thus from 12 kg of C and 32 kg of O_2 we get 4×10^8 j of energy. This amounts to 3.3×10^7 j/kg of C. We may regard the carbon as the fuel which must be purchased; the oxygen is ordinarily freely available in our atmosphere.

While it is more convenient in atomic physics to use the electron-volt as the unit of energy rather than the much larger joule, we find that in engineering a still bigger unit called the *kilowatt-hour* is preferred. By definition

$$\begin{aligned}
1 \text{ kilowatt-hour} = 1 \text{ KWH} &= 1000 \text{ watt-hr} \\
&= 1000 \times 3600 \text{ watt-sec} \\
&= 3.6 \times 10^6 \text{ j.}
\end{aligned}$$

Thus the energy released in the burning of 1 kg of carbon amounts to

$$\begin{aligned}
\frac{Q}{\text{mass of C}} &= \frac{4 \times 10^8 \text{ j}}{12 \text{ kg}} \\
&= \frac{10^8 \text{ j}}{3 \text{ kg} \times 3.6 \times 10^6 \text{ j/KWH}} \\
&\doteq 10 \text{ KWH/kg of C.}
\end{aligned}$$

One atom of C contains 12 nucleons, and there are 6×10^{26} atoms in 12 kg of C. Thus the energy Q is released by an amount of matter that contains 72×10^{26} nucleons. Hence

$$\begin{aligned}
\frac{Q}{\text{No. of nucleons}} &= \frac{4 \times 10^8 \text{ j}}{72 \times 10^{26} \text{ nucleons} \times 1.6 \times 10^{-19} \text{ j/ev}} \\
&= 0.35 \text{ ev/nucleon.}
\end{aligned}$$

(b) *Fission.* The fission process was mentioned briefly in Section 19–5. It derives its name from the fact that it involves the *splitting in two* of a heavy nucleus (see Fig. 20–1) rather than the transformation of a nucleus into another one of about the same mass.

The story of the discovery of fission is another of the great dramas in the history of physics. As early as 1934 Enrico Fermi had conducted experiments in which various nuclei were bombarded with neutrons and radioactive products resulted. In the case of the bombardment of uranium, Fermi thought that he had produced

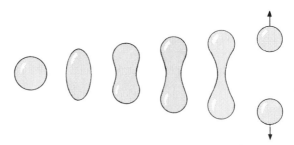

FIG. 20-1.   Schematic representation of the fission of a heavy nucleus.

transuranic (beyond uranium) elements. We now know that this was partly true, but what Fermi did not realize was that he had also caused the fission of some uranium nuclei.

Two German physical chemists, Otto Hahn and F. Strassmann, published on January 6, 1939, a paper in which they described the puzzling results of their work on the chemical identification of the products formed when uranium was bombarded with neutrons. They wrote that the evidence pointed to the formation of nuclei much lighter than uranium, but this seemed incredible to them in view of the fact that all previous experiments in nuclear transmutation had involved only a change of 1 or 2 in the atomic number of the affected nucleus. However, Lise Meitner, a former colleague of Hahn, and Otto Frisch did believe in the fission interpretation of Hahn's and Strassmann's results and they so informed Neils Bohr, who, in turn, announced their conclusions at a meeting of the American Physical Society in Washington, D.C., on January 26, 1939. Almost overnight American physicists undertook, in different laboratories, confirmatory experiments.

The importance of the discovery lies in the fact that the fission of a uranium nucleus requires an impinging neutron, while as a result of the fission one obtains not only the two product nuclei plus a relatively large release of energy, but *several neutrons* as well. It was easy to see that if one neutron could produce two, two might produce four, four produce eight, and so on (Fig. 20-2). This would be a *chain reaction*, making possible the release of nuclear energy on a large scale. The atomic bomb and the many nuclear power plants on land and in submarines testify to man's success in overcoming the various technical problems that had to be surmounted. Thus January 1939 marks the beginning of the age of nuclear energy on our earth.

In the typical fission reaction

$$U^{235} + n^1 \rightarrow Ba^{141} + Kr^{92} + 3n^1 + Q; \qquad (20\text{-}2)$$

Q may be calculated from our knowledge of nuclear masses and the principle of the conservation of mass-energy. It is found that Q is about 210 Mev/U nucleus. Since 930 Mev are equivalent to 1 amu (see Example in Section 19-3), we see that here Q is equivalent to $\frac{210}{930}$ amu $= 0.225$ amu, which is about 0.1% of the mass (235 amu) of the U nucleus. Hence the fission of 1 kg of U is accompanied by the release of energy equivalent to, or associated with, 0.1% $\times$ 1 kg $= 10^{-3}$ kg of

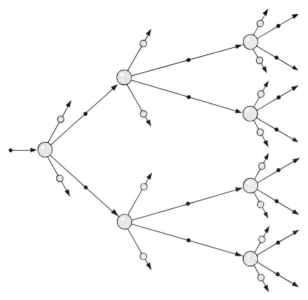

FIG. 20–2.   Simplified sketch of a chain reaction in U^{235}.

mass.   From Einstein's relation $E = mc^2$, we have

$$\frac{Q}{\text{mass of U}} = (10^{-3} \text{ kg/kg}) \times (3 \times 10^8 \text{ m/sec})^2 = 9 \times 10^{13} \text{ j/kg}$$

$$= \frac{9 \times 10^{13} \text{ j}}{1 \text{ kg} \times 3.6 \times 10^6 \text{ j/KWH}}$$

$$= 25 \times 10^6 \text{ KWH/kg}.$$

This number is two and one-half million times greater than in the case of the combustion of carbon!

A U^{235} nucleus contains 235 nucleons, so that

$$\frac{Q}{\text{No. of nucleons}} = \frac{210 \text{ Mev}}{235 \text{ nucleons}} = 0.9 \text{ Mev/nucleon}.$$

It is this great concentration of energy in fission fuel that gives such a fuel its great importance.   A nuclear reactor utilizes the fission process in a controlled manner and an A-bomb uses it in an explosive, uncontrolled reaction.

(c) *Fusion.*   The direct combination of two hydrogen atoms and two neutrons should give a helium atom and a Q of 28 Mev (see problem 6 of Chapter 19). This process of *combining* lighter particles to form a heavier nucleus is called *fusion.*   Actually it is not practical to try to get four particles to collide simultaneously, but in the following fusion process only two particles need collide:

$$H^2 + H^3 \rightarrow He^4 + n^1 + Q, \tag{20–3}$$

where Q is about 17 Mev/He nucleus. Here the H^2 is the nucleus of the heavy hydrogen atom found in a concentration of 0.015% in all of our water. The H^3 may be obtained from the process represented by

$$H^2 + H^2 \rightarrow H^3 + H^1. \qquad (20\text{-}4)$$

The H^3 is radioactive, but as its half-life is 12 years it is feasible to stockpile it.

Since 17 Mev are equivalent to $\frac{17}{930}$ amu $= 0.018$ amu, which is 0.36% of the mass (5 amu) of the combining nuclei, we may say that here the energy released per kg is that equivalent to, or associated with, 0.0036 kg. Thus from $E = mc^2$ we have

$$\frac{Q}{\text{mass of H}} = (0.0036 \text{ kg/kg}) \times (3 \times 10^8 \text{ m/sec})^2$$

$$= \frac{3.24 \times 10^{14} \text{ j}}{1 \text{ kg} \times 3.6 \times 10^6 \text{ j/KWH}}$$

$$= 90 \times 10^6 \text{ KWH/kg}.$$

This represents over three times the concentration of energy in fission fuel.

Since H^2 and H^3 together contain 5 nucleons, we have

$$\frac{Q}{\text{No. of nucleons}} = \frac{17 \text{ Mev}}{5 \text{ nucleons}}$$

$$= 3.4 \text{ Mev/nucleon}.$$

The reaction in Eq. (20–3) will take place only if the colliding nuclei have high initial speeds; otherwise they will not, as it were, stick together. As two nuclei approach each other the Coulomb force of repulsion between their like (positive) charges predominates until they are sufficiently close for nuclear attractive forces (see the following section) to take control. To ensure collisions at high speeds one must heat the hydrogen sufficiently so that a significant fraction of the particles have, according to the kinetic theory, the kinetic energies associated with the required speeds. Since it turns out that the fusion reaction will only take place at temperatures of many millions of degrees, it is termed a *thermonuclear reaction*. In the H-bomb the required temperature is acquired through the explosion of an A-bomb and then the fusion process is utilized in an uncontrolled manner. The controlled use of the fusion process would make it possible to utilize sea water as a source of energy, a source available in abundance to every nation. The great experimental problem of today is to find how to build a practical device in which the fusion process is made to proceed in a controlled manner. One attempt to solve this problem is being carried on at Princeton University's Forrestal Laboratory, where the device is called a *stellerator* because the fusion process is believed to be the one through which the stars (and our sun) release their energy. It is interesting to note that the design of the stellerator has required the application of nearly every one of the fundamental principles discussed in the previous chapters.

20–2 Nuclear forces

We have seen that in nuclear processes the energy released is around ten million (10^7) times greater than in chemical processes. The release of energy by an atomic system implies that forces in the atom must have done work equivalent to the energy given out. Work equals force times distance. Nuclear distances are of the order of 10^{-15} m, while atomic diameters are 10^5 times greater. For a nuclear force F_n to do, in the distance $s_n = 10^{-15}$ m, an amount of work equal to 10^7 times that done by an electromagnetic force F_e in the distance $s_e = 10^{-10}$ m, we must have

$$F_n \times 10^{-15} = 10^7 \times F_e \times 10^{-10}, \qquad F_n = 10^{12} \times F_e = 100\,(10^{10}\,F_e).$$

We must remember that electromagnetic forces vary inversely as the square of the distance between interacting charges. Therefore at a separation of 10^{-15} m the Coulomb force between two charges would be 10^{10} times what it is for a separation of 10^{-10} m, that is, $10^{10}\,F_e$. Thus for a separation of 10^{-15} m the nuclear force between two nucleons must be nearly 100 times the electrostatic Coulomb force.

More information about nuclear forces has been obtained from scattering experiments in which a beam of protons or neutrons is scattered by protons (H^1 nuclei) or by protons and neutrons (nuclei of H^2 or other elements). The stability of the deuteron, which is a proton-neutron combination, and the binding energies of the various known isotopes of all the elements also tell us much about nuclear forces. The following facts about nuclear forces are known.

(1) Nuclear forces are *attractive*; they hold the nucleons together in a nucleus.

(2) Nuclear forces are very *strong*; they are the strongest forces so far discovered in nature.

(3) Nuclear forces are *short-ranged*; they are important only at distances of 10^{-15} m or less.

(4) Nuclear forces are *charge-independent*; similar nuclear attractions exist between proton and proton, proton and neutron, neutron and neutron.

(5) Nuclear forces are *not central-type* forces; they do not always act along the line joining the interacting particles. Recall that gravitational and electrostatic forces are central, while magnetic forces usually are not.

(6) Nuclear forces are *asymmetric*. By this we mean that the force between two nucleons depends on the angles that their joining line makes with the direction of the spin axis of each particle.

(7) Nuclear forces involve an *exchange* of a meson particle between the interacting pair of nucleons.

From the above facts we may conclude that the strong nuclear forces represent a new type of force, one not previously described. A fundamental law (perhaps laws) for such forces, analogous to Newton's law of gravitation, Coulomb's law of electrostatic force, and Ampère's law of magnetic force, is being sought. At present it is not clear whether or not this new law may be stated as simply as have the others; it is felt that more information is needed before it will be possible to make a final statement of the relation between nuclear forces and the various quantities upon which nuclear forces depend. Such a statement could be our *Fundamental Law XV*.

20–3 The weak interactions of elementary particles

Processes which involve the strong nuclear forces just discussed take place *very* rapidly. Once an α-particle enters a nitrogen nucleus, the ensuing reaction (emission of a proton and formation of an O^{17} nucleus) follows in about 10^{-23} seconds. However, in processes such as radioactive decay with the emission of a beta ray or electron (plus or minus) it is found that the mean decay time is 10^{-10} seconds or longer. This large difference in time suggests that forces much weaker than either those of nuclear attraction or those of electromagnetism are involved in the decay process. It is estimated that these weak forces are not more than 10^{-14} times as strong as are nuclear forces, so they must constitute still another fundamental type of force in the physical world.

All beta-decay processes involve the transformation of one elementary particle into another, and it seems likely that in every case the same fundamental principles are involved. If this is so, we would like to know what fundamental law, new to us, is involved in weak interactions.

20–4 Symmetry in nature

Physicists have become increasingly interested of late in the question of what symmetries nature possesses.

We have seen that certain things may be deduced more quickly by appealing to symmetry considerations rather than by carrying out the detailed application of a physical law to a special situation. For example, in the case of two oppositely charged parallel plates, the electric field is normal to the plates in the region where edge effects may be neglected. This result may be obtained by using Coulomb's law and performing a mathematical integration, but we reached the same conclusion by asking "If the field is *not* normal to the plates, why should one direction be preferred to another?" Obviously the only unique direction is the normal one. Other examples of this kind of reasoning occurred in connection with the magnetic field around a long straight wire carrying a current. In the same way the symmetry of a snowflake may be deduced from the assumption of certain conditions and physical laws, but to most people it is an example of nature's symmetry and as such it appeals to our aesthetic sense.

The appeal to symmetry or aesthetic considerations may not always be justified, since it assumes environmental conditions that may not exist. Due to the gravitational, electric, and magnetic fields of the earth, sun, our galactic system, etc., we actually live in a world where perfect symmetry can only be approximated.

There is another kind of symmetry that is being discussed; it has to do with transformations and conservation laws. For example, we saw that according to the relativity principle, natural laws are invariant under a transformation from one inertial system to another; the results of a physical experiment should be the same in any inertial system. Let us now ask whether the laws of physics would still hold in a world just like ours except that (1) every charged particle has the opposite charge, (2) matter and antimatter are reversed, (3) everything is the mirror image of what it is in our world.

(a) *Charge reversal.* Suppose that we could make a copy world just like our own except that every electron and antiproton would bear a positive charge, every proton and antielectron a negative one, and so on. In this copy world Coulomb's law and Ampere's law would hold because both involve the *product* of two charges and $q_1 \times q_2 = (-q_1) \times (-q_2)$. Newton's laws and our other laws that do not relate to charge would certainly be unaffected. Atoms built up out of negative nuclei (containing neutrons and negatively charged protons) with orbiting positively charged electrons would have the same chemical properties as their counterparts in our ordinary world. So far no evidence has been obtained against the proposition that *the laws of nature are invariant under charge conjugation.*

Related to this principle is the fact that there are two kinds of charge, positive and negative, and that charges of one sign may be separated from charges of the opposite sign, but the net charge in a closed system remains constant.

(b) *Matter conjugation.* Now imagine a copy world in which every particle in our world is replaced by its antiparticle, i.e., a positron replaces an electron, a negative antiproton is substituted for a proton, an antineutron for a neutron, a neutron for an antineutron, an antineutrino for a neutrino, a neutrino for an antineutrino, etc. Note that this conjugation involves not only a charge reversal but something more, since it affects neutral particles as well. Would such a world behave like ours? The evidence so far is that in the main it would obey the same fundamental laws. We may speculate that in some distant part of the universe such a world may actually exist, but, if so, let us hope that we shall never encounter it because, if we did, our world and this world of antimatter would annihilate each other! Perhaps the universe contains equal amounts of matter and antimatter and it is only due to statistical fluctuations that in our world there is an excess of our kind of matter.

Related to this apparent particle-antiparticle symmetry we have the conservation of matter principle, namely, that particles of opposite kind may be created in pairs and separated from one another, but the net count of particles (counting antiparticles as a negative number) in a closed system remains constant.

(c) *Mirror reflection. Parity.* Let us finally imagine a world which is the mirror image of our own, or what our world would look like if always viewed in a mirror. This amounts to interchanging right-handedness and left-handedness. If a right-hand screw is pointed at a mirror and turned clockwise, as viewed from its rear, the screw will advance toward the mirror (see Fig. 20–3). In the mirror the screw will appear to advance toward the viewer; the viewer will see the screw turning clockwise as viewed from in front, so that he would regard it as turning counterclockwise as viewed from the rear. A screw that advances when turned counterclockwise is a *left-hand* screw. In the mirror world the left hand replaces the right and the right replaces the left.

Would the laws of nature be different in a mirror world than in our own? If so, we could use the laws of nature alone to distinguish right from left. Up until 1956 physicists thought that the laws of nature would be invariant under a mirror-type conjugation. This principle was related to a conservation law called *the conservation of parity.* Parity is defined in terms of the symmetry of the wave functions describing an atomic system or particle and it has no counterpart in large-scale

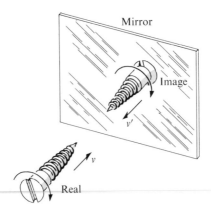

FIG. 20–3.   A right-hand screw advancing to the right appears in a mirror as a left-hand screw advancing to the left.

physics.   It was assumed that in an atomic process parity did not change, or was conserved.   Then in 1956 the theoretical physicists T. D. Lee and C. N. Yang proposed crucial experiments to test the conservation of parity principle.   These and other experiments since performed have shown that parity is not conserved in weak interactions of the beta-decay type (see Section 19–5) and that in such processes nature does distinguish not only between right-handedness and left-handedness, but also between matter and antimatter.   However, results so far indicate that antimatter in a mirror world behaves like matter in our world, or that *the laws of nature are invariant under a simultaneous matter conjugation and mirror reflection.* Further testing of this postulate must be awaited.

ILLUSTRATION.   When a positive pion (π^+) decays, a positive muon (μ^+) and neutrino (ν) are formed, so that we have

$$\pi^+ \rightarrow \mu^+ + \nu. \qquad (20\text{–}5)$$

The conservation of momentum (based on Newton's laws) requires that the

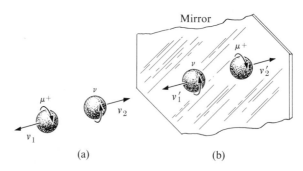

FIG. 20–4.   Decay of a π^+ particle into a μ^+ and neutrino results in the situation shown in (a), but not that shown in (b).   (b) is the mirror image of (a).

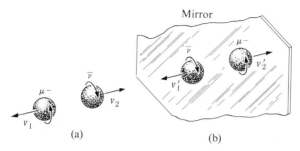

FIG. 20–5. Decay of a π^- particle into a μ^- and antinuetrino results in the situation shown in (a), but not that shown in (b).

particles μ^+ and ν be emitted in opposite directions and with opposite spins, as shown in Fig. 20–4(a). We see that both particles are advancing as would left-hand screws. The mirror image of this experiment is shown in Fig. 20–4(b), in which both particles are advancing as would right-hand screws. This mirror-image process has never been found to occur in nature.

If we perform a matter conjugation upon the process of Eq. (20–5), we have

$$\pi^- \rightarrow \mu^- + \bar{\nu}, \tag{20-6}$$

where $\bar{\nu}$ is the antineutrino; π^+ and π^-, as well as μ^+ and μ^-, form particle-antiparticle pairs. The decay process of Eq. (20–6) does occur in nature, but only as shown in Fig. 20–5(a), in which both particles are seen to be advancing as *right-hand* screws. The mirror image of this actual process is shown in Fig. 20–5(b) and it does *not* occur. Hence we see that if we take the process shown in Fig. 20–4(a), which does occur, and perform upon it both a matter conjugation and a mirror reflection, then we end up with another actual process, one allowed by the laws of nature.

20–5 Other problems

Particle physics is reaching the stage attained by atomic physics when the spectral lines of the various atomic spectra had been carefully measured, but no one knew why hydrogen emitted one type of spectrum, sodium another, mercury a third, and so on. The advent of the Bohr theory made possible a theoretical explanation of the hydrogen spectrum and quantum mechanics has enabled physicists to explain the spectra of all the elements. In particle physics we are confronted with much factual knowledge, but no fundamental theory that explains it all. Such a theory must involve the principle of nuclear forces and that of the weak interaction, but it may also require one or more additional postulates. Perhaps we shall find that just as atoms possess quantized energy states, so matter also has its quantized states represented by the various elementary particles.

We would like to know why the proton and the electron have the masses they do. Why should we not go further and ask ourselves why the speed of light is 3×10^8 m/sec and not some other value? Why is $G = 6.67 \times 10^{-11}$ n-m^2/kg^2? Thought has been given to the possibility of relationships between the fundamental constants. Any satisfactory theory along this line will have to encompass more than one branch of physics, and so it will need to be a unifying theory, one in which two or more of our fundamental postulates may be combined into a more comprehensive law.

Some physicists have turned from the minute world of the atom to the seemingly infinite one of the universe. In this field of endeavor speculation is rife. Many theories have been proposed to account for the origin of the solar system and the present distribution of stars and interstellar matter in the universe. All such theories must meet the test of explaining known facts, but they cannot be given the thorough testing in the laboratory that we have given the fundamental laws discussed in previous chapters. Cosmic theories will, in the long run, be judged by the same criteria that we apply to other physical theories, such as their rationality, simplicity, fruitfulness, and adaptability.

Are you interested in following man's progress in his search for new fundamental truths? If so, you may choose for your reading from an increasing number of excellent books, magazines and newspaper articles written for the educated layman. You are particularly urged to read the *Scientific American*, many of whose articles pertain to the scope of this book.

20–6 General philosophical principles

It should be kept in mind that the fundamental laws of nature so far discussed relate physical concepts and describe what happens and what does not happen in our world. There are also some general postulates of a different nature that are more or less tacitly assumed, such as the following.

    I. Fundamental laws of nature do exist.
    II. Fundamental laws of nature are basicly simple.
    III. The fundamental laws of nature are independent of time.

Postulate III states our belief that nature is not capricious, that an experiment repeated under the same conditions will yield the same result. While not all scientists accept each of these principles, physicists generally put considerable faith in them. We have assumed these postulates in this book.

20–7 Goedel's theorem

Kurt Goedel, one of the most brilliant mathematicians of this century, is now at the Institute for Advanced Study in Princeton. In 1931, when he was at the University of Vienna, he published a profound and significant paper on the internal consistency of mathematical systems. Goedel proved what has become a famous theorem, which states among other things that if one builds a mathematical system based on a set of consistent axioms, or postulates, then within the system statements will be discovered such that (1) no exception to these statements is ever found, yet (2) these statements cannot be *proved*, i.e., derived from the axioms of the system.

ILLUSTRATION. A prime number is defined as one that is not divisible by any integer except itself and unity. In number theory it has been found that one can choose any even integer and express it as the sum of two prime numbers, for example, $10 = 7 + 3, 20 = 17 + 3, 24 = 19 + 5$, etc. No one has ever found a proof of this theorem as applied to *all* even integers.

We may regard Goedel's theorem as having great import for physics as well as for mathematics. It tells us that if man ever builds what he regards as a complete theory of the physical world, one based on a set of fundamental laws such as we have discussed, then new truths will still be discovered, and these truths will require additional laws for their explanation. In other words, if at some time man wonders whether or not he has discovered *all* of the fundamental laws of nature, he can be sure that he has *not* and that there is at least *one more* fundamental law to look for. The search for new truths should never end!

PROBLEMS

1. (a) Why do heavy isotopes contain a greater proportion of neutrons than do light isotopes? (b) Why are elements with atomic numbers greater than 92 unstable or non-existent?

2. (a) Why is it possible to release nuclear energy by fusion of light nuclei and by fission of heavy ones? (b) What nuclei are the most stable? (c) Why is iron a poor prospect for a source of nuclear energy?

3. Compute the energy released per kg and per nucleon in the hypothetical fusion of H^1 atoms and neutrons to form helium.

4. Consider as a possible illustration of Goedel's theorem the famous four-color map problem. It is taken as a rule, or axiom, that in a map of several countries, or states, those countries with a common border must be colored differently in order to make them more distinguishable. Under this condition no arrangement of countries has been *found* to exist, or has been imagined to exist, for which more than *four* colors are needed when coloring the map of the countries, but no one has yet *proved* that less than *five* colors will suffice in general. Construct some real or fictitious maps and show that for them four colors are sufficient, as in Fig. 20–6.

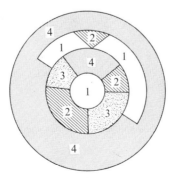

FIG. 20–6.   The four-color map problem. The numbers 1, 2, 3, 4, refer to four different colors.

5. Explain how magnetic forces are not symmetric and not usually central. (See Chapter 13.)

6. Show that Ampere's law would hold in a mirror world. Consider the force between two long straight current-carrying wires as an example.

7. How would the laws of physics be affected by a rotation of the axes of our inertial system?

8. How would the laws of physics be affected by a reversal of time, i.e., by replacing t with $-t$ in all of our relations?

9. Find the so-called *kinetic temperature* T at which the mean thermal energy of a particle ($3kT/2$) is equal to 10^3 electron-volts. At such a temperature would any of the particles possess 10^6 electron-volts of energy?

REFERENCES

GARDNER, MARTIN, *The Annotated Alice*, C. N. Potter, 1960.

Appendixes

APPENDIX 1

SINES AND COSINES OF COMMON ANGLES

Angle θ	sin θ	cos θ
0°	0.000	1.000
5°	0.087	0.996
10°	0.174	0.985
15°	0.259	0.966
20°	0.342	0.940
25°	0.423	0.906
30°	0.500	0.866
35°	0.574	0.819
37°	0.602	0.799
40°	0.643	0.766
45°	0.707	0.707
50°	0.766	0.643
53°	0.799	0.602
55°	0.819	0.574
60°	0.866	0.500
65°	0.906	0.423
70°	0.940	0.342
75°	0.966	0.259
80°	0.985	0.174
85°	0.996	0.087
90°	1.000	0.000

APPENDIX 2

UNIVERSAL CONSTANTS

Name	Symbol	Value
Gravitational constant	G	6.67×10^{-11} n-m^2/kg^2
Coulomb's law constant	k_e	8.98×10^9 n-m^2/coul^2
Ampere's law constant	k_m	1.00×10^{-7} n-sec^2/coul^2
Speed of light in vacuo	c	2.998×10^8 m/sec
Planck's constant	h	6.63×10^{-34} j-sec
Boltzmann's constant	k	1.38×10^{-23} j/°K
Avogadro's number	N_0	6.02×10^{26} molecules/kg-mole
Gas constant	$R = N_0 k$	8.31×10^3 j/kg-mole-°K
Electronic charge unit	e	1.60×10^{-19} coul
Faraday's constant	$F = N_0 e$	9.64×10^7 coul/kg-mole
Rest mass of electron	m_0	9.11×10^{-31} kg
Ratio of mass of proton to mass of electron	m_p/m_0	1836

Appendix 3

Useful Data

Quantity	Symbol	Value
Acceleration due to gravity at		
0° latitude and sea level	g	9.78 m/sec^2
Washington, D.C.	g	9.80 m/sec^2
Speed of sound at standard		
temperature and pressure	v_s	332 m/sec
Freezing point of water at 1 atmosphere	T_0	$273.15°\text{K}$
Mechanical equivalent of heat	J	4185 j/cal*
Pressure of normal atmosphere	p_0	$1.013 \times 10^5 \text{ n/m}^2$
Mass of earth	M_E	$5.98 \times 10^{24} \text{ kg}$
Mean radius of earth	R_E	$6.37 \times 10^6 \text{ m}$
Mass of moon	M_M	$M_E/81.5$
Mass of sun	M_S	$2.0 \times 10^{30} \text{ kg}$
Mean distance to moon	R_{ME}	$3.84 \times 10^8 \text{ m}$
Mean distance to sun	R_{SE}	$1.5 \times 10^{11} \text{ m}$
Rydberg constant for hydrogen	R_H	$1.097 \times 10^7 \text{/m}$
Electron-volt	ev	$1.60 \times 10^{-19} \text{ j}$
Angstrom unit	A	10^{-10} m
Atomic mass unit	amu	$1.66 \times 10^{-27} \text{ kg}$

* This is the large calorie, or "kilocalorie."

Answers to Problems

Answers to Problems

CHAPTER 1

2. All hats are red.
3. Explorer will get the right answer. If native is a liar he must lie twice.
4. Shorter native tells the truth, taller one lies.
5. $9567 + 1085 = 10652$
6. $8694 \div 63 = 138$
7. $12128316 \div 124 = 97809$
8. Helen
9. (a) After a red card play a higher card, after a black card play a lower one.
   (b) After odd-numbered card play one of another suit, after an even-numbered card play one of the same suit.

CHAPTER 2

1. 10^4
2. $2 \times 10^{-1} = 0.2$
3. 3.96×10^{-2}
4. (a) 3.17, (b) 31.7, (c) 5.02×10^3
5. 75 cm and 25 cm
6. -12
7. $M = GR^2/g = 6 \times 10^{24}$ kg
8. $1 + \frac{3}{2}x + \frac{1}{4}x^2 - \frac{1}{24}x^3 + \frac{1}{64}x^4 \cdots$
9. $3(1 + \frac{1}{18} - \frac{1}{648} + \cdots)$
10. (a) Not convergent, (b) converges to 0.3065 , ...
11. $57.3°$
12. About 37° and 53°.
15. 141.4 ft east and 141.4 ft south.
16. $10° = 0.175$ rad, $\sin 10° = 0.174$, $\cos 10° = 0.985$.
17. $\frac{3}{4}$, 1, and $\frac{5}{4}$ seconds. Plot s vs. t^2. Slope $= g/2$.
18. $p \propto 1/V$. Hyperbola. $1/p$.
19. $P \propto \sqrt{l}$. Plot P^2 vs. l (slope $= 4 \times 10^{-2}$ sec^2/cm), or l vs. P^2 (slope $= 25$ cm/sec^2).
20. 810, 729, 656, 531. 6.5 days. Plot log of activity vs. time.
21. 3

CHAPTER 3

1. (a) 1.26×10^{-3} m^2, (b) 3×10^{-5} m^3, (c) 3.35×10^{-3} m^3
2. 6.44×10^6 m
4. 3.05×10^{-1} m/sec
6. 60π radians/sec
7. 0.24 m/sec, 0.48 m/sec
8. 192 cm/sec^2, 1/92 m/sec^2
9. 4.45 n, yes

10. 1.1×10^5 n/m^2
11. n-m^2/kg^2, or m^3/kg-sec^2
12. 6.67×10^{-8} cm^3/gm-sec^2
13. 4.0×10^{-47} n

CHAPTER 4

1. (a) 0.4 sec, or 1%, (b) 2%
2. 41.7 sec, 0.7 sec, 1.6%, 2.6%
3. Dependence of period on arc definitely indicated.
4. (a) 0.007, 0.010, 0.016, 0.020, 0.016, 0.004 m. (c) No
5. About 0.29 m
7. (a) 0.5%, (b) 1%, (c) 2.5%
8. (a) About 1%, (b) about 3%
9. 202 (m/kg)$^{1/2}$, 1.3%
10. (a) $\frac{1}{16}$, (b) $\frac{1}{4}$, (c) $\frac{3}{8}$. (d) Not exactly.
11. Actual error 0.35%, mean deviation 0.2%.

CHAPTER 5

3. $\frac{1}{2}$
4. 9×10^{16} joules
5. $E = vB$
6. $e/m = E^2/2B^2V$
7. (a) Yes. (b) Restricted law. (c) Frictional force per unit weight. No.
8. Depends on the pressure and is a property of a particular substance.
9. $0 + 0 = 0$, $0 + 1 = 1$, $1 + 0 = 1$, $1 + 1 = 0$
10. (a) 11100001. (b) $0 \times 0 = 0$, $0 \times 1 = 1$, $1 \times 0 = 0$, $1 \times 1 = 1$
11. (a) Use cubical structure of 4 floors, each with 16 rooms; must mark 4 rooms in a line to win. (b) Two squares in a line.

CHAPTER 6

1. (a) 0.4 mi/hr-sec, (b) 24 mi/hr-min, (c) 1440 mi/hr^2, (d) 1.11×10^{-4} mi/sec^2
2. (a) 9.8, 19.6, 29.4, 39.2, 49.0 m/sec   (b) 4.9, 14.7, 24.5, 34.3, 44.1 m/sec
   (c) 4.9, 14.7, 24.5, 34.3, 44.1 m   (d) 4.9, 19.6, 44.1, 78.4, 122.5 m
3. (a) 4 m/sec^2, (b) 30 and 34 m.
4. (a) 30 n, 12.5 kg, (c) yes
5. (a) 1 n, 3.33 kg, (c) yes
7. 6×10^{26}
8. (a) 9.78 m/sec^2, (b) 9.31 m/sec^2, (c) 2.45 m/sec^2
9. (a) 735 n, (b) 733.5 n, (c) 184 n
10. (b) $R_x = -46.0$ n, $R_y = 35.4$ n, $R = 57.8$ n
11. 30.6 n
12. 1110 n, or 250 lb-wt
13. 0, 2.5, 5.0, 7.5 m/sec^2
14. $F = mv/\Delta t = 1.45 \times 10^4$ n $= 3.26 \times 10^3$ lb-wt
15. (a) 8 n-sec/m, (b) 16 n, 110 m/sec^2, (c) 0, (d) -50 m/sec^2
16. (a) 80 kg-wt, (b) 88 kg-wt, (c) 72 kg-wt

18. 9.8, 4.9, 0, -4.9, -9.8, -14.7 m/sec
19. $v_{ox} = 21$ m/sec, $v_{oy} = 7$ m/sec, $v = 22.2$ m/sec
20. (a) 19.6 m/sec, 9.8 m/sec^2, (b) $v = gt$, $a = g$

CHAPTER 7

1. (a) 100 n by the rope, -100 n by the ground.
   (b) -100 n by boy in (a), 100 n by other boy.
   (c) The 100 n in (a) and the -100 n in (b).
2. 196 n. No
3. (a) 2 m/sec^2, (b) 100 n by the rope on weaker boy, -110 n by the rope and 210 n by the ground on stronger boy. (c) 105 n.
4. (a) Always up. (b) Same direction when climbing, opposite when skiing down.
   (c) Greater going up.
5. 81 times greater for the moon.
7. 1.27 m/sec^2, 6.53 n, 3.27 n
8. (a) 0.95 m/sec^2, 8.85 n, 5.90 n, 2.95 n
   (b) Additional inertia due to hanging block.
9. (a) 1.96 m/sec^2, (b) 2.35 n
11. 10 mi/hr
12. 3.33 mi/hr
13. 173.4 mi/hr
14. (a) 0.5 ft/sec, (b) 0
15. 150 m/sec, 200 m/sec, 250 m/sec
16. (a) 5×10^5 n, (b) 1.12×10^5 lb-wt, or 56 ton-wt, (c) 15.2 m/sec

CHAPTER 8

1. 3.9×10^{-47} n
2. (a) 3.2×10^{-9} n, 7.2×10^{-10} lb-wt, (b) 1.28×10^{-8} m/sec^2
3. (a) 1.51×10^3 ft, 10.8 sec, (b) 4.20×10^3 ft, 18 sec
4. $\tan \theta = \sin \theta / \cos \theta = v^2/gr$
5. (a) If not, plane's weight will cause it to fall faster than in the circular loop.
   (b) 2, -2, (c) 1, -3
6. (a) 4.2×10^7 m, or 26,000 mi, (b) 22,000 mi
8. 3.6×10^{22} n
9. 0.72 AU, 1.5 AU
10. (a) Mass of parent, but not that of satellite, appears in Eq. (8–7). (b) By observing its T and R and using Eq. (8–7).
11. 54 R_E from earth's center.

CHAPTER 9

1. (a) 2940 joules, (b) 2.94×10^5 joules
2. (a) 368 watts, 0.49 H.P.
   (b) 70 watts, 0.093 H.P.
3. 49 joules; no
4. $W = 59$ joules, $\Delta V = 49$ joules, $\Delta U = 10$ joules
5. (a) 400 joules, (b) 1.6×10^4 joules, (c) 100 joules
6. (a) 6.25, (b) 2.5, (c) s proportional to weight

7. (a) K.E. $= 98$ j, P.E. $= 98$ j
   (b) K.E. $= 176.4$ j, P.E. $= 19.6$ j
   (c) $\Delta U = 215.6$ j
8. $kA^2/2$
9. $V = -100GmM_e/81D$, if $V = 0$ at infinity
10. $M/(m + M)$
11. No, K.E. is less after collision than before.
12. $-\frac{4}{3}$ and $\frac{8}{3}$ m/sec
14. (a) Microphone, (b) loudspeaker, (c) photoelectric cell, (d) battery, (e) motor, (f) piston engine

CHAPTER 10

1. (a) 400 n/m^2, (b) 600 n/m^2
2. 500 m/sec, 590 m/sec
3. No
4. 0.43 cm^3
5. (a) 2.68×10^{19}, (b) 2.68×10^4
6. (a) 6.2×10^{-21} joule, (b) 3.88×10^{-2} electron-volt
7. (a) Violates conservation of energy principle, (b) too efficient; violates second law of thermodynamics.
8. Takes in 1250 joules, gives up 250 joules.
9. Walls of engine would melt.
10. 2800 joules absorbed, 3000 joules ejected.
11. (a) $\frac{1}{15}$, (b) 4
12. Yes
13. (a) 3:2, (b) 5:2, (c) the most probable distribution becomes more likely the greater the number of events.

CHAPTER 11

3. (a) 3×10^9/sec, (b) 6×10^{14}/sec
4. (b) 10, $(\frac{2}{3})$ m, 3/sec, 2 m/sec
5. 15 in all
6. Do, mi, fa, sol, la, do; 11 pleasant 2-note and 5 pleasant 3-note chords
9. (a) 3 ft, (b) right and left inverted.
12. (a) 42°, (b) light enters perpendicular to a small side, (c) light enters perpendicular to hypotenuse.
13. 20 cm
14. (a) 13°, 26°, 41°, (b) 19°, 41°, 82°
15. 1.5×10^{-5} m
16. (a) Red, (b) blue, (c) black

CHAPTER 12

1. (a) 64×10^{-5} n, (b) 64×10^{-5} n
2. (a) Charges changed from unlike to like.
   (b) 4×10^{-9} coul, (c) $\pm 12 \times 10^{-9}$ coul, $\mp 4 \times 10^{-9}$ coul
3. 4500 n/coul, directed in second quadrant.
4. 630 volts

5. (a) 0.93 m beyond the negative charge.

(b) 0.36 m beyond the negative charge, also 0.15 m from negative and 0.35 m from positive charge.

6. (a) 5.0×10^3 n/coul, (b) 2, 4, 6 mm from the grounded plate.

7. 5.4, 2.7, 1.8 and 1.35 m

10. (a) 8×10^{-16} n   (b) 6.4×10^{-18} joule

(c) 6.4×10^{-18} joule   (d) 3.78×10^6 m/sec

13. (a) 400 volts, (b) 2×10^4 v/m, (c) no, (d) yes, from work of separation.

14. (a) 100 volts, (b) 5×10^3 v/m, (c) yes, (d) no, electric energy decreases, voltage supply gains energy.

15. (b) In parallel, plates of like charge connected.

16. (a) $-Q_2$, (b) $Q_1 + Q_2$

CHAPTER 13

1. 1.28 amps up

2. 8×10^{-5} amp

3. 3020 sec

6. (a) Around the magnetic poles, (b) near the magnetic equator.

8. 1.5×10^{-4} n   or 1.53×10^{-2} gm-wt, 6×10^{-4} n   or 6.12×10^{-2} gm-wt, 13.5×10^{-4} n or 13.8×10^{-2} gm-wt, 24×10^{-4} n or 24.5×10^{-2} gm-wt

10. $16\pi k_m I/5\sqrt{5}\, R$

11. 2.1×10^{-3} n toward center of square.

12. Attract

13. 1 amp, due to relative motion of observer and positive ions in wire.

14. 10^4 v/m, 10^{-3} w/m^2, 10^7 m/sec

15. (a) 5×10^7 coul/kg, (b) 6.4×10^{-27} kg, (c) 10^6 volts

CHAPTER 14

3. (a) 300 v/m, (b) 0

4. (a) 300 j, (b) 1200 j, (c) yes

5. (a) 300 j, (b) 900 j, (c) no

6. (a) 40 volts, (b) 12 watts, (c) 0.3 n, (d) 12 watts

7. (a) 5×10^{-2} volt, (b) 2.5×10^{-2} volt

8. (a) 2.5×10^{-4} coul, (b) 2.5×10^{-4} coul

9. (a) $\pi l^2 nB$, (b) $\pi l^2 nB/4$

10. 26 volts clockwise and 28 volts counterclockwise.

11. 14 volts clockwise and 8 volts counterclockwise.

12. $2\pi^2 a^2 k_m N_1 N_2/b$

14. (a) 2200 v, 0.5 a, (b) 2200 v, 0.45 a

15. 1.59×10^{-2} v/m

CHAPTER 15

2. In theory of heat conduction the concepts of density and velocity of moving substance are lacking, but a new concept, temperature, is introduced.

3. (a) Negative, (b) positive, (c) 0

4. 2×10^{-10} joule/m^3
5. Neither gains nor loses energy.
6. Gains
7. Zero, because isolated magnetic poles do not exist.

CHAPTER 16

1. (a) 50 sec, 62.5 sec, (b) 80 ft
2. (b) 0.44 fringe
3. (a) 2.6×10^8 m/sec, (b) 400 lb, (c) 33 years
4. (a) $p = m_o U / \sqrt{1 - U^2/c^2}$
5. (a) 5.1×10^4 ev, (b) 5.1×10^5 ev, (c) 4.6×10^6 ev, (d) 5.06×10^7 ev
6. (a) 9.42×10^7 ev, (b) 9.42×10^8 ev, (c) 8.48×10^9 ev, (d) 9.33×10^{10} ev
7. (a) 2.56×10^3 ev, (b) 7.86×10^4 ev, (c) 6.60×10^5 ev, (d) 3.1×10^6 ev
8. 6.1×10^{-12} kg
9. (a) 1.5×10^{-10} joule, or 9.3×10^8 ev
   (b) 0.37%
   (c) 9.3×10^7 KWH/kg
10. 4.4×10^9 kg/sec
11. 5.7 years
12. 350 days
13. (a) 2300 kg, (b) 130,000 kg

CHAPTER 17

1. (a) 2, (b) 1
3. 6.17×10^3 °K
4. (a) 5.06, (b) 2.38
5. (a) $(hc/\lambda) - E$, (b) $(hc/\lambda) + E$
7. (a) 3.90×10^{-15} j-sec/coul, (b) 6.24×10^{-34} j-sec, (c) 1.6 ev
8. 1.10×10^7/m
9. 1215 A, 6562 A, 4861 A, 4340 A
10. 13.6 ev
11. hc/eV
13. $\frac{2}{3}$
14. (a) 6.63×10^{-32} m, (b) 7.3×10^{-11} m
16. (b) $\Delta E > 0.4 \times 10^6$ ev

CHAPTER 18

1. 3.85×10^{-5}
2. (b) 1.47×10^{-10} m
3. 21×10^{-30} m^3, 2.76×10^{-10} m
4. 18 states for $n = 3$, 32 for $n = 4$.
5. $n = 4$, $l = 3$, $m_l = 3, 2, 1, 0, -1, -2, -3$, $m_s = \frac{1}{2}, -\frac{1}{2}$
6. It has 10 electrons in $n = 3$, $l = 2$ states.
7. (a) K^+, I^-, (b) Cu^+, Cl^-, (c) Cu^{2+}, Cl^-, (d) Mg^{2+}, O^{2-}, (e) Al^{3+}, Cl^-, (f) Al^{3+}, O^{2-}

9. N≡N bond coordinate covalent, N=O bond covalent; $-e$ on outer N, $+e$ on middle N
10. $Na^+ - (OH)^-$ bond ionic, O—H bond covalent.

CHAPTER 19

1. 15 gm of water evaporated
2. 5.33 kg
3. 43 gm
4. 4.17 ev, 0.35 ev/nucleon, 0.095 ev/nucleon
5. (a) Alpha particle, (b) neutron, (c) proton, (d) proton, (e) neutron, (f) neutron
6. 28.2 Mev, 7.05 Mev/nucleon
7. (a) 7.66 Mev/nucleon, (b) 7.90 Mev/nucleon
8. 17.5 Mev
9. 17.3 Mev
10. 0.78 Mev
12. (a) 16 days, (b) 53 days, (c) 80 days
13. (a) 36%, (b) 59%
14. Not counted, but π^+ and π^- are antiparticles to each other.
15. (a) Matter, (b) proton, electron, neutrino, two antineutrinos, (c) $+1$

CHAPTER 20

1. (a) Because of electrostatic repulsion between protons, (b) same as (a).
2. (a) Binding energy per nucleon greatest for nuclei of medium mass. (b) ones with mass number near 60. (c) binding energy per nucleon near the maximum.
3. 1.88×10^8 KWH/kg, 7.05 Mev/nucleon
7. Invariant
8. All fundamental laws invariant except V.
9. 7.7×10^6 °K, yes

Index

A, mass number, 354
Abductive reasoning, 6
Absolute temperature scale, 35
Absolute zero, 177
Absorption spectra, 311
Abundance of stable isotopes, 354
Acceleration, 37, 84, 108
   centripetal, 127
   due to gravity, 65, 91
   motion under constant, 84
Accuracy, of a single reading, 54
   of the average of several readings, 55
Action-reaction law of Newton, 110
Addition of forces, 92
Airplane, forces on, 114
Algebra, 16
Alpha particle, 352, 358
   scattering of, 329
Ampere, the unit of current, 235
Ampere balance, 243
Ampere's law, 227
Amplitude, 182
Analogy, reasoning by, 6
   electromechanical, 261
Annihilation of matter, 299, 362
Antimatter, 363
Antiproton, 363
Area, 37
Aristotle, 45
Artificial radioactive isotopes, 359
Asteroids, 50
Atom, size of, 329, 334, 339
Atomic mass unit, 354, 356
Atomic number, 353
Atomic weight, 78
Avogadro's number N_0, 78, 167, 348

Background radiation, 359, 367
Balmer series, 312
Baryons, 364
Becquerel, 358
Beta decay, 360
Beta rays, 359
Betatron, 263
Binding energy, 366
Binomial theorem, 18
Blackbody radiation, 302

Bode-Titus law, 49
Bohr's theory, 311
Boltzmann's constant, k, 167, 348
Bombs, atomic, 359, 373, 374
Bonds, chemical, 342
Brightness, 184
British units, 42

c (*See* Speed of light)
Calorie, 155
Capacitance, 215
Carnot cycle, 169
Cavendish experiment, 7, 134, 139
Centrifugal force, 129
Centrifuge, 130
Centripetal acceleration, 127
Centripetal force, 129
Chadwick, 357
Charge, 35
Charge reversal, 377
Charge to mass ratio of particles, 239
Chemical energy, 154
Circular motion experiment, 138
Cockcroft and Walton, 35
Collisions, 117
Color, 184
Combustion, 371
Components of a vector, 86, 96
Compton effect, 316
Compton wavelength, 318
Conservation, of charge, 270
   of elementary particles, 364
   of energy principle, 157
   of mass-energy, 299
   of matter, 350
   of mechanical energy, 149
   of momentum, 118, 295
   of parity, 377
Conservative forces, 147
Constants, in physics, 77
   universal, 77
Controlled experiments, 46
Constructs, 9
Coordinate covalence, 345
Copernicus, 126
Corpuscular theory of light, 195
Cosine of an angle, 21

Coulomb, the unit of charge, 86
Coulomb balance, 220
Coulomb's law, 201
Covalence, 344
Critical angle, 192
Curie, Madame, 358
Curie-Joliot, M. and Mme., 357
Current element, 223
Cycle, 169
Cyclotron, 240

Dalton's atomic hypothesis, 353
Dating by radioactivity, 360
DeBroglie wavelength, 320
Decay, radioactive, 29, 360
Decay constant, 368
Decibel, 184
Deductive reasoning, 6
Definition, role in physics, 31
Degradation of energy, 173
Density, 38
Derivative, 103
Derived quantities, 37
Deviation, 55
Diffraction, 186, 192
Dipole, electric, 208
Direction of natural processes, 173
Dispersion of light, 184, 191, 195
Displacement current, 273
Dual nature, of atomic particles, 318
  of light, 315
Dynamics, 110

e to m ratio for electrons, 245
Einstein, 282
Einstein's mass-energy equivalence, 297
  photoelectric equation, 308
Electric charge, 35
Electric current, 222
Electric field, 204
Electric flux, 272
Electric forces, 201
Electric potential, 208
Electrolysis, 224, 244
Electromagnetic spectrum, 182
Electromagnetic waves, 270, 277
Electromotive force, 248
Electron, 215
Electron-volt, 218, 309, 356
Electrons, free and bound, 331
Electrostatic bond, 344
Elementary particles, 364
Emission spectra, 310, 313
Empirical laws, 48

Endothermal vs. exothermal processes, 351
Energy, 38, 144
  chemical, 154
  of electrical field, 217
  forms of, 159
  internal, 152
  kinetic, 145
  of magnetic field, 260
  nuclear, 370
  potential, 146
Energy states, 311
Engines, heat, 168
Entropy, 172
Equation of state, 167
Equilibrium, static, 98
Equipotential surfaces, 210, 212
Errors, 51ff
Escape velocity, 151
Ether theory, 274, 284
Exclusion principle, 339
Excited states, 313
Explosions, 118
Exponential decay, 29, 368

Farad, the unit of capacitance, 216
Faraday, 204, 247
Faraday's law, 255, 267
Fermi, 361, 371
Fields, 219
Fission, 371
Flux, electric, 272
  magnetic, 253
Focus, 189
Foot-pound, 42
Force, concept of, 86
  definition of, 37
  electrostatic, 201
  gravitational, 131
  magnetic, 225
  net, or unbalanced, 86
  nuclear, 375
Force table, 109
Four-color map problem, 381
Free-fall experiment, 64
Frequency, 38
Fresnel, 187
Friction, moving, 86
  static, 113
  work done against, 153
Fundamental laws, 75
Fundamental quantities, 33
Fusion of nuclei, 373

G (See Gravitational constant)

Galileo, 46, 57, 84
Gamma rays, 359
Gas constant, R, 167, 348
Gas thermometer, 35, 177
Generator, electric, 252, 255
Goedel's theorem, 380
Graphs, 23, 59
Grating, diffraction, 194, 198
Gravitation, Newton's law of, 7, 72, 131
Gravitational constant, G, 7, 32, 133
Gravitational forces, 124, 136
Greek scientists, 45
Grimaldi, 192

h (*See* Planck's constant)
Half-life, 29, 360, 368
Hahn and Strassmann, 372
Heat, 155
    of reaction, 351
Heat capacities of metals, 332
Heavy hydrogen, 354
Heisenberg's uncertainty principle, 321
Henry, Joseph, 258
Henry, the unit of inductance, 257
Hertz, 270, 304
Hooke's law, 48, 66
Horsepower, 42
Huygens' principle, 187
Hyperbolas, 21
Hyperons, 364

Inclined plane, 161
Induced currents, 247
Induced electric field, 263
Induced magnetic field, 276
Inductive reasoning, 6
Inertial systems, 281
Infinite series, 17
Intensity, 183
Interference, 187, 192, 194
    in thin films, 197
Internal energy, 152
Ionic valence, 342
Isotopes, 354

Joule, the unit of work and energy, 40
Joule's law, 249

k (*See* Boltzmann's constant)
Kelvin temperature scale, 35
Kepler's laws, 49, 126
Kilogram, 34
Kilowatt-hour, 371
Kinematics, 110

Kinetic energy, 145
    relativistic, 297
Kinetic theory, 163

Laser, 314
Laws, derived, 71
    empirical, 48
    fundamental, 75, 76
    restricted, 75
Le Chatelier's principle, 256
Length, 33
Lenses, 191
Lenz's law, 255
Leptons, 364
Light, speed of, 199
    theories of, 195
Light quanta, 307
Logarithms, 26
Logic, 5
Lorentz space-time transformation, 286
Lorentz-Fitzgerald contraction, 288
Loudness, 183

Magnetic field, 230, 236
Magnetic flux, 253
Magnetic force, between parallel currents,
        235
    on current element, 231
    on moving charge, 232
Magnetic forces, 225, 229
Magnetic poles, 225
Mass, 33, 88, 123
    inertial vs. gravitational, 133
    variation with velocity, 294
    vs. weight, 90
Mass-energy equivalence, 159, 297
Mass number, 354
Mathematics, contrasted with theoretical
        physics, 80
    role in physics, 9, 71
Matter conjugation, 377
Maxwell, 269
Maxwell's postulate, 274
Mean deviation, 55
Mendeléeff, 335
Mesons, 364
Meter, 33
Michelson-Morley experiment, 283
Millikan's oil-drop experiment, 214
Mirror reflection, 377
Mirrors, 189
Mks system, 36
Models in physical theory, 69
Molecular speeds, 165

Momentum, 37
  conservation of, 118, 119, 295
  of a photon, 316
Monomolecular layers, 348
Moon, period of, 133
Motion, equation of, 102
  Newton's first law of, 99
  Newton's second law of, 91
Motor, electric, 252
Muons, 364
Mutual inductance, 257

Neutrino, 158, 361
Neutron, 357
Newton, 7, 127, 195
Newton, the unit of force, 40
Newton's law of cooling, 369
Nucleus, size of, 329
Nuclear chemistry, 352
Nuclear energy, 370
Nuclear forces, 375
Nuclear transmutations, 356
Null method, 57

Observable quantities, 301, 324
Oersted, 226
Ohm, the unit of resistance, 249
Operator, 324
Optical pumping, 314
Order and disorder, 174

Pair annihilation and production, 362
Parabolas, 20
Parallel plates, field between, 207, 211
  force between, 211, 220
Parity, 377
Particle, 93
Pauli's exclusion principle, 339
Pendulum, energy of, 150
  period of, 65
Period, 38, 180
Periodic table, 335
Periodic wave, 180
Phase, 182, 188
Philosophy, 5
Phosphorescence, 358
Photoelectric effect, 306, 326
Photon, 307, 315, 364
Pi, determination of, 62
Pions, 364
Pitch, 184
Planck, 303
Planck's constant, h, 304, 310
Planetary theories, 125

Positron, 361, 364
Postulates, 67, 76
Potential, electric, 208
Potential difference, 210
Potential energy, 147
Pound-weight, 92
Power, 38
Prefixes to units, 41
Pressure, 38
  kinetic theory concept of, 164
Prism, 191
Projectile, motion of, 101
Ptolemy, 125

Quanta of light, 307
Quantum numbers, 312, 330
Quantum principle, 323
Quantum states, 331, 340

R (See Gas constant)
Radian, 20
Radioactive decay, 29, 360
Radioactivity, 358
Radium, 358
Rays, 185
Reflection, 185, 188
Refraction, 185, 190
Refractive index, 186
Refrigerator, 171
Relativistic dynamics, 294
Relativity, principle of, 282
  special theory of, 282
Relaxation phenomena, 368
Resistance, electrical, 249
Resultant of two or more forces, 93
Rutherford, 328, 352

Satellites, motion of, 135
Scalars, 94
Scattering of alpha particles, 329
Search coil, 253
Second, the, 34
Self-inductance, 258
Shells, electron, 340
Significant figures, 15
Simple harmonic motion, 101
Simultaneity, 289
Sine of an angle, 21
Slope of a line, 25
Snell's law, 186
Sound, speed of, 107
Space travel, 292
Specific heat capacity, 156

Speed, 37
    instantaneous, 103
    of light, 197
    root mean square, 166
    of sound, 107
Spin of electron, 331
Square roots, extraction of, 15
State, equation of, 167
Statics, 98
Statistical approach, 163
Statistical fluctuations, 367
Stellerator, 374
Stopping potential, 309
Syllogism, 6
Symmetry in nature, 376
Synchrotron, 241
System, physical, 115

Temperature, 34
    kinetic theory concept of, 166
Theories, list of famous, 75
Theory, 67
Thermodynamics, first law of, 156
    second law of, 171
Thermometer, gas, 35, 177
Thermonuclear reaction, 374
Thought experiments, 84, 85
Time, 34
    dilation, 291
Tonal quality, 184
Total reflection, 192
Transformer, 259
Trigonometry, 21
Tunnel effect, 322
Twin paradox, 292

Uncertainty in physics, 9
Uncertainty principle, 321
Units, British, 42
    for derived quantities, 39
    for fundamental quantities, 33
    mks, 36

Van de Graaff generator, 213
Vectors, 86, 94
Velocities, addition of, 293
Velocity, average, 85
Vibrating string, 47
Volta, 225
Volume, 37

Watt, the unit of power, 40
Wave, definition of, 178
Wave function, 179
Wave propagation, 185
Wavefront, 185
Waves, types of, 179
Weak interactions, 125, 376
Weber, the unit of magnetic flux, 233
Weight, 90, 91
Weightlessness, 92
Work, concept of, 141
    definition of, 38, 142
Work function of a metal, 308

Young's double slit experiment, 193

Z, atomic number, 353
Zartman and Ko's experiment, 165